ART OF ALGEBR

DEVELOPING ADVANCED ALGEBRA CONCEPTS THROUGH NON-TRADITIONAL PROBLEMS

ALGEBRA 1

BOX ALGEBRA

ALGEBRA 2

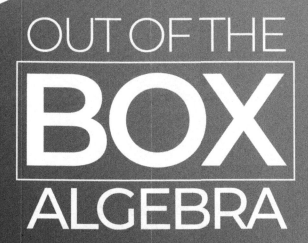

OUT OF THE BOX ALGEBRA

- ADVANCED ALGERBA COURSES
- MATHEMATICS CONTESTS
- AMC 10/12
- MATHCON
- MATH LEAGUES

MATHTOPIA PRESS

SINAN KANBIR, Ph.D.
MATHEMATICS EDUCATION

Paper Book

978-1-7356252-6-3

Graphic Designer - Typesetting

cemnilsen@gmail.com

PREFACE

What is BOX Algebra and what makes this book special and unique?

This book grew from working with algebra honor course students, math contest participants, and problem-solving communities. It covers all algebra 1 and most algebra 2 and pre-calculus topics and presents some non-traditional school algebra concepts. Through short explanations and carefully crafted problems, it shows how all algebraic concepts are well-connected. Working through cognitively challenging problems and their well-presented solutions, students will expand their understanding and develop advanced mathematical concepts. Students will feel challenged but eventually feel connected and enjoy the book's problems.

Possible target audiences of this book

- Algebra 1&2, honor algebra, and pre-calculus course takers.
- Participants in mathematics contests such as AMC 8, AMC 10, AMC 12, MATHCOUNTS, MathCON, and Math Leagues.
- Math Circle students and organizers.
- Pre-service and in-service mathematics teachers.
- Parents of mathematically promising students.
- General math enthusiasts.

How to use this book

Students should engage each chapter's concepts by trying themselves first, then move to examples as they work through them. Solutions are presented very clearly; however, algebra learners are supposed to explore and discover themselves when they first engage with the problems. Examples and set problems have multiple entry points and solutions that every algebra learner can begin with. There is no time pressure; students should enjoy their deep algebraic thinking over speed. Notetaking is an essential skill for algebra learners. We encourage students to take their notes and become good mathematical note-takers.

Acknowledgments

I would like to thank MathTopia Academy teaching assistants Andrew Carratu, Sarah Zuge, and Ava Kumar for holding problem-solving sessions, reading the drafts of this book, and giving very valuable comments. I am also thankful to Semra Betul Kaleli, Eshaani Singh, and Lomahn Sun for test solving and reading the drafts of this book, and giving very valuable comments as students and algebra learners. Lastly, I would like to thank Ertan Kaya for making valuable contributions and the University of Wisconsin-Stevens Point Mathematical Sciences department faculties for giving valuable feedback.

TABLE OF CONTENTS

CHAPTER 1

NUMBERS

Order of Operations

Consider the expression $5+3\times4$. Should you add 5 and 3 first, then multiply by 4? If so you get 32. Or, should you multiply 3 and 4 first, then add 5? If so you get 17. Let's take a look at the following three situations:

1. I have 3 packs of 10 pencils plus 7 extra.
   So I do: $3\times10+7 = 37$.

2. It's like 4 packs of 10 pencils with three missing.
   So I do: $4\times10-3 = 37$.

Or,

3. I have 7 pencils plus 4 packs of 10 pencils,
   so I do: $7+4\times10 = 47$.

In the final example, it does not make sense to add 7 and 4 first.

Remark 1.1

First of all, parentheses must be performed (but some exceptions) and exponents are next. Division or multiplication have the same priority, and addition or subtraction have the same priority. Again, we need to use the following conventions on order of operations.

- All powers (exponents) are considered first
- Multiplication and division are considered from left to right.
- Addition and subtraction are considered from left to right.

MathTopia Press

Problem 1.1

Evaluate the expression
$5-3\times4^3\div(7-1)$

Solution 1.1

$$5-3\times4^3\div(7-1) = 5-3\times4^3\div6$$
$$= 5-192\div6$$
$$= 5-32$$
$$= -27$$

Problem 1.2

Simplify $2+2\times2-2\div2+2$

Solution 1.1

$$2+2\times2-2\div2+2 = 2+4-1+2$$
$$= 6-1+2$$
$$= 5+2$$
$$= 7$$

Problem 1.3

Simplify $(3^3-3)^2 \div 4 \times 6 \div 1$.

Solution 1.3

$$(27-3)^2 \div 4 \times 6 \div 1 \; = 576 \div 4 \times 6 \div 1$$
$$= 144 \times 6 \div 1$$
$$= 864$$

Problem 1.4

Use parentheses to obtain 4 from the expression

$4 \times 4 - 4 \div 4 + 4$

Solution 1.4

$4 \times (4-4) \div 4 + 4 = 4$

Problem 1.5

To make the statement $(10\;?\;5) + 4 - (10-9) = 5$ true, the question mark between 10 and 5 should be replaced by

A) $\times$ B) $-$ C) $+$ D) $\div$ E) None

Solution 1.5

$(10 \div 5) + 4 - (10-9) = 2 + 4 - 1 = 5$.
The answer is $\div$.

Remark 1.2

Holistic thinking for numbers, structures and operations. We need to look for operations holistically before deciding on whether to use one of the order of operations mnemonic (PEMDAS or BOMDAS). For example, $24 \times 12 - 23 \times 12$, we see that students just memorize the PEMDAS mnemonic they learned could start with multiplication and then subtraction which takes additional step. Instead, knowing appropriate number properties such as the associative property of multiplication or, the distributive property of multiplication over addition or subtraction would definitely be more efficient for comprehensive understanding of numbers and operations.

Example 1.1

Simplify $555(143-88) - 45 \times 6 - 549(143-88)$.

Notice that this expression can be though of as

$(143-88)(555-549) - 45 \times 6 = 6(143-88) - 45 \times 6$

$= 6(143-88-45) = 6 \times 10 = 60$.

Problem 1.6

Simplify the following:

a) $4 \times 128 \times \left(\frac{1}{4}\right)$

b) $81 \times 5^2 - 71 \times 5^2$

c) $25 \times (13 \times 4)$

Solution 1.6

a) Using associative and commutative properties of multiplication,

$$4 \times \left(128 \times \frac{1}{4}\right) = 4 \times \left(\frac{1}{4} \times 128\right)$$
$$= \left(4 \times \frac{1}{4}\right) \times 128$$
$$= 1 \times 128$$
$$= 128$$

b) Using the distributive property of multiplication over subtraction

$$81 \times 5^2 - 71 \times 5^2 = (81-71) \times 5^2$$
$$= 10 \times 25$$
$$= 250$$

c) Using associative and commutative properties of multiplication

$$25 \times (13 \times 4) = 25 \times (4 \times 13)$$
$$= (25 \times 4) \times 13$$
$$= 100 \times 13$$
$$= 1300$$

Definition 1.1 — Natural Numbers.

$\mathbb{N} = \{1, 2, 3, 4, 5, ...\}$ The natural numbers are also called the counting numbers.

MathTopia Press

Problem 1.7

If $a, b \in \mathbb{N}$ and $a \cdot b = 16$, then $(a+b)_{min} = ?$, and $(a+b)_{max} = ?$ (e: belongs to / element of)

Solution 1.7

a	b	a+b
1	16	17
2	8	10
4	4	8

$(a+b)_{min} = 8$ and $(a+b)_{max} = 17$

Definition 1.2 — Whole Numbers.

Whole numbers are positive numbers, including zero, without any decimal or fractional parts. They are numbers that represent whole things without pieces. The set of whole numbers is represented mathematically by the set

$\mathbb{W} = \{0, 1, 2, 3, 4, 5 ...\}$

MathTopia Press

Problem 1.8

Let a;b be whole numbers, then how many different a values satisfy $4a + 5b = 220$?

A. 6　　B. 8　　C. 12　　D. 15　　E. 16

Solution 1.8

If we divide both sides of the given equation by 5 and find b, then we get $b = 44 - \frac{4a}{5}$.

It is easy to see that a has to be multiple of 5. Since wholenumbers are greater than zero or equal to zero, $b = 44 - \frac{4a}{5} \geq 0$ and $a \leq 55$ that is $a = \{0, 5, 10, 15, \ldots, 55\}$ which is 12 different whole numbers.

Correct answer is C.

Problem 1.9

If x, y, z are distinct whole numbers and $2x + 3y + 4z = 75$, then what is the maximum value of z ?

A. 20　　B. 19　　C. 18　　D. 17　　E. 16

Solution 1.9

If x and y have minimum values, then z gets its maximum. For $x = 0$ and $y = 1$ we get

$$2 \cdot 0 + 3 \cdot 1 + 4 \cdot z = 75$$
$$4z = 72$$
$$z = 18$$

Correct answer is C.

Definition 1.3 — Integers.

Any number that is not a fraction or decimal.
- Positive integers, $\mathbb{Z}^+ = \{1, 2, 3, ...\}$,
- Negative integers, $\mathbb{Z}^- = \{..... , -3, -2, -1\}$,
- Integers, $\mathbb{Z} = \mathbb{Z}^- \cup \{0\} \cup \mathbb{Z}^+$, 0 has no sign.

Problem 1.10

If $a, b \in \mathbb{Z}$, $a \cdot b = 6$ and $b \cdot c = 15$, then $(a \cdot b \cdot c)_{min} = ?$

Solution 1.10

If $a \cdot b = 1 \cdot 6 = (-1)(-6) = 2 \cdot 3 = (-2) \cdot (-3)$ and $b \cdot c = 1 \cdot 15 = (-1) \cdot (-15) = 3 \cdot 5 = (-3) \cdot (-5)$, then $(a \cdot b \cdot c)_{min} = (-6) \cdot (-1) \cdot (-15) = -90$

Problem 1.11

If a, b, c are positive integers, $a+b = 10$ and $b + c = 8$, then $(a \cdot c)_{max} = ?$

A. 40　　B. 48　　C. 54　　D. 63　　E. 80

Solution 1.11

To find $(a \cdot c)_{max}$ we should find a_{max} and c_{max} that is $b = 1$.

If $b = 1$, then $a = 9$ and $c = 7$, so $(a \cdot c)_{max}$ $= 9 \cdot 7 = 63$.

Correct answer is D.

Problem 1.12

If a, b, c are positive integers, $a + b = 12$ and $b - c = 6$, then $(a \cdot b \cdot c)_{min} = ?$

A. 30   B. 35   C. 36   D. 48   E. 64

Solution 1.12

To find $(a \cdot b \cdot c)_{min}$ we should find a_{min}, b_{min} and c_{min} that is since $b > c$, then $c = 1$.

If $c = 1$, then $b = 7$ and $a = 5$ that is $(a \cdot b \cdot c)_{min}$ $= 5 \cdot 7 \cdot 1 = 35$.

Correct answer is B.

Definition 1.4 — Odd and Even Numbers.

An odd number is an integer which is not a multiple of two. An integer that is not an odd number is an even number.

If an odd number is divided by two the result is a fraction. One is the first odd positive number. The next four bigger odd numbers are three, five, seven, and nine. Alternatively, a single symbol for the set of even numbers is 2a. Likewise, since any odd number must have the form 2a+1 for some integer a. Odd and even numbers are either positive or negative.

- Odd Numbers $= \{..., -5, -3, -1, 1, 3, 5, ...\}$
- Even Numbers $= \{..., -6, -4, -2, 0, 2, 4, ...\}$

Addition-Subtraction and Multiplication table of Odd and Even Numbers

∓	odd	even	x	odd	even
odd	even	odd	odd	odd	even
even	odd	even	even	even	even

Remark 1.3

If x is an odd number and y is an even number, then for $n \in \mathbb{Z}^+$, x^n is odd and y^n is even.

Example 1.2

Let a, b, c be integers and $(2a+b)^{20} = 2c+3$.
Is b even or odd?
$2c+3$ is always odd. If $(2a+b)^{20}$ is odd, then $(2a+b)$ is odd.
If $(2a+b)$ is odd, then b is odd.

Problem 1.13

If a is an even natural number, then which of the following is odd number?

A. a^5+2^7 B. a^2-a^5+a8 C. $3^a+a^a+5^{11}$

D. $a^7+3a^3+5^a$ E. $a^{11}+10^{12}$

Solution 1.13

$a^7+3a^3+5^a = \underbrace{(a^7+3a^3)}_{even}+5^a = even+odd = odd$

Correct answer is D.

Problem 1.14

Let a; b and c be positive integer numbers,

if $\dfrac{2a}{b+c} = 3$, then which one of the following cannot not correct?

A. b and c are odd numbers

B. if b is even, then c is even

C. if b is odd, then c is odd

D. if c is odd, then b is even

E. c is even

MathTopia Press

Solution 1.14

If $\dfrac{2a}{b+c} = 3$, then $2a = 3(b+c)$. Since $2a$ is even number, $3(b+c)$ is even and also $(b+c)$ is even.

If $(b+c)$ is even, then b and c are either both even or both odd.

Correct answer is D.

Remark 1.4

Multiplication of two consecutive integers is always even. Let x be an integer, $x(x+1)$ is always even.

Example 1.3

Let a, b, c be integers and $\dfrac{(a-2)b+7}{c} = c+1$.

Find if a, b are odd or even?

$\dfrac{(a-2)b+7}{c} = c + 1 \implies (a-2) \cdot b+7 = c(c+1)$

where $c(c+1)$ is always even

$(a-2)b+7$ is even $\implies (a-2)b$ is odd$) \implies (a-2)$ is odd and b is odd

$a-2$ is odd $\implies$ a is odd $\implies$ a and b are both odd.

Example 1.4

Let a, b, c, d be integers and $ab+6c = 4d+10$. Find if a, b are odd or even?

$6c$, $4d + 10$ are even $\implies$ ab is even

ab is even $\implies$ at least one of a and b is even

Problem 1.15

Let n be a positive integer. Which of the followings is always even?

A. $(3n-5)^3$ B. $2n^3+3$ C. $(2n-1)^4$

     D. $(n+1)(n+4)$ E. $(n+1)^3+3$

Solution 1.15

$(n+1)(n+4)$ is always even. If n is even, then $n+1$ is odd and $n+4$ is even so the. Product is even. If n is odd, then $n+1$ is even so the product is even.

Correct answer is D.

Remark 1.5

To get the nth odd number, use $2n-1$. The difference between the two consecutive squares

Remark. The difference between the two consecutive squares is $a^2+2a+1-a^2 = 2a+1$

Remark. Sum of cubes of first n natural numbers is $2^3+4^3+\cdots+(2n)^3 = 2(n(n+1))^2$.

Remark. Sum of cube of first n odd natural numbers $1^3+3^3+\cdots+(2n-1)^3 = n^2(2n^2-1)$.

Problem 1.16

Suppose a and b are integers such that $ab = a+b+91$. Which of the following is always true for a and b, respectively?

A) odd, odd   B) even, even   C) a+b is odd

          D) odd, even   E) even, odd

Solution 1.16

If b is even, then left side will be even. On the right side we have $a+b+91$, that is $a+even+91 = a+odd$, so a is odd. Similarly; If b is odd, then left side would be even or odd. On the right side we have $a+b+91$, that is $a+odd+91 = a+even$, so a could be even or odd.

The answer is D.

Remark 1.6

Multiplication rules of same or dif-ferent signs.

a) $(+)(+) = (+)$ and $(-)(-) = (+)$.

b) $(+)(-) = (-)$ and $(-)(+) = (-)$.

Gauss Sums

The sum of consecutive positive integers up to n is given by

$$1+2+3+\ldots+n = \frac{n(n+1)}{2}.$$

This formula is also called "Gauss Sums".

Problem 1.17

Find the sum of $11+12+\ldots+99+100$.

Solution 1.17

$$
\begin{aligned}
11+12+\ldots+100 &= (1+2+\ldots+100) \\
&\quad -(1+2+\ldots+10) \\
&= \frac{100 \cdot 101}{2} - \frac{10 \cdot 11}{2} \\
&= 5050-55 = 4995
\end{aligned}
$$

Problem 1.18

Find the sum of $2+4+6+\ldots+50$.

Solution 1.18

$$
\begin{aligned}
2+4+6+\ldots+50 &= 2 \cdot 1+2+\ldots+2 \cdot 25 \\
&= 2(1+2+\ldots+25) \\
&= 2 \cdot \frac{25 \cdot 26}{2} \\
&= 650
\end{aligned}
$$

Remark 1.7

Remark Sum of Even/Odd Numbers.

$2+4+6+\ldots+2n = n(n+1)$

$1+3+5+\ldots+(2n-1) = n^2$

Number of integers between two integers

If a and b are integers with $a < b$, then there are $(b-a)-1$ numbers between numbers a and b, not including a or b and there are $(b-a)+1$ numbers including a and b.

Example 1.5

There are $(77-13)-1 = 63$ integers between 13 and 77, not including 13 and 77.

Example 1.6

Find the number of integers between 1 and 1000 (exclusive) that are divisible by 3. Those numbers are 3, 6, . . . ,333 and they have the same number of integers with 1, 2, . . . , 999. So, there are 333 numbers between 1 and 1000 are divisible by 3.

Problem 1.19

How many numbers between 18 and 792 are divisible by 6 (inclusive)?

Problem 1.20

Compute $21 + 23 + 25 + \ldots + 99$.

MathTopia Press

1. Simplify $80 - 64 \div 8 \times 4$.

   A) –16   B) 0   C) 32   D) 48   E) 78

4. Simplify $6 + 3(8 - 3) \div 5 - 2^3$.

   A) –2   B) –1   C) 0   D) 1   E) 2

2. Simplify $16 - 4 \div (1 \div 4) + 1$.

   A) –4   B) 0   C) 1   D) 4   E) 5

5. Evan uses only the whole number 1–9, no more than one time each in order to obtain the smallest number by filling the following boxes

   $$\boxed{}\boxed{} \times \boxed{}\boxed{}$$

   What's the difference between two numbers?

   A) 7   B) 8   C) 9   D) 10   E) 11

3. Compute the following and find the sum of all digit:

   $7346 \times 1425 + 2654 \times 1425$.

   A) 10   B) 12   C) 16   D) 18   E) 20

6. Let X and Y be the following sum of sequence
   $$X = 20 + 22 + 24 + ... + 100$$
   and
   $$Y = 22 + 24 + ... + 102$$
   What is the value of $Y - X$?

   A) 82   B) 102   C) 122   D) 162   E) 202

MathTopia Press

7. What is the largest value of the expression $a \times b^c$ when a, b, and c are replaced with 2, 3, and 4 using each number once?

   A) 36   B) 48   C) 64   D) 128   E) 162

8. Consider the following student work:
   $84 \times 45 = 20 + 400 + 160 + 320$.
   Which of the following is correct?

   A) There is an error with 20
   B) There is an error with 160
   C) There is an error with 320
   D) There is an error with 400
   E) There is no error

9. Simplify $2.5 \times 1.8 + 2.5 \times 8.2$.

   A) 15   B) 17.5   C) 18.5   D) 22.5   E) 25

10. How many terms are in the following sequences 13, 16, 19, ..., 79, 82, 85?

    A) 20   B) 21   C) 24   D) 25   E) 31

11. What is the largest value of the expression $a + b^c$ when a, b, and c are replaced with 2, 3, and 4 using each number once?

    A) 48   B) 66   C) 72   D) 83   E) 625

12. How many ordered pair of positive integers (m, n) that satisfy $n + m^2 \leq 17$?

    A) 12   B) 34   C) 38   C) 42   E) 51

1. How many positive integers less than 10 can be obtained by using 1, 2, 3, 4 only once while four basic operations and parentheses are allowed?

   A) 4   B) 6   C) 7   D) 8   E) 9

2. Given the equation

   AB + CD = EFG (EFG is a 3-digit number,

   AB and CD are 2-digit numbers)

   place each of the digits 0, 1, 2, 3, 4, 5 and 6 in one of the letters.

   What is EFG?

   A) 102   B) 104   C) 105   D) 106   E) None

3. Suppose a and b are integers and a + b is an odd number. Which of the following is always true?

   I. a − 2b is even

   II. ab is even

   III. 4a + b is even

   A) Only I   B) Only II   C) Only III
            D) I and II   E) I, II and III

4. Let A, B and C be non-negative integers such that A + B + C = 8. What is the maximum value of A × B × C + A × B + A × C + B × C?

   A) 36   B) 39   C) 42   D) 45   E) 48

5. If a, b, c $\in$ Z$^+$, a · b = 13 and b · c = 12, then what is the value of a + b + c?

   A) 23   B) 24   C) 25   D) 26   E) 27

6. If a, b are distinct digits, then what is the maximum value of 7a + 5b?

   A) 101   B) 103   C) 107   D) 110   E) 117

MathTopia Press

7. If $x, y, z \in \mathbb{W}$, $x = 3y + 4$ and $y = z + 5$, then what is the minimum value of x?

   A) 19   B) 20   C) 21   D) 22   E) 23

8. Let x and y be distinct positive integers. How many distinct x values satisfy the given equation $5x + 6y = 120$?

   A) 2   B) 3   C) 4   D) 5   E) 6

9. If sum of the four distinct two-digit numbers is 320, then what is the minimum value of the smallest number?

   A) 25   B) 26   C) 27   D) 28   E) 29

10. If $a < b < 0 < c$, then which one of the followings is always positive?

    A) $(a - c)(b - a)$ B) $(c - b)(b + a)$ C) $a^2 b^3$

    D) $-b^2(b - c)$ E) $(-b^2)(-a)^2$

11. If $x, y \in \mathbb{Z}$ and $x = \dfrac{y + 15}{y}$, then find the number of distinct values of x.

    A) 10   B) 9   C) 8   D) 7   E) 6

12. Suppose a is an odd number and b is an even number. Which of the following is always be an odd number?

    A) $a(a + 1) + b$ B) $b^2 + a^2 + 1$
    C) $a^2 - (b + 1)^2$ D) $ab + a + b$
    E) $3a + 2b + 1$

MathTopia Press

Problem Set 1

1. Multiplication and division operations have priority over addition and substraction. If multiplication and division operations are used in a single expression, the left-most operation (multiplication or division) is dealt with first. Therefore,

   $80 - 64 \div 8 \times 4 = 80 - 8 \times 4$

   $= 80 - 32 = 48$

   The answer is D

2. For any a and b integers ($b \neq 0$),

   $a \div (1 \div b) = a \times b$. Therefore,

   $16 - 4 \div (1 \div 4) + 1 = 16 - 4 \times 4 + 1$

   $= 16 - 16 + 1 = 1$

   The answer is C

3. Multiplication has distribution property over addition. Hence,

   $7346 \times 1425 + 2654 \times 1425$

   $= (7346 + 2654) \times 1425 = 10000 \times 1425$

   $= 14250000$

   The sum of all digit of 14250000 is

   $1 + 4 + 2 + 5 + 0 + 0 + 0 + 0 = 12$.

   The answer is B

4. Parentheses have priority over other mathematical operations. Therefore,

   $6 + 3(8 - 3) \div 5 - 2^3 = 6 + 3 \times 5 \div 5 - 8$

   $= 6 + 15 \div 5 - 8 = 6 + 3 - 8 = 1$

   The answer is D

5. To obtain the smallest number, we should use only 1, 2, 3 and 4. AB $\times$ CD can be

   $13 \times 24 = 312$, $14 \times 23 = 322$ or $12 \times 34 = 408$. We do not need to compute other possibilities since they are clearly not the smallest number can be obtained

   (for example, $31 \times 24 > 13 \times 24$).

   Hence, two numbers are 24 and 13, and

   $24 - 13 = 11$.

   The answer is E

6. Let's define $Z = 22 + 24 + \cdots + 100$. It can be seen that $X = 20 + Z$ and $Y = 102 + Z$. Hence,

   $Y - X = (102 + Z) - (20 + Z) = 102 - 20 = 82$

   The answer is A

7. Since all numbers are positive integers, we should choose b and c greater than a to obtain the largest value. So, there are two possibilities,

   $2 \times 3^4 = 162$ or $2 \times 4^3 = 128$.

   The largest value is 162.

   The answer is E

MathTopia Press

8. We can write 84 as 80 + 4 and 45 as 40 + 5.

$84 \times 45 = (80 + 4) \times (40 + 5)$

$= 3200 + 400 + 160 + 20$

Therefore, 320 in the given equation should have been 3200.

The answer is C

9. Multiplication has distribution property over addition. Therefore,

$2.5 \times 1.8 + 2.5 \times 8.2 = 2.5 \times (1.8 + 8.2)$

$= 2.5 \times 10 = 25$

The answer is E

10. There is a formula for number of terms of an arithmetic sequence as follows

Number of terms =

$$\frac{\text{Last term} - \text{Firs term}}{\text{Common difference of successive members}} + 1$$

Therefore, number of terms is

$\frac{85 - 13}{3} + 1 = 25$.

The answer is D

11. We should choose b and c greater than a to obtain the largest value because power functions are increasing faster than linear functions.

So, there are two possibilities,

$2 + 3^4 = 83$ or $2 + 4^3 = 66$.

The largest value is 83.

The answer is D

12. Since n is a positive integer, $n \geq 1$, and thus, $16 \geq m^2$. So, m can be 1, 2, 3 or 4.

If m = 1, $n \leq 16$, and there are 16 pairs of (m, n).

If m = 2, $n \leq 13$, and there are 13 pairs of (m, n).

If m = 3, $n \leq 8$, and there are 8 pairs of (m, n).

If m = 4, $n \leq 1$, and there are 1 pairs of (m, n).

In total, there are 38 pairs of positive integers (m, n).

The answer is C

Problem Set 2

1. There are two ways to approach to this question. In both cases, we can obtain all 1, 2, . . . , 9 numbers. If it is allowed not to use all 1, 2, 3, 4 numbers, $1 = 1, 2 = 2, 3 = 3, 4 = 4, 5 = 2 + 3$, $6 = 2 \times 3, 7 = 3 + 4, 8 = 2 \times 4$, and $9 = 2 + 3 + 4$.

If all numbers have to be used,

$1 = (4 - 3) \times (2 - 1), 2 = 1 + 2 + 3 - 4$,

$3 = (4 - 1) \times (3 - 2), 4 = 1 + 2 - 3 + 4$,

$5 = (4 + 1) \times (3 - 2), 6 = 1 - 2 + 3 + 4$,

$7 = (4 + 3) \times (2 - 1), 8 = -1 + 2 + 3 + 4$, and $9 = 4 + 3 + (2 \div 1)$.

Therefore, there are 9 positive integers can be obtained.

The answer is E

MathTopia Press

2. Since AB and CD are 2-digit numbers,

AB + CD ≤ 64 + 53 = 117.

So, E = 1 and F = 0. If neither A nor C is 6,

then AB + CD ≤ 56 + 43 < 100.

Hence A or C is 6. Without loss of generality, assume A = 6. In this case, C cannot be less than 4, otherwise,

AB + CD ≤ 65 + 34 < 100. Also C cannot be 5 because AB + CD ≤ 60 + 50 ≤ 110.

So, C = 4. Therefore,

AB + CD = 6B + 4D = 100 + B + D = 100 + G,

in other words, B + D = G.

It is 2 + 3 = 5. Therefore, G = 5, EFG = 105.

The answer is C

3. If a + b is odd, then exactly one of a and b is odd, other one is even. Hence, ab is even. However, a − 2b or 4a + b does not have to be even.

For (a, b) = (5, 2), a − 2b = 1 is odd.

For (a, b) = (0, 1), 4a + b = 1 is odd.

Therefore, only II is always true.

The answer is B

4. Let's change variables as

A = a − 1, B = b − 1, and C = c − 1.

a + b + c = A + B + C + 3 = 11, and

ABC + AB + AC + BC = (a − 1)(b − 1)(c − 1) +

(a − 1)(b − 1) + (a − 1)(c − 1) + (b − 1)(c − 1)

= abc − a − b − c + 2 = abc − 9

So we need to find the maximum value of abc. Because the sum of a, b, c is given (constant), the maximum value of their product is obtained when varibles are close to each other.

For (a, b, c) = (4, 4, 3), abc − 9 = 48 −9 = 39.

The answer is B

MathTopia Press

5. By the given equations, b divides both 13 and 12. Hence, b divides gcd (13, 12) = 1. So, b = 1.

As a result, a = 13, c = 12, and a + b + c= 26.

The answer is D

6. Since a and b are distinct digits, then

a + b ≤ 9 + 8 = 17. Therefore,

7a + 5b = 2a + 5(a + b) ≤ 2 × 9 + 5 × 17 = 103

Equality is satisfied when a = 9 and b = 8.

The answer is B

7. Since $z \geq 0$, then $y = z + 5 \geq 5$. Therefore,

   $x = 3y + 4 \$ 3 \geq 5 + 4 = 19$.

   Equality holds when $(x, y, z) = (19, 5, 0)$.

   The answer is A

8. Because 120 and 5x are divisible by 5, 6y is also divisible by 5. Similarly, 5x is divisible by 6.

   So, there exist a and b positive integers such that $x = 6a$ and $y = 5b$.

   $5(6a) + 6(5b) = 30(a + b) = 120) a + b = 4$

   Therefore, a can be 1, 2, 3.

   For each a, there exists exactly one x value.

   So, there are 3 different x values.

   The answer is B

9. To find minimum value of the smallest number, other numbers should be chosen as 99, 98, and 97. In this case, the smallest number is

   $320 - (99 + 98 + 97) = 320 - 294 = 26$.

   The answer is B

10. If we choose $(a, b, c) = (-2, -1, 1)$,

    $(a - c)(b - a) = -3 < 0$

    $(c - b)(b + a) = -9 < 0$

    $a^2 b^3 = -4 < 0$

    $(-b^2)(-a)^2 = -4 < 0$

    Expressions in A, B, C, and E might not be positive.

    However, $-b^2(b-c) > 0$ since $b - c$ and $-b^2$ are negative.

    The answer is D

11. If we write equation as $x = 1 + \dfrac{15}{y}$, we can see that y divides 15.

    So, y can be $-15, -5, -3, -1, 1, 3, 5, 15$.

    For each y, there is exactly one x value.

    Hence, there are 8 different values of x.

    The answer is C

12. For $a = 1$ and $b = 0$, all options are even. So, none of them have to be odd number. For the version the suggestion applied, $ab + a + b$ is even since ab is even, a is odd, and b is even.

    The answer is D

MathTopia Press

RATIONAL NUMBERS

Definition 2.1 — Rational Numbers.

A rational number is any number that can be expressed as the quotient or fraction p/q of two integers, a numerator p and a non-zero denominator q. Since q may be equal to 1, every integer is a rational number. The rational numbers are designated by $\mathbb{Q}$.

Remark 2.1

For integers a and b,

- $\frac{0}{b} = 0$ when $b \neq 0$, and $\frac{b}{0}$ is undefined otherwise.

- If the numerator of a fraction is smaller than its denominator, it is called a proper (or simple) fraction. If $\frac{a}{b}$ is simple fraction, then $-1 < \frac{a}{b} < 1$

- If the numerator of a fraction is greater than or equal to its denominator, it is called an improper fraction. If $\frac{a}{b}$ is improper fraction, then $\frac{a}{b} \leq -1$ or $\frac{a}{b} \geq 1$

- A number which consists of a whole number and a proper fraction is called a mixed number.

  $a\frac{b}{c} = a + \frac{b}{c} = \frac{a \cdot c + b}{c}$

- Let a, b, k be natural numbers with $b \neq 0$ and $k \neq 0$. Then $\frac{ak}{bk} = \frac{a}{b}$

MathTopia Press

Problem 2.1

Find a fraction with denominator 120 equivalent to $\frac{13}{24}$.

Solution

Observe that $120 \div 24 = 5$. Thus
$$\frac{13}{24} = \frac{13 \cdot 5}{24 \cdot 5} = \frac{65}{120}.$$

Problem 2.2

Order the rational numbers, $\frac{6}{7}, \frac{1}{7}, \frac{5}{7}, \frac{9}{7}$ from largest to smallest.

Solution

If all the rational numbers have a common denominator, then the rational number with the biggest numerator is the biggest number,

$$\frac{9}{7} > \frac{6}{7} > \frac{5}{7} > \frac{1}{7}$$

Problem 2.3

Compare and order the following rational numbers.
$\frac{4}{7}, \frac{5}{9}, \frac{2}{3}, \frac{10}{17}$ from

Solution

Let us equalize the numerators.

- Find the least common multiple of the numerators:
  LCM(4, 5, 2, 10) = 20

- Equalize the numerators:
  $$\frac{4\cdot5}{7\cdot5}=\frac{20}{35}, \frac{5\cdot4}{9\cdot4}=\frac{20}{36}, \frac{2\cdot10}{3\cdot10}=\frac{20}{30}, \frac{10\cdot2}{17\cdot2}=\frac{20}{34}$$

- Compare the numbers:
  $$\frac{20}{30}>\frac{20}{34}>\frac{20}{35}>\frac{20}{36} \Rightarrow \frac{2}{3},\frac{10}{17},\frac{4}{7},\frac{5}{9}$$

Problem 2.4

Order the rational numbers:
$$\frac{11}{5},\frac{11}{13},\frac{11}{3},\frac{11}{12}$$

Solution

If all the rational numbers have a common numerator, then the rational number with the smallest denominator is the biggest number:
$$\frac{11}{3}>\frac{11}{5}>\frac{11}{12}>\frac{11}{13}$$

Remark 2.2

Adding or Subtracting rational numbers with different denominators, first we equalize the denominators by enlarging each rational number by the lowest common denominator (LCD). Then we add or subtract the numerators.

Problem 2.5

Add: $\frac{3}{5}+\frac{4}{7}$.

Solution

A common denominator is $5\cdot7=35$.
We thus find
$$\frac{3}{5}+\frac{4}{7}+\frac{3\cdot7}{5\cdot7}+\frac{4\cdot5}{7\cdot5}=\frac{21}{35}+\frac{20}{35}=\frac{41}{35}$$

Example 2.1

To perform the addition $\frac{2}{7}+\frac{1}{5}+\frac{3}{2}$, observe that $7\cdot5\cdot2=70$ is a common denominator. Thus
$$\frac{2}{7}+\frac{1}{5}+\frac{3}{2}=\frac{2\cdot10}{7\cdot10}+\frac{1\cdot14}{5\cdot14}+\frac{3\cdot35}{2\cdot35}$$
$$=\frac{20}{70}+\frac{14}{70}+\frac{105}{70}$$
$$=\frac{20+14+105}{70}$$
$$=\frac{139}{70}.$$

Remark 2.3

Multiplication of Fractions

Let a, b, c, d be natural numbers with $b\neq0$ and $d\neq0$.
Then $\frac{a}{b}\cdot\frac{c}{d}=\frac{ac}{bd}$.

Example 2.2

We have
$$\frac{2}{3}\cdot\frac{3}{7}=\frac{6}{21}=\frac{2}{7},$$
Alternatively, we could have cancelled the common factors, as follows,
$$\frac{2}{\cancel{3}}\cdot\frac{\cancel{3}}{7}=\frac{2}{7},$$

Problem 2.6

Find the exact value of the product
$$\left(1-\frac{2}{5}\right)\left(1-\frac{2}{7}\right)\left(1-\frac{2}{9}\right)\cdots\left(1-\frac{2}{99}\right)\left(1-\frac{2}{101}\right)$$

Solution

We have,
$$\left(1-\frac{2}{5}\right)\left(1-\frac{2}{7}\right)\left(1-\frac{2}{9}\right)\cdots\left(1-\frac{2}{99}\right)\left(1-\frac{2}{101}\right)$$
$$\frac{3}{5}\cdot\frac{5}{7}\cdot\frac{7}{9}\cdot\frac{9}{11}\cdots\frac{97}{99}\cdot\frac{99}{101}=\frac{3}{101}$$

Remark 2.4

To divide rational expressions, multiply by the reciprocal of the divisor.

$$\frac{a}{b} \div \frac{c}{d} = \frac{a}{b} \cdot \frac{d}{c}$$

Example 2.3

We have,

$$\frac{24}{35} \div \frac{20}{7} = \frac{24}{35} \cdot \frac{7}{20} = \frac{4 \cdot 6}{7 \cdot 5} \cdot \frac{7 \cdot 1}{4 \cdot 5} = \frac{6 \cdot 1}{5 \cdot 5} = \frac{6}{25}.$$

Problem 2.7

Which of the expressions below is equivalent to $((X \div (Y \div Z)) \div ((X \div Y) \div Z)$?

Solution

We have,

$$((X \div (Y \div Z)) \div ((X \div Y) \div Z) = \frac{x/(y/z)}{(x/y)/z} = \frac{x \cdot \frac{z}{y}}{\frac{x}{y} \cdot \frac{1}{z}}$$

$$= \frac{\frac{xz}{y}}{\frac{x}{yz}} = \frac{xz}{y} \times \frac{yz}{x} = \frac{xyz^2}{xy} = z^2.$$

Problem 2.8

$$2 + \cfrac{2 + \cfrac{1}{2 + \cfrac{1}{2}}}{2} = ?$$

Solution

$$2 + \cfrac{2 + \cfrac{1}{2 + \cfrac{1}{2}}}{2} = 2 + \cfrac{2 + \cfrac{1}{\frac{5}{2}}}{2} = 2 + \cfrac{2 + \frac{2}{5}}{2}$$

$$= 2 + \cfrac{\frac{12}{5}}{2} = 2 + \frac{12}{10} = \frac{32}{10} = \frac{16}{5} = 3\frac{1}{5}$$

MathTopia Press

Problem 2.9

Simplify $\left(1 + \frac{1}{2}\right) \cdot \left(1 + \frac{1}{3}\right)\left(1 + \frac{1}{4}\right) \cdots \left(1 + \frac{1}{99}\right)$.

Solution

Adding each fraction:

$$\frac{3}{2} \cdot \frac{4}{3} \cdot \frac{5}{4} \cdots \frac{100}{99},$$

which simplifies to $100/2 = 50$.

Remark 2.5

Repeating Decimals

If the decimal is repeating then we can multiply the number with powers of 10 to get the same decimal parts and by subtracting, we get an integer

Example 2.4

$0.\overline{129} = 0.129\ 129\ 129 \ldots = N$

Multiplying both sides by 1000, (since three digits are repeating), we get $1000N = 129.\overline{129}$

Which has the same decimal part as N. Subtracting N from this we get $999N = 129.\ (1000N - N)$

So, $N = \frac{129}{999} = \frac{43}{333}$.

Problem 2.10

Show that $0.9999 \ldots = 1$

Solution

We have $\quad 0.\overline{1} = \frac{1}{9}$

$$0.\overline{9} = \frac{9}{9}$$

$$\Rightarrow 0.\overline{9} = 1$$

Alternate: $A = 0.9999 \ldots \Rightarrow 10A = 9.999 \ldots$

$$10A - A = 9 \Rightarrow 9A = 9 \Rightarrow A = 1$$

Remark 2.6

$$0.\overline{a} = \frac{a}{9} \qquad 0.\overline{ab} = \frac{ab}{99} \qquad 0.a\overline{bc} = \frac{abc - a}{990}$$

Problem 2.11

Find a reduced fraction equivalent to the repeating decimal $0.\overline{123} = 0.123123123. \ldots$

Solution

Let $N = 0.123123123. \ldots$

Then $1000N = 123.123123123. \ldots$

Hence $1000N - N = 123$, whence

$N = \dfrac{123}{999} = \dfrac{41}{333}$ or $N = 0.\overline{123} = \dfrac{123}{999} = \dfrac{41}{333}$.

Problem 2.12

Suppose a and b represent positive numbers. Of the two numbers, a is the smaller and b the larger. What number represents the point one third of the way between a and b on a number line?

Solution

We want to find point C. The distance between a and b is $b - a$.

The distance between a and x is $\dfrac{b-a}{3}$.

To get point C we need to add a and $\dfrac{b-a}{3}$.

$a + \dfrac{b-a}{3} = \dfrac{3a}{3} + \dfrac{b-a}{3} = \dfrac{2a+b}{3}$.

Problem 2.13

Find the point on the number line two-thirds of the way from $\dfrac{3}{4}$ to $\dfrac{4}{3}$.

Solution

$\dfrac{3}{4} = \dfrac{9}{12} = \dfrac{27}{36}$ $\dfrac{4}{3} = \dfrac{16}{12} = \dfrac{48}{36}$

$\dfrac{48-27}{36} = \dfrac{21}{36} = \dfrac{7}{36}$ (each $\dfrac{1}{3}$ distance).

Hence, $x = \dfrac{27+14}{36}$ or $\dfrac{48-7}{36}$

Therefore, $x = \dfrac{41}{36} = 1\dfrac{5}{36}$.

Problem 2.14

If a proper fraction in lowest terms is subtracted from its reciprocal, the difference is $\dfrac{77}{18}$. What is the proper fraction?

Solution

Let $\dfrac{b}{a}$ be our fraction

$\dfrac{a}{b} - \dfrac{b}{a} + \dfrac{77}{18}$ ($\dfrac{a}{b}$ is the reciprocal of $\dfrac{b}{a}$)

$\dfrac{^{ax}a}{_{ax}b} - \dfrac{b^{xb}}{a_{xb}} = \dfrac{77}{18}$

$\dfrac{a^2 - b^2}{ab} = \dfrac{77}{18}$

$\dfrac{(a-b)(a+b)}{ab} = \dfrac{77}{18}$.

Hence, $a = 9$ and $b = 2$.

The proper fraction is $\dfrac{2}{9}$.

Problem 2.15

In an online math practice test, Junaid attempts exactly $\dfrac{3}{4}$ of the problems and answers $\dfrac{5}{8}$ of those problems correctly. When he submits the test, he finds that he answered 105 problems correctly. How many math problems were on this test?

Solution

Answered problems

21 21 21 21 21 21 21 21

| | | | | | | | | $= 21 \times 8 = 168$

105 correct answers

$168 = \dfrac{3}{4}$ of the total number of math problems.

$168 = \dfrac{3}{4} \times T$

$T = 168 \times \dfrac{4}{3} = 224$.

MathTopia Press

Problem 2.16

$$(-5)^2 \times \left(-\frac{1}{5}\right)^3 - 2^3 \div \left(-\frac{1}{2}\right)^2 - (-1)^{1999}.$$

Solution

$$(-5)^2 \times \left(-\frac{1}{5}\right)^3 - 2^3 \div \left(-\frac{1}{2}\right)^2 - (-1)^{1999}$$

$$= 5^2 \times \left(-\frac{1}{125}\right) - 8 \div \left(\frac{1}{4}\right)^2 - (-1)$$

$$= -\frac{1}{5} - 8 \times 4 + 1 = -\frac{1}{5} - 31 = -31\frac{1}{5}.$$

Problem 2.17

Find the value of:

$$\left(1+\frac{1}{1}\right) \times \left(1+\frac{1}{2}\right) \times \left(1+\frac{1}{3}\right) \times \left(1+\frac{1}{4}\right) \times ... \times \left(1+\frac{1}{2022}\right)$$

Solution

We have $1 + \frac{1}{n} = \frac{n+1}{2}$.

We can write the product as follows

$$\frac{2}{1} \times \frac{3}{2} \times \frac{4}{3} \times ... \times \frac{2023}{2022} = 2023$$

The answer is 2023.

Problem 2.18

$$\frac{1}{2} + \frac{1}{6} + \frac{1}{12} + \frac{1}{20} + \frac{1}{30} + \frac{1}{42} + \frac{1}{56} = ?$$

Solution

$$\frac{1}{2} + \frac{1}{6} + \frac{1}{12} + \frac{1}{20} + \frac{1}{30} + \frac{1}{42} + \frac{1}{56}$$

$$\frac{1}{1 \times 2} + \frac{1}{2 \times 3} + \frac{1}{3 \times 4} + ... + \frac{1}{7 \times 8}$$

$$\left(1 - \frac{1}{2}\right) + \left(\frac{1}{2} - \frac{1}{3}\right) + ... + \left(\frac{1}{7} - \frac{1}{8}\right)$$

$$= 1 - \frac{1}{8} = \frac{7}{8}$$

The answer is $\frac{7}{8}$.

Problem 2.19

If $x = \frac{8}{3} + \frac{11}{4} + \frac{14}{5}$, then what is the value of

$\frac{2}{3} + \frac{3}{4} + \frac{4}{5}$ in terms of x?

Solution

Let $\frac{2}{3} + \frac{3}{4} + \frac{4}{5}$ be Y.

Then $x - y = \left(\frac{8}{3} - \frac{2}{3}\right) + \left(\frac{11}{4} - \frac{3}{4}\right) + \left(\frac{14}{5} - \frac{4}{5}\right)$

$x - y = 2 + 2 + 2 \Rightarrow x - y = 6$.

Therefore, $y = 6 - x$.

Problem 2.20

The fraction $\frac{7}{13}$ is equal to

$0.\overline{538461} = 0.5384615384615....$

What is the 2020th digit to the right of the decimal point?

Solution

Since the number of repeating digit is 6 we divide 2020 by 6.

$2020 = 336 \times 6 + 4$

2016th digit is 1.

2020th digit is 4.

Problem 2.21

If $a = \frac{11}{12} + \frac{13}{14} + \frac{15}{16} + \frac{17}{18}$ then, what is the value of

$\frac{1}{12} + \frac{1}{14} + \frac{1}{16} + \frac{1}{18}$ in terms of a?

MathTopia Press

Problem 2.22

Suppose x, y, and z are positive integers such that

$x + \dfrac{1}{y + \dfrac{1}{z}} = \dfrac{11}{3}$, what is $x + y + z$?

Problem 2.24

Find the sum

$$\frac{1}{3 \times 5} + \frac{1}{5 \times 7} + \frac{1}{7 \times 9} + \frac{1}{9 \times 11} + \frac{1}{11 \times 13}$$

MathTopia Press

Problem 2.23

Suppose a, b, and c are different integers.

What is $a \cdot b \cdot c$ if $\dfrac{2}{a} + \dfrac{3}{b} + \dfrac{b}{c}$ gets the largest possible value?

A) 15   B) 24   C) 27   D) 30

Problem 2.25

$a = 0.\overline{24}$

$b = 0.2\overline{75}$

$c = 106 = ?$

1. 2.999... + 3.999... = ?

    A) 4   B) 5   C) 6   D) 7   E) 8

2. How many integers x satisfy $\frac{1}{15} < \frac{x}{60} < \frac{1}{4}$?

    A) 7   B) 8   C) 9   D) 10   E) 11

3. For how many positive integers x is $\frac{15}{2x-3}$ improper fraction?

    A) 3   B) 6   C) 9   D) 12   E) 15

4. Find $\frac{x+y}{z}$ where x, y, and z are the midpoints of the given intervals.

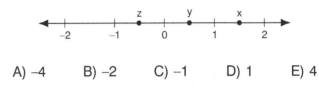

    A) –4   B) –2   C) –1   D) 1   E) 4

5. $\frac{x}{y} = \frac{2}{3}$ and $\frac{y}{z} = \frac{3}{4}$. Find $(x-z) \cdot \frac{1}{y} + \frac{y}{x-z}$.

    A) –1   B) $-\frac{7}{6}$ C) $-\frac{5}{3}$ D) $-\frac{13}{6}$ E) $-\frac{5}{2}$

6. $A = \frac{0.01}{0.2} + \frac{0.02}{0.3} + \frac{0.03}{0.4}$ and

    $B = \frac{0.19}{0.2} + \frac{0.14}{0.15} + \frac{0.37}{0.4}$.

    Find A + B.

    A) 0.3   B) 0.1   C) 3   D) 3.6   E) None

MathTopia Press

7. Simplify $1 - \dfrac{3}{1 - \dfrac{4}{2 + \dfrac{1}{4}}} \div \dfrac{3}{7}$

A) $-\dfrac{4}{7}$　　B) $-\dfrac{20}{3}$　　C) $-\dfrac{20}{7}$　　D) $-\dfrac{40}{7}$

E) None of the preceding

8. What is the value of

$\left(1 - \dfrac{9}{2}\right)\left(1 - \dfrac{9}{3}\right)\left(1 - \dfrac{9}{4}\right)\left(1 - \dfrac{9}{5}\right)\ldots\ldots\left(1 - \dfrac{9}{71}\right)$?

A) $\dfrac{70}{71}$　　B) $\dfrac{9}{13}$　　C) 0　　D) 1　　E) $\dfrac{9}{71}$

9. Suppose x, y, and z are positive integers such that $x + \dfrac{1}{y + \dfrac{1}{z}} = \dfrac{11}{3}$, what is x + y + z?

A) 6　　B) 7　　C) 8　　D) 9　　E) 10

10. What is the exact point at three forth of the way between

$1\dfrac{1}{3}$ and $1\dfrac{3}{4}$?

A) $\dfrac{19}{12}$　　B) $\dfrac{35}{24}$　　C) $\dfrac{79}{48}$　　D) $\dfrac{37}{48}$　　E) $\dfrac{39}{48}$

11. Let x, y, and z are decimal numbers such that

x = 1.45a, y = 1.4a3, z = 1.a53 where a is a digit. If $x < y < z$, then what is the smallest possible value of a?

A) 3　　B) 4　　C) 5　　D) 6　　E) None

12. Suppose $\dfrac{2000}{2001} + \dfrac{2002}{2003} + \dfrac{2004}{2005} = a$,

what is the value of

$\dfrac{1}{2001} + \dfrac{1}{2003} + \dfrac{1}{2005}$ in terms of a?

A) $4 - a$　B) $3 - a$　C) $a + 3$　D) $a + 4$　E) $2005a$

MathTopia Press

1. Find the sum of all possible values that make

$$\dfrac{3}{2-\dfrac{1}{4-a}}$$ undefined.

  A) 4   B) $\dfrac{7}{2}$ C) 0   D) $\dfrac{15}{2}$ E) $\dfrac{17}{2}$

2. The fraction $\dfrac{\frac{2}{4}}{3}$ is 6 times of the fraction $\dfrac{\frac{3}{2}}{x}$.

  Find x.

  A) 9   B) 6   C) 4   D) 2   E) 1

3. If $x = \dfrac{8}{3} + \dfrac{11}{4} + \dfrac{14}{5}$, then what is the value of

  $\dfrac{2}{3} + \dfrac{3}{4} + \dfrac{4}{5}$ in terms of x?

  A) $x + 3$ B) $x - 6$ C) $x - 2$

        D) $x - 4$ E) None

4. Suppose a; b, and c are positive integers such

  that $a + \dfrac{1}{b + \dfrac{1}{c}} = \dfrac{23}{4}$.

  Find $a + b + c$.

  A) 5   B) 6   C) 8   D) 9   E) 10

5. Suppose n is an integer such that $\dfrac{n}{21}$ is between

  $\dfrac{5}{14}$ and $\dfrac{5}{12}$. What is n?

  A) 4   B) 5   C) 6   D) 7   E) 8

6. Suppose x, y, z, and t are positive integers and

  $x + \dfrac{1}{y + \dfrac{1}{z + \dfrac{1}{t}}} = \dfrac{23}{7}$.

  What is $x + y + z + t$?

  A) 6   B) 7   C) 8   D) 9   E) 11

MathTopia Press

7. If $A = \dfrac{21}{19} + \dfrac{11}{29}$, what is $\dfrac{18}{29} - \dfrac{2}{19}$ in terms of A?

   A) $2 - A$ B) $1 - A$ C) A

           D) $A + 1$ E) $A + 2$

8. For how many n integers is $\dfrac{1}{3} \le \dfrac{n}{2003} \le \dfrac{1}{2}$?

   A) 333   B) 334   C) 335   D) 336   E) 337

9. Let m and n are integers such that $\dfrac{3}{4} < \dfrac{n}{m} < \dfrac{4}{5}$. What is the smallest value of m?

   A) 7   B) 9   C) 12   D) 20   E) 40

10. Find the product of

$$\left(1 - \frac{4}{1}\right) \cdot \left(1 - \frac{4}{9}\right) \cdot \left(1 - \frac{4}{25}\right) \cdots \left(1 - \frac{4}{625}\right).$$

   A) $-\dfrac{17}{25}$ B) $-\dfrac{23}{25}$ C) $-\dfrac{27}{25}$

           D) $-\dfrac{31}{29}$ E) $-\dfrac{37}{25}$

11. If the fraction $\dfrac{39}{14}$ can be written as

$$2 + \cfrac{1}{1 + \cfrac{1}{x + \cfrac{1}{y + \cfrac{1}{z}}}}$$

What is (x, y, z)?

   A) (3, 1, 2)   B) (2, 1, 3)   C) (1, 1, 3)

           D) (14, 11, 3)   E) (2, 14, 3)

12. What is the product of the following fractions

$$\left(1 - \frac{1}{4}\right) \cdot \left(1 - \frac{1}{9}\right) \cdot \left(1 - \frac{1}{16}\right) \cdots \left(1 - \frac{1}{(n + 1)^2}\right)?$$

   A) $\dfrac{n + 2}{2n + 2}$ B) $\dfrac{n + 2}{2n + 3}$ C) $\dfrac{n + 1}{2n + 3}$

           D) $\dfrac{n + 1}{2n + 5}$ E) None

MathTopia Press

Problem Set 1

1. For any non-negative integer a,

   $a.999\cdots = a + 1$. Therefore,

   $2.999\cdots + 3.999\cdots = 3 + 4 = 7$

   The answer is D

2. If we multiply the inequality with 60, we will obtain that $4 < x < 15$

   Hence, $x \in \{5, 6, \ldots, 14\}$, there are 10 integers.

   The answer is D

3. For a, b integers with $b \neq 0$, $\frac{a}{b}$ is called improper fraction if $a \geq b$.

   Hence, $15 \geq 2x - 3$ and $9 \geq x$.

   There are 9 possible positive integers.

   The answer is C

4. In the given line, $x = \frac{3}{2}$, $y = \frac{1}{2}$, and $z = -\frac{1}{2}$

   Therefore, $\frac{x + y}{z} = -4$

   The answer is A

5. If we say $x = 2k$, others are found as $y = 3k$ and $z = 4k$.

   $(x - z) \cdot \frac{1}{y} + \frac{y}{x - z} = \frac{-2k}{3k} + \frac{3k}{-2k} = -\frac{13}{6}$

   The answer is D

6. By summing them directly,

   $A + B = \left(\frac{0.01}{0.2} + \frac{0.19}{0.2}\right) + \left(\frac{0.02}{0.3} + \frac{0.28}{0.3}\right) +$

   $\left(\frac{0.03}{0.4} + \frac{0.37}{0.4}\right) = 1 + 1 + 1 = 3$

   The answer is C

7. Let's organize the expression,

   $1 - \dfrac{3}{1 - \dfrac{4}{2 + \frac{1}{4}}} \div \dfrac{3}{7} = 1 - \dfrac{3}{1 - \dfrac{4}{\frac{9}{4}}} \times \dfrac{7}{3}$

   $= 1 - \dfrac{3}{1 - \frac{16}{9}} \times \dfrac{7}{3} = 1 - \dfrac{3}{-\frac{7}{9}} \times \dfrac{7}{3} = 1 - (-9)$

   $= 10$

   The answer is E

8. Since $\left(1 - \frac{9}{9}\right) = 0$ is one of the factors,

   the value is 0.

   The answer is C

9. Let's organize $\frac{11}{3}$,

   $\frac{11}{3} = 3 + \frac{2}{3} = 3 + \dfrac{1}{\frac{3}{2}} = 3 + \dfrac{1}{1 + \frac{1}{2}}$

   So, $x = 3$, $y = 1$, and $z = 2$. Their sum is 6.

   The answer is A

10. For a and b numbers with $a < b$, if we divide the way between a and b into 4 pieces, boundaries of pieces will be a,

    $a + \dfrac{(b - a)}{4}$, $a + \dfrac{2(b - a)}{4}$, $a + \dfrac{3(b - a)}{4}$, and b.

    Hence, for $a = 1\frac{1}{3}$ and $a = 1\frac{3}{4}$,

    point at three forth of the way will be

    $1\frac{1}{3} + \dfrac{3\left(1\frac{3}{4} - 1\frac{1}{3}\right)}{4} = \dfrac{79}{48}$

    The answer is C

11. Let's compare x and y.

    $1.45a < 1.4a3 \Rightarrow a \geq 5$

    but $a \neq 5$ because $1.455 > 1.453$. So, $a \geq 6$.

    For $a = 6$, $x < y < z$ is satisfied.

    The answer is D

12. Let the sum $\frac{1}{2001} + \frac{1}{2003} + \frac{1}{2005}$ be b.

If we calculate a + b,

$a + b = \left(\frac{2000}{2001} + \frac{1}{2001}\right) + \left(\frac{2002}{2003} + \frac{1}{2003}\right) +$

$\left(\frac{2004}{2005} + \frac{1}{2005}\right) = 1 + 1 + 1 = 3$

Therefore, b = 3 − a.

The answer is B

Problem Set 2

1. If the given expression is undefined, then denominator of a fraction is 0. There are two possibilities, $4 - a = 0$ or $2 - \frac{1}{4-a} = 0$.

In the first case, a = 4. Second case,

$2 = \frac{1}{4-a} \Rightarrow 4 - a = \frac{1}{2} \Rightarrow a = 4 - \frac{1}{2} = \frac{7}{2}$

Their sum is $\frac{15}{2}$

The answer is D

2. The given fractions are equal to $\frac{3}{2}$ and $\frac{3}{2r}$.

Since it is given that $\frac{3}{2} = 6 \cdot \frac{3}{2r}$,

we will find that $\frac{3}{2} = \frac{9}{x}$ and x = 6.

The answer is B

3. Assume that $y = \frac{2}{3} + \frac{3}{4} + \frac{4}{5}$.

If we calculate x − y,

$x - y = \left(\frac{8}{3} - \frac{2}{3}\right) + \left(\frac{11}{4} - \frac{3}{4}\right) + \left(\frac{14}{5} - \frac{4}{5}\right)$

$= 2 + 2 + 2 = 6$

Hence, y = x − 6.

The answer is B

4. Let's organize $\frac{23}{4}$,

$\frac{23}{4} = 5 + \frac{3}{4} = 5 + \frac{1}{\frac{4}{3}} = 5 + \cfrac{1}{1 + \frac{1}{3}}$

So, a = 5, b = 1, and c = 3. Their sum is 9.

The answer is D

5. The given information is equivalent to

$\frac{5}{14} < \frac{n}{21} < \frac{5}{12}$. If we multiply this inequality with

84, we will obtain that

$30 < 4n < 35 \Rightarrow 4n = 32$ So, n = 8.

The answer is E

6. Let's organize $\frac{23}{7}$,

$\frac{23}{7} = 3 + \frac{2}{7} = 3 + \frac{1}{\frac{7}{2}} = 3 + \cfrac{1}{3 + \frac{1}{2}}$

$= 3 + \cfrac{1}{3 + \cfrac{1}{1 + \frac{1}{1}}}$

So, x = 3, y = 3, z = 1, and t = 1.

Their sum is 8.

The answer is C

7. Assume that $B = \frac{18}{29} - \frac{2}{19}$.

If we calculate A + B,

$A + B = \left(\frac{21}{19} - \frac{2}{19}\right) + \left(\frac{11}{29} + \frac{18}{29}\right) = 1 + 1 = 2$

Hence, B = 2 − A.

The answer is A

8. If we multiply the inequality with 2003, we will find that

$$\frac{2003}{3} \le n \le \frac{2003}{2} \;\Rightarrow\; 668 \le n \le 1001$$

Therefore, $n \in \{668, 669, \ldots, 1001\}$.

There are $(1001 - 668) + 1 = 334$-many n integers.

The answer is B

9. To find a value for m, let's organize the inequality

$$\frac{3}{4} < \frac{n}{m} < \frac{4}{5} \;\Rightarrow\; \frac{6}{8} < \frac{n}{m} < \frac{8}{10}$$

We can choose $(m, n) = (9, 7)$, therefore, m can be 9. For smaller values, we can check that

$$\frac{3m}{4} \le n \le \frac{4m}{5}.$$

There is no n integer for $m < 9$.

The answer is B

10. All factors in the product are in form of

$$\left(1 - \frac{4}{n^2}\right) = \frac{(n-2)(n+2)}{n^2} \text{ for } n \in \mathbb{Z}^+. \text{ Hence,}$$

$$\left(1 - \frac{4}{1}\right)\left(1 - \frac{4}{9}\right)\left(1 - \frac{4}{25}\right)\cdots\left(1 - \frac{4}{625}\right)$$

$$= (-3) \cdot \frac{1 \cdot 5}{3^2}\, \frac{3 \cdot 7}{5^2} \cdots \frac{23 \cdot 27}{25^2}$$

$$= (-3) \cdot \frac{1 \cdot 3 \cdot 5 \cdots 23}{3 \cdot 5 \cdot 7 \cdots 25}\, \frac{5 \cdot 7 \cdot 9 \cdots 27}{3 \cdot 5 \cdot 7 \cdots 25}$$

$$= (-3)\frac{1}{25}\frac{27}{3} = -\frac{27}{25}$$

The answer is C

11. Let's organize $\frac{39}{14}$,

$$\frac{39}{14} = 2 + \frac{11}{14} = 2 + \frac{1}{\frac{14}{11}}$$

$$= 2 + \frac{1}{1 + \frac{3}{11}}\quad 2 + \frac{1}{1 + \frac{1}{\frac{11}{3}}}$$

Hence, $x + \dfrac{1}{y + \frac{1}{z}} = \dfrac{11}{3}$.

$$\frac{11}{3} = 3 + \frac{2}{3} = 3 + \frac{1}{\frac{3}{2}} = 3 + \frac{1}{1 + \frac{1}{2}}$$

Therefore, $x = 3,\ y = 1,\ z = 2$.

The answer is A

12. For positive integer n,

$$1 - \frac{1}{(n+1)^2} = \frac{n(n+2)}{(n+1)^2}$$

Hence, the product is

$$\left(1 - \frac{1}{4}\right)\left(1 - \frac{1}{9}\right)\left(1 - \frac{1}{16}\right)\cdots\left(1 - \frac{1}{(n+1)^2}\right)$$

$$= \frac{1 \cdot 3}{2 \cdot 2} \cdot \frac{2 \cdot 4}{3 \cdot 3} \cdot \frac{3 \cdot 5}{4 \cdot 4} \cdots \frac{n(n+2)}{(n+1)\cdot(n+1)}$$

$$= \frac{n! \cdot \frac{(n+2)!}{2}}{((n+1)!)^2} \cdot \frac{n+2}{2(n+1)}$$

The answer is A

MathTopia Press

MY NOTES

MathTopia Press

PRIMES

Definition 3.1 — Factor

Suppose, p, q, and r are natural numbers and are such that p × q = r. Then, p and q are called factors of r.

That leads to the following definition: A natural number p is a factor of another natural number r if and only if there exists a natural number, q say, which is such that p × q = r.

Thus, if three natural numbers p, q, and r are such that p × q = r, then p and q are factors of r. Also, r is said to be a multiple of p (and also a multiple of q).

Example 3.1

- 20 is composite because 20 can be written as 20 = 5 × 4 or 2 × 10.
- 29 is prime because 29 can only be factored as 29 = 1 × 29, which means the only positive divisors of 29 are 1 and 29.
- 121 is composite because 121 = 11 × 11.
- 703 is composite because 703 = 19 × 37.

MathTopia Press

Definition 3.2 — Prime number

Any natural number which has exactly two different natural number factors, namely itself and 1, is a prime number. All natural numbers which are not prime are called composite.

Thus, 2 is the first prime number, 3 is the second, and 5 the third. What is the tenth prime number?

Sieve of Eratosthenes

To obtain all the prime numbers less than 100 do the following with the given array of natural numbers: (a) cross out 1; (b) encircle 2 and the cross out all multiples of 2 (c) encircle 3 and then cross out all multiples of 3 (d) encircle 5 and then cross out all multiples of 5; etc. Eratosthenes, who was Greek mathematician who lived about 2200 years ago, used this method to identify prime numbers.

Sieve of Eratosthenes

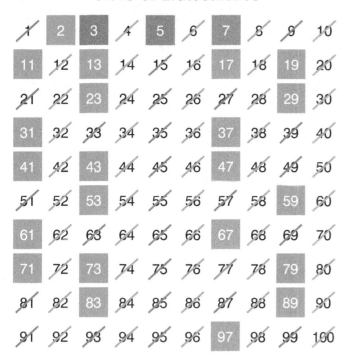

Remark 3.1

The unique even prime number is 2. All other primes are odd primes.

Remark 3.2

If a and b are relatively prime it can be represented by $(a,b) = 1$

Let $(a, b) = 1$ and $(x, y) = 1$. If $\dfrac{a}{b} = \dfrac{x}{y}$, then $a = x$ and $b = y$.

Problem 3.1

If $(a + b, a - b) = 1$ and $\dfrac{a+b}{a-b} = \dfrac{25}{55}$, then $a = ?$

A) 4   B) 6   C) 8   D) 10   E) 12

Solution

If $\dfrac{a+b}{a-b} = \dfrac{25}{55} = \dfrac{a+b}{a-b} = \dfrac{5}{11}$ and $(a + b, a - b) = 1$,

then $a + b = 5$ and $a - b = 11$ that is $a = 8$

Correct answer is C.

Remark 3.3 — Primality Tests

Primality Tests provide shortcuts to check whether or not a number is prime; in other words, they are methods to determine whether or not a specific number is prime, without having to check all the possible divisors.

We can determine whether a given natural number is prime by successively dividing the given number by prime numbers, starting with 2, then if necessary dividing by 3, 5, 7, etc. We only need to test up to the highest prime number less than the square root of the given number. Thus, for example, suppose we were asked to check whether 967 was prime. Since $\sqrt{967}$ is between 31 and 32, we only need to check whether 967 is divisible by 2, 3, 5, 7, 11, 13, 17, 19, 23, 29, and 31. In fact none of these is a divisor of 967, and therefore 967 is a prime number.

Primality Test If an integer $n > 1$ has no prime divisor p such that $p \le \sqrt{n}$, then n is prime.

Example 3.2

Is 397 composite or prime?

The possible primes p such that $p^2 \le 397$ are 2, 3, 5, 7, 11, 13, 17, and 19.

Because none of the primes 2, 3, 5, 7, 11, 13, 17, and 19 divide 397 is prime.

MathTopia Press

Definition 3.3 — The Fundamental Theorem of Arithmetic

Any composite number can be factored into prime numbers in one and only one way (disregarding the order in which the factors are stated).

For example,

$12 = 2 \times 2 \times 3$. (We write $12 = 2^2 \times 3$)

$105 = 3 \times 5 \times 7$

$360 = 2 \times 2 \times 2 \times 3 \times 3 \times 5 = 2^3 \times 3^2 \times 5$

$2592 = 2^5 \times 3^4$

These examples demonstrate what is known as the prime factorization of a composite number.

To find the prime factorization of a given natural number a systematic approach is recommended. You should successively divide through by the lowest prime factor.

Example 3.3

Suppose you were asked to find the prime factors of 54600:

Hence: $54600 = 2^3 \times 3 \times 5^2 \times 7 \times 13$

So 54600 has

$4 \times 2 \times 3 \times 2 \times 2 = 96$

different natural number factors

(including 1 and 54600).

```
2|54600
2|27300
2|13650
3|6825
5|2275
5|455
7|91
13|13
```

Example 3.4

Finding prime factorizations of 260.

(a)	(b)	(c)	(d) Alternative form
2⌊260	2⌊260	2⌊260	⌊260
130	2⌊130	2⌊130	2⌊130
	65	5⌊65	2⌊65
		13⌊13	5⌊13
		1	13⌊1

MathTopia Press

Problem 3.2

Find the prime factorization of 320.

Solution

Since prime factorizations are unique, starting with any factors of 320 will produce the same final answer. Here is one way to get to the prime factorization.

$$320 = 10 \cdot 32 = (2 \cdot 5)(2^5) = 2^6 \cdot 5$$

Note that starting with different factors still ends at the same prime factorization:

$320 = 2 \cdot 160 = 2 \cdot (8 \cdot 20) = 2 \cdot 2^3 \cdot (4 \cdot 5)$

$= 2 \cdot 2^3 \cdot 2^2 \cdot 5 = 2^6 \cdot 5$

Remark 3.4 — How many Prime numbers are there?

How many Prime numbers are there?

Assume that there is a finite number of different prime numbers, and that altogether there are exactly n different prime numbers. Let us denote the largest of these n prime numbers by pn.

Then consider a number, Q say, which is one more than the product of all the prime numbers. Thus:

$Q = 1 + (2 \times 3 \times 5 \times 7 \times 11 \times 13 \times \ldots \times pn)$, where pn is the largest prime number.

Now the number Q is clearly larger than pn. Furthermore, Q is not divisible by any of the prime numbers (because if one divides by any of the prime numbers one will always get a remainder of 1— Why is that?). Hence Q itself is prime.

But the conclusion that Q itself is a prime number contradicts the initial assumption that pn is the largest prime number, because Q > pn.

Thus, the original assumption must be wrong. Thus pn is not the largest prime number.

Thus, it is not true that there is a finite number of prime numbers.

Hence, the set of prime numbers is an infinite set. There is no largest prime number.

The above particularly elegant proof is an example of a reductio ad absurdum proof. It is credited to Euclid, a great Greek mathematician who lived over 2300 years ago. Euclid's proof is a beautiful example of what Bishop (1988) classified as "Explaining."

Number of Divisors

For any number, you can build its divisors by multiplying distinct combinations of prime factors.

n	Prime Factorization	of Divisors
20	$2^2 \times 5^1$	$3 \times 2 = 6$
30	$2^1 \times 3^1 \times 5^1$	$2 \times 2 \times 2 = 8$
50	$2^1 \times 5^2$	$2 \times 3 = 6$
60	$2^2 \times 3^1 \times 5^1$	$3 \times 2 \times 2 = 12$

Example 3.5 — How many divisors does 360 have?

$360 = 2^3 \times 3^2 \times 5^1$,

So if we want to build a divisor of 360, we have 4 choices for the number of 2s, 3 choices for the number of 3s, and 2 choices for the number of 5s.

| 4 choices | 3 choices | 2 choices |
| $2^0, 2^1, 2^2, 2^3$ | $3^0, 3^1, 3^2$ | $5^0, 5^1$ |

$$2^2 \times 3^0 \times 5^1 = 20$$

In all, then, we have $4 \times 3 \times 2 = 24$ choices, so there are 24 divisors of 360.

Remark 3.5

In general, if n has the prime factorization

$n = p_1^{k_1} \times p_2^{k_2} \times \ldots \times p_m^{k_m}$,

then n has

$(k_1 + 1) \times (k_2 + 1) \times \ldots \times (k_m + 1)$

divisors.

MathTopia Press

Problem 3.3

Find the number of positive divisors of 1,000,000.

Solution

The prime factorization of 1,000,000 is

$10^6 = (2 \cdot 5)^6 = 2^6 \cdot 5^6$.

2^6 has $6 + 1 = 7$ divisors, and 5^6 has $6 + 1 = 7$ divisors.

$2^6 \cdot 5^6$ has $(7)(7) = 49$ divisors.

Problem 3.4

If the number of positive composite divisors of 6^{4n} is 622, then n = ?

A) 3   B) 4   C) 5   D) 6   E) 8

Solution

If $6^{4n} = (2 \cdot 3)^{4n} = 2^{4n} \cdot 3^{4n}$, then there are only two prime divisors and 1. So the number of all positive divisors are $622 + 3 = 625$ which means

$625 = 25^2 = (4n + 1)(4n + 1)$

$\Rightarrow 4n + 1 = 25 \Rightarrow n = 6$

Correct answer is D.

Problem 3.5

If $a, b \in \mathbb{Z}^+$ and $120a = b^2$, then $(a + b)_{min} = ?$

A) 30   B) 45   C) 60   D) 80   E) 90

Solution

If the prime factorization of 120 is $2^3 \cdot 3 \cdot 5$, then $2^3 \cdot 3 \cdot 5 \cdot a = b^2$. Since a and b are both integers, to get the minimum value of a + b; the power of 2,3 and 5 should be 4,2 and 2 respectively.

If $a = 2 \cdot 3 \cdot 5 = 30$ and $2^2 2^2 3^2 5^2 = b^2$, then $b = 60$ and $(a + b)_{min} = 30 + 60 = 90$.

Correct answer is E.

What is the smallest natural number with exactly n factors?

An Apparently Promising Method Which Doesn't Quite Hold in All Cases

If you want to find the smallest natural number which has exactly n natural number factors (including 1 and the natural number itself), then the following procedure works in almost all cases (but there are a couple of exceptions – see later):

Step 1: Factorise n into the product of primes, but do not write the powers of primes (simply repeat the prime). For example, if n = 20, then write n = 2 × 2 × 5.

Step 2: The answer to the question is found by raising 2 to the power one less than the largest factor, multiplied by 3 to the power one less than the second largest factor, multiplied by 5 to the power one less than the third largest factor, etc.

Problem 3.6

What is the smallest natural number with exactly 20 natural number factors?

Solution

Since 20 = 2 × 2 × 5, the answer is:

$$2^{5-1} \times 3^{2-1} \times 5^{2-1}$$
$$= 2^4 \times 3^1 \times 5^1$$
$$= 16 \times 3 \times 5$$
$$= 240$$

Check: Factors of 240 are 1, 2, 3, 4, 5, 6, 8, 10, 12, 15, 16, 20, 24, 30, 40, 48, 60, 80, 120, and 240. There are twenty factors altogether.

Problem 3.7

What is the smallest natural number with exactly 42 natural number factors?

Solution

Since 42 = 2 × 3 × 7, the answer is:

$$2^{7-1} \times 3^{3-1} \times 5^{2-1}$$
$$= 2^6 \times 3^2 \times 5^1$$
$$= 64 \times 9 \times 5$$
$$= 2880$$

Problem 3.8

How many positive integers less than 120 have exactly three different prime divisors?

Solution

If 2 and 3 are the smallest prime divisors, then the third prime divisor can be 5, 7, 11, 13, 17, or 19.

If 2 and 5 are the smallest prime divisors, then the third prime divisor can be 7 or 11.

If 3 and 5 are the smallest prime divisors, then the third prime divisor must be 7, giving 105.

The number of solutions is 6 + 2 + 1 = 9

Problem 3.9

How many odd factors does 780 have?

Solution

We start with the prime factorization of 780:

$$780 = 2^2 \cdot 3 \cdot 5 \cdot 13$$

If we're looking only for odd factors, then we don't want to include any multiple of 2. That means that we only include combinations that include the multiples of 3,5 and 13

So the number of possible combinations is 2 *2 *2 = 8.

Problem 3.10

For how many n is $|n^2\ 6n + 5|$ prime?

Solution

Since $|n^2\ 6n + 5| = |n - 5|\ |n - 1|$ is prime,

$|n - 5| = 1$ or $|n - 1| = 1$.

$|n - 5| = 1 \Rightarrow n = 4$ or $n = 6$.

$|n - 1| = 1 \Rightarrow n = 0$ or $n = 2$.

Checking cases gives.

n	$|n^2 - 6n + 5|$
0	5 (prime)
2	3 (prime)
4	3 (prime)
6	5 (prime)

The answer is 4 n values.

Problem 3.11

Let

$N = 59^5 + 5 \cdot 59^4 + 10 \cdot 59^3 + 10 \cdot 59^2 + 5 \cdot 59 + 1$

How many positive integers are factors of N?

Solution

This given expression is the 5th power of $(59 + 1)$.:

$N = 59^5 + 5 \cdot 59^4 + 10 \cdot 59^3 + 10 \cdot 59^2 + 5 \cdot 59 + 1$

$= (59 + 1)\wedge 5 = (60)\wedge 2 = 2\wedge 4 * 3\wedge 2 * 5\wedge 2$.

There are $(4 + 1)(2 + 1)(2 + 1) = 45$ factors of N.

Problem 3.12

How many positive integers less than 40 have an odd number of positive integer divisors?

Solution

Notice that every positive integer with an odd number of divisors is a perfect square.

In particular (with p and q being prime): If a number has 3 divisors, then it is $p\wedge 2$ for some prime p. If a number has 9 divisors, then it is $(p\wedge 2)(q\wedge 2)$ for some primes p and q.

So, there are only possibilities of 6 numbers until 40.

1, 4, 9, 16, 25, 36.

Problem 3.13

How many positive integer values of x are there that makes the given fraction integer;

$$\frac{x^2 - 7x + 60}{x}$$

A) 24   B) 16   C) 12   D) 10   E) 8

Solution

$$\frac{x^2 - 7x + 60}{x} = \frac{x^2}{x} - \frac{7x}{x} + \frac{60}{x} = x - 7 + \frac{60}{x}$$

$$\Rightarrow \frac{60}{x} \in \mathbb{Z}$$

so x divides 60. Since $60 = 2^2 \cdot 3 \cdot 5$,

then the number of positive integer divisors is

$(2 + 1) \cdot (1 + 1) \cdot (1 + 1) = 12$.

Correct answer is C.

Remark 3.6

If the prime factorization of n is $p_1^{\alpha_1} p_2^{\alpha_2} \cdots p_k^{\alpha_k}$, then the sum of the positive divisors of n is

$\sigma(n) = (1 + p_1 + p_1^2 + \cdots + p_1^{\alpha_1})(1 + p_2 + p_2^2 + \cdots + p_2^{\alpha_2})$
$\cdots (1 + p_k + p_k^2 + \cdots + p_k^{\alpha_k})$

$$= \frac{p_1^{\alpha_1+1} - 1}{p_1 - 1} \cdot \frac{p_2^{\alpha_2+1} - 1}{p_2 - 1} \cdots \frac{p_k^{\alpha_k+1} - 1}{p_k - 1}$$

MathTopia Press

Problem 3.14

Find the sum of the positive integer divisors of 72000.

Solution

Since $72000 = 2^6 \cdot 3^2 \cdot 5^3$

$\sigma(72000) = \dfrac{2^7-1}{2-1} \cdot \dfrac{3^3-1}{3-1} \cdot \dfrac{5^4-1}{5-1}$

$= 127 \cdot 13 \cdot 156 = 257556$

Problem 3.15

Find the sum of the non-prime positive integer divisors of 72000.

Solution

$257{,}556 - (2 + 3 + 5) = 257546$

Problem 3.16

Find the sum of the even positive integer divisors of 1000.

Solution

Since $1000 = 2^3 \cdot 5^3$, the sum of the even positive integer divisors of 1000 is

$(2^1 + 2^2 + 2^3)(5^0 + 5^1 + 5^2 + 5^3) = 14 \cdot \dfrac{5^4-1}{5-1}$

$= 14 \cdot 156 = 2184$

Problem 3.17

Find the sum of the positive divisors of 360 which are multiples of 3.

Solution

Since $360 = 2^3 \cdot 3^2 \cdot 5$, we get

$(3 + 3^2)(1 + 2 + 2^2 + 2^3)(1 + 5) = 12 \cdot 15 \cdot 6 = 1080$

Problem 3.18

Find the smallest natural number with exactly:

(a) 6 natural number factors.

(b) 10 natural number factors.

(c) 32 natural number factors.

Problem 3.19

The sum of four consecutive prime numbers is 258. Find the largest of the primes.

Problem 3.20

Find the sum of the reciprocals of all the positive factors of 30. Express your answer as a fraction in the simplest form.

Problem 3.21

How many prime numbers does the following number sequence?

$345! + 2,\ 345! + 3,\ 345! + 4,\ \ldots,\ 345! + 345$

Problem 3.22

Suppose $x < y < z$ prime numbers scuh that $x + y + z = 68$ and $xy + yz + xz = 437$.

MathTopia Press

The Four 4s Problem

Use the digit 4 exactly four times to write number sentences equivalent to the numbers from 1 to 25.

You may use any mathematical operations and symbols (e.g., 4.4, 44, 4^4, 4!, $\sqrt{4}$). Use parentheses as needed to clarify the order of operations.

Answer	Solution 1	Solution 2
1	$(4 + 4 - 4) / 4$	$(4 + 4) \div (4 + 4)$
2		
3		
4		
5		
6		
7		
8		
9		
10		
11		

Answer	Solution 1	Solution 2
12		
13		
14		
15		
16		
17		
18		
19		
20		
21		
22		
23		
24		
25		

MathTopia Press

1. The sum of two prime numbers is 61.

   What is the product of these two prime numbers?

   A) 60   B) 61   C) 118   D) 122   E) 930

2. How many ways can 2017 be written as the sum of two primes?

   A) 0   B) 1   C) 2   D) 3   E) 4

3. What is the smallest positive integer that is neither prime nor square and that has no prime factor less than 20?

   A) 251   B) 621   C) 667   D) 713   E) None

4. Three positive integers have a product of 1800 and are pairwise relatively prime. What is their sum?

   A) 40   B) 42   C) 48   D) 80   E) None

5. Find the number of prime divisors of $9! + 10! + 11!$.

   A) 2   B) 3   C) 4   D) 5   E)

6. The sum of all the positive divisor and the sum of their reciprocals of a number N are 195 and $\frac{64}{24}$ respectively. Find N.

   A) 68   B) 72   C) 80   D) 144   E) 195

MathTopia Press

7. Let a and b relatively prime numbers $a > b > 0$ and $\dfrac{a^2 - b^2}{(a-b)^2} = \dfrac{17}{3}$.

   What is $a - b$?

   A) 1   B) 2   C) 3   D) 4   E) 5

10. Given that $2^8 3^2 = xy$, where both x and y are positive integers. Find the smallest possible value for $x + y$.

   A) 24   B) 48   C) 50   D) 96   E) 128

8. Which of the following numbers is a perfect square?

   A) 8!9!   B) 8!10!   C) 9!10!   D) 9!11!   E) 10!11!

11. The number of positive divisors of $40 \cdot 3^x$ is 16. What is the value of x?

   A) 1   B) 2   C) 3   D) 4   E) 5

9. Let n be a positive number that satisfier $999 \times 333 = 3 \cdot (3n)^2$.

   Find the value of n.

   A) 8   B) 11   C) 22   D) 111   E) 444

12. Let a, b be positive integers; if $72(a - 2) = b^3$, then $(a + b)_{min} = ?$

   A) 5   B) 7   C) 9   D) 11   E) 13

MathTopia Press

1. If $\dfrac{12}{x+2}$ is an integer then find the number of whole numbers of x?

   A) 12   B) 10   C) 8   D) 6   E) 5

4. If a and b are distinct positive integers such that $44 \times a = b^2$.

   Find the minimum value of a?

   A) 10   B) 11   C) 12   D) 13   E) 14

2. The number of non-prime positive divisor of 14^{2n} is 387. What is the value of n?

   A) 8   B) 9   C) 10   D) 11   E) 12

5. If a and b are positive integers such that $32 \times a^2 = b^2$.

   What is the minimum value of a + b?

   A) 8   B) 12   C) 16   D) 18   E) 24

MathTopia Press

3. If a and n are distinct whole numbers such that $120 \cdot n = a^3$.

   Find the minimum value of a?

   A) 10   B) 15   C) 20   D) 25   E) 30

6. Suppose that m and n are positive integers such that $250 \times m = n^3$.

   What is the minimum possible value of m + n?

   A) 10   B) 12   C) 14   D) 24   E) None

7. How many positive integer values of x makes the given equation $\dfrac{x^2 - 7x + 60}{x}$ integer?

   A) 24   B) 16   C) 12   D) 10   E) 8

8. How many digit long is the result of the multiplication $(2^{11})^4(5^{22})^2$.

   A) 22   B) 33   C) 45   D) 55   E) None

9. The number $25^4 4^8$ is a square of a positive integer of N. What is the sum of the digits of N?

   A) 7   B) 11   C) 14   D) 15   E) 100

10. How many two-digit prime numbers can be written such that the sum of their digits' square is also become prime numbers?

    A) 6   B) 5   C) 4   D) 3   E) 2

11. What is the sum of the prime factors of $11^2 + 33^2$?

    A) 18   B) 17   C) 16   D) 15   E) None

12. Which of the following numbers can not divide the number $27! + 28!$?

    A) 48   B) 62   C) 130   D) 170   E) 230

MathTopia Press

Problem Set 1

1. It is given that the sum of two prime numbers is 61. Let these prime be p and q.

    Then we have $p + q = 61$. This implies that one of primes is even. It can only be possible by choosing $p = 2$ and $q = 59$ or $q = 2$ and $p = 59$. Therefore,

    $p \times q = 2 \times 59 = 59 \times 2 = 118$

    The answer is C

2. Assume p and q are these primes. Then we have, $p + q = 2017$. Now consider where p and q are odd. If p and q are both odd then we have $p + q$ is even, however 2017 is not even. So there is no possible solution for this case.

    So at least one of p or q must be even. Therefore, we might try $p = 2$, $q = 2015$. However, 2015 is not prime. So there is no possible solution for this case either. Therefore, the answer is 0.

    The answer is A

3. The smallest two primes which are greater than 20 are 23 and 29. So, this number is can be minimum $23 \times 29 = 667$.

    The answer is C

4. First, let's factorize 1800.

    $1800 = 18 \times 100 = 2^3 \times 3^2 \times 5^2$.

    Here 2,3 and 5 are relatively prime.

    So $2^3, 3^2, 5^2$ are also relatively prime.

    Therefore, we have $2^3 + 3^2 + 5^2 = 42$.

    The answer is B

5. $9! + 10! + 11! = 9!(1 + 10 + 10 \cdot 11) = 9! \cdot 12!$.

    So we have 2, 3, 5, 7 and 11 as prime divisors.

    Therefore, the number of prime divisors is 5.

    The answer is D

6. Let this number be N. If N is a perfect square, assume that

    $$\sqrt{N}, a_1, a_2, \dots, a_n, \frac{N}{a_1}, \frac{N}{a_2}, \dots, \frac{N}{a_n}$$

    are all positive divisors of N. So,

    $$195 = \sqrt{N} + \left(\frac{N}{a_1} + a_1\right) + \left(\frac{N}{a_2} + a_2\right) + \dots + \left(\frac{N}{a_n} + a_n\right)$$

    $$\frac{65}{24} = \frac{1}{\sqrt{N}} + \left(\frac{a_1}{N} + \frac{1}{a_1}\right) + \left(\frac{a_2}{N} + \frac{1}{a_2}\right) + \dots + \left(\frac{a_n}{N} + \frac{1}{a_n}\right)$$

    So, $\frac{65N}{24} = 195$. Same equality can be found in the same way if N is not a perfect square.

    So, $N = 72$.

    The answer is B

7. Now let's write it as the following.

    $$\frac{a^2 - b^2}{(a-b)^2} = \frac{(a-b) \times (a+b)}{(a-b) \times (a-b)} = \frac{a+b}{a-b} = \frac{17}{3}$$

    This implies that

    $17a - 17b = 3a + 3b \Rightarrow 14a = 20b \Rightarrow 7a = 10b$

    Now let $a = 10k$ and $b = 7k$. Putting these values into the above equation, we have $a = 10$ and $b = 7$. Therefore, $a - b = 3$.

    The answer is C

8. Now let's check

$8! \times 9! = (8!)^2 \times 3^2 \Rightarrow$ Perfect square

$8! \times 10! = (8! \times 9!) \times 10 \Rightarrow$ Not perfect square

$9! \times 10! = (9!)^2 \times 10 \Rightarrow$ Not perfect square

$9! \times 11! = (9!) \times 110 \Rightarrow$ Not perfect square

$10! \times 11! = 10! \times 11 \Rightarrow$ Not perfect square

So the answer is A

9. Consider left and right sides.

Then we have, $333^2 = (3n)^2$.

This implies $333 = 3n$ and $n = 111$.

The answer is D

10. In order to find the smallest value that $x + y$ can take, we should consider where the numbers are closest to each other or if it is possible where they are equal. So consider two cases.

Case 1: $x \neq y$

$\qquad x = 36, y = 64$ and $x + y = 100$

Case 2: $x = y$

$\qquad x = 48, y = 48$ and $x + y = 96$

Therefore, the answer is 96.

The answer is D

11. When we make given expressions prime factorization $2^3 \cdot 5 \cdot 3^x$

Number of positive divisons $(3 + 1)(1 + 1)(XH)$

$= 4 \cdot 2 \cdot (x+1) = 16$. Therefore $x = 1$.

The answer is A

12. Let's rewrite as follows.

$72 \times (a - 2) = 2^3 \times 3^2 \times (a - 2) = b^3$.

As we have a third power on the right side, we need to make the left side a perfect cube. So we need $a - 2$ to be, 3 since we want the minimum value of $a + b$.

This implies that $a = 5$ and, $2^3 \times 3^3 = b^0$.

Hence, we have $a = 5$, $b = 6$ and $a + b = 11$.

The answer is D

Problem Set 2

1. Because $x + 2$ divides 12 with no remainder and $x + 2 \geq 2$, $x + 2$ can be 2, 3, 4, 6, 12.

By that, x can be 0, 1, 2, 4, 10.

The answer is E

2. Because $14^{2n} = 2^{2n} \cdot 7^{2n}$, the number of non-prime positive divisor is $(2n + 1)^2 - 2$.

So, $(2n + 1)2 - 2 = 387$. Therefore n is 8.

The answer is A

3. Since $120 = 2^3 \cdot 3 \cdot 5$, to obtain a perfect cube n must have $3^2 \cdot 5^2$ as a divisor. So, n can be at least $3^2 \cdot 5^2$, and $a = 2 \cdot 3 \cdot 5 = 30$.

The answer is E

MathTopia Press

4. Since $44 = 2^2 \cdot 11$, to obtain a perfect square a must have 11 as a divisor. So, a can be at least 11, and b = 22.

    The answer is B

5. Since b^3 is divisible by 2^5, b is divisible by 4. However, b cannot be 4 because a^2 is not a perfect square in this case. For b = 8, a = 4.

    Hence, their sum is 12.

    The answer is B

6. Since $250 = 2 \cdot 5^3$, to obtain a perfect cube m must have 4 as a divisor. So, m can be at least 4, and n = 10. Their sum is 14.

    The answer is C

7. Since $\dfrac{x^2 - 7x + 60}{x} = x - 7 + \dfrac{60}{x}$ is an integer, x is a divisor of $60 = 2^2 \cdot 3 \cdot 5$.

    Hence, the number of positive divisors of 60 is $(2 + 1)(1 + 1)(1 + 1) = 12$ and x can be any of these divisors.

    The answer is C

8. Let's calculate directly
    $$(2^{11})^4 \cdot (5^{22})^2 = 2^{44} \cdot 5^{44} = 10^{44}$$
    which has 45 digits.

    The answer is C

9. Square root of the given number is
    $N = 5^4 \cdot 2^8 = 160000$. The sum of its digits is 7.

    The answer is A

10. Assume that ab = p is a 2-digit prime number and $a^2 + b^2 = q$ is also a prime.

    If q = 2, then ab = 11. If q ≠ 2, then $a^2 + b^2$ is odd and b is odd, and a is even. In this case, p can be 23, 29, 41, 43, 47, 61, 67, 83, 89.

    However, only for p = 23, 41, 61, 83, q is prime.

    Hence, there are 5 prime numbers.

    The answer is B

11. If we calculate the sum
    $$11^2 + 33^2 = 11^2 (1^2 + 3^2) = 2 \cdot 5 \cdot 11^2$$
    Its prime divisors are 2, 5,8 and their sum is 18.

    The answer is A

12. If we reorganize the sum,
    $$27! + 28! = 27!(1 + 28) = 27! \cdot 29.$$
    Because $48 = 2 \cdot 24$, $62 = 2 \cdot 31$, $130 = 10 \cdot 13$, $170 = 10 \cdot 17$, and $230 = 10 \cdot 23$, only 62 cannot divide 27! + 28!.

    The answer is B

MY NOTES

MathTopia Press

LCM and GCD

Definition 4.1 — GCD

The greatest common divisor (gcd) of two or more natural numbers is the greatest element in the set of common factors. We write gcd(a, b) to mean the greatest common divisor of a and b.

We can use prime factorization as a short way to find the greatest common factor of two or more numbers. To find the greatest common factor of two numbers, follow the steps.

1. Write the prime factorization of each number.
2. Draw a circle round each common factor.
3. Multiply the common factors.

Example 4.1

Find the greatest common factor of 40 and 60. If we know the prime factorizations of 40 and 60, we can just write them and circle the common factors. $40 = 2 \cdot 2 \cdot 2 \cdot 5$, $60 = 2 \cdot 2 \cdot 3 \cdot 5$. Multiply the bold numbers: $2 \cdot 2 \cdot 5 = 20$. Therefore, the greatest common factor of 40 and 60 is 20. We can write gcd(40, 60) = 20.

MathTopia Press

Problem 4.1

b is a natural number. When we divide 29 and 41 by b the remainder is 5 in each case. Find the greatest possible value of b.

Solution

If b divides 29 with remainder 5, then $29 - 5 = 24$ is divisible by b. If b divides 41 with remainder 5, then $41 - 5 = 36$ is also divisible by b. So b is a common factor of 24 and 36. The greatest possible value of b must be the greatest common factor of 24 and 36. The common prime factors are 2, 2, and 3. Therefore, gcd(24, 36) = $2 \cdot 2 \cdot 3 = 12$. Therefore, the greatest possible value of b is 12.

Problem 4.2

A man has a rectangular field whose sides are 160 m and 250 m long respectively. He wants to put trees around the field so that the distance between each tree is the same. Find the least number of trees that the man needs, and the distance between them.

Solution

If the distance between each tree is the same then the distance must be a divisor of both 160 and 250. Because we want to find the least number of trees, the distance between each tree must be as great as possible. Therefore, to solve the problem we need to find gcd(160, 250).

160	250	2
80	125	2
40	125	2
20	125	2
10	125	2
5	125	**5**
1	25	5
	5	5
	1	

$gcd(160, 250) = 2 \cdot 5 = 10$

Therefore, the greatest possible distance between each tree is 10m. To find the number of trees we divide the perimeter of the rectangular field by the distance between each tree. The perimeter is $2 \cdot (160 + 250) = 820$m, and so the number of trees is $820 : 10 = 82$

Problem 4.3

The sides of a rectangular area are 16 m and 24 m long respectively. A person wants to divide the area into square sections so that each section is as big as possible. Find the number of sections.

Solution

The length of one side of a square section is GCF(16, 24)

16	24	2
8	12	2
4	6	2
2	3	2
1	3	3
	1	

$GCF(16, 24) = 2 \cdot 2 \cdot 2 = 8$

The area of the rectangular section is $16 \cdot 24 = 384$ m^2 and the area of each square section is $8 \cdot 8 = 64$ m^2.

Therefore, the number of square section is

$$\frac{16 \cdot 24}{8 \cdot 8} = \frac{384}{64} = 6.$$

MathTopia Press

MathTopia Press

Definition 4.2 — LCM

The least common multiple (lcm) of two or more natural numbers is the smallest element in the set of common multiples of the numbers. We write lcm(a, b) to mean the least common multiple of a and b.

Example 4.2

For example, let us find the least common multiple of 6 and 8.

- The multiples of 6 are {6, 12, 18, 24, 30, 36, 42, 48, ...}.
- The multiples of 8 are {8, 16, 24, 32, 40, 48, 56, ...}.
- The common multiples of 6 and 8 are {24, 48, ...}. Therefore, the least common multiple of 6 and 8 is 24. We can write lcm(6, 8) = 24.

Example 4.3

We can use prime factorization as a short way to find the least common multiple of two or more numbers. First we find the prime factorization of the numbers, then we multiply all the prime factors together. For example, let us find lcm(10, 12).

10	12	2
5	6	2
5	3	3
5	1	5
1	1	1

Look at the result of the division method. The prime factors are 2, 2, 3, and 5.

Therefore,

$lcm(10;12) = 2 \cdot 2 \cdot 3 \cdot 5 = 60$

Example 4.5

When the students in a class are divided into groups of eight or groups of twelve, there are five students remaining each time. What is the least possible number of students in the class?

8	12	2
4	6	2
2	3	2
1	3	3
	1	

First we must find lcm(8, 12).

lcm(8, 12) = $2^3 \cdot 3 = 24$.

Therefore, the least possible number of students in this class is

24 + 5 = 29

Problem 4.5

Find the GCD of {676, 21125, 709800}

Solution

Since 676 = $2^2 \times 13^2$, 21125 = $13^2 \times 5^3$,

and 709800 = $2^3 \times 3 \times 5^2 \times 7 \times 13^2$, it follows that the GCD of {676, 21125, 709800} is 13^2 or 169 (because 13^2 factor appears in the three prime factorizations, but no other prime number is a factor of all three).

Problem 4.6

A is a natural number. When we divide A by 12, 14, and 18, the remainders are 8, 10, and 14 respectively. Find the least possible value of A.

Solution

When A is divided by 12, 14, and 18, the remainders are 8, 10, and 14, respectively.

By the division algorithm:

A = $(12 \cdot x) + 8$

A = $(14 \cdot y) + 10$

A = $(18 \cdot z) + 14$

If we add 4 to each side of the equations we can write:

A + 4 = $(12 \cdot x) + 12 = 12(x + 1)$

A + 4 = $(14 \cdot y) + 14 = 14(y + 1)$

A + 4 = $(18 \cdot z) + 18 = 18(z + 1)$

So A + 4 is a common multiple of 12, 14 and 18. Since we are looking for the least possible value of A we must find LCM(12, 14, 18)

12	14	18	2
6	7	9	2
3	7	9	3
1	7	3	3
	7	1	7
	1		

LCM(12, 14, 18) = $2^2 \cdot 3^2 \cdot 7 = 252$.

So A + 4 = 252, and A = 248.

Problem 4.4

To build the smallest possible cube using bricks with dimensions 3cm · 4cm · 6cm.

• Find the dimensions of the cube.

• How many bricks are needed?

Solution

The length of one side of the cube must be a multiple of 3, 4, and 6. The least common multiple of these numbers is lcm(3, 4, 6) = 12.

• The dimensions of the cube are
  12cm · 12cm · 12cm:

• The volume of the cubic wall is $(12 \cdot 12 \cdot 12)cm^3$. The volume of one brick is $(3 \cdot 4 \cdot 6)cm^3$.

  Therefore, the total number of bricks is

  $$\frac{12 \cdot 12 \cdot 12}{3 \cdot 4 \cdot 6} = 4$$

MathTopia Press

▮ ▯ ▮▮ ▯▮

Remark 4.1

Let a and b be two natural numbers, then
$\gcd(a, b) \cdot \operatorname{lcm}(a, b) = a \cdot b$.

Remark 4.2

If a and b are relatively prime then, $\gcd(a, b) = 1$

Remark 4.3

To find the gcd and lcm of two rational numbers
$\frac{a}{b}$ and $\frac{c}{d}$

- $\gcd\left(\frac{a}{b}, \frac{c}{d}\right) = \dfrac{\gcd(a \cdot d, b \cdot c)}{\operatorname{lcm}(b, d)}$

- $\operatorname{lcm}\left(\frac{a}{b}, \frac{c}{d}\right) = \dfrac{\operatorname{lcm}(a, c)}{\gcd(b, d)}$

Remark 4.4

Number of ordered pairs possible for

$\operatorname{lcm} = N = p_1^a \cdot p_2^b \cdot p_3^c$ is $(2a + 1)(2b + 1)(2c + 1)$

Problem 4.7

Find the gcd and lcm of two rational numbers
$\frac{6}{5}$ and $\frac{12}{7}$.

Solution

$\gcd\left(\frac{6}{5}, \frac{12}{7}\right) = \dfrac{\gcd(6 \cdot 7, 12 \cdot 5)}{\operatorname{lcm}(5, 7)} = \dfrac{\gcd(42, 60)}{\operatorname{lcm}(5, 7)}$

$= \dfrac{6}{35}$

$\operatorname{lcm}\left(\frac{6}{5}, \frac{12}{7}\right) = \dfrac{\operatorname{lcm}(6, 12)}{\gcd(5, 7)} = \dfrac{12}{1} = 12$

Problem 4.8

$x \in \mathbb{W}$, when x is divided by $\frac{9}{5}$, $\frac{12}{7}$ and $\frac{15}{11}$ the result is always integer.

What is the minimum value of x?

A) 90   B) 180   C) 240   D) 270   E) 360

Solution 1:

If the value of $\dfrac{x}{\frac{9}{5}} = \dfrac{5x}{9}$, $\dfrac{x}{\frac{12}{7}} = \dfrac{7x}{12}$, $\dfrac{x}{\frac{15}{11}} = \dfrac{11x}{15}$ are

integers, then x is divisible by 9, 12, 15.
So the minimum value of x is $\gcd(9, 12, 15) = 180$

Solution 2:

$x = \operatorname{lcm}\left(\frac{9}{5}, \frac{12}{7}, \frac{15}{11}\right) = \dfrac{\operatorname{lcm}(9, 12, 15)}{\gcd(5, 7, 11)} = 180$

Problem 4.9

Find the lcm of 676, 21125, 709800

Solution

Since $676 = 2^2 \times 13^2$, $21125 = 13^2 \times 5^3$, and
$709800 = 2^3 \times 3 \times 5^2 \times 7 \times 13^2$, it follows that the
lcm of the three numbers is $2^3 \times 3 \times 5^2 \times 7 \times 13^2$

Problem 4.10

How many integers between 2000 and 4000 have all three of the numbers 25; 30; and 45 as factors?

MathTopia Press

Problem 4.11

Let A, B, and a be natural numbers with

$A = GCF(a, 12)$ and $B = LCM(a, 12)$.

If $A \cdot B = 216$, find a.

Problem 4.12

A box of marbles can be shared equally among 6, 7, or 8 students with 4 marbles left each time.

What is the least possible number of marble in the box?

Problem 4.13

Suppose p and q represent two composite natural numbers whose prime factorizations are given by

$$p = 2^3 \times 3^2 \times 7^2 \text{ and } q = 3^4 \times 5^2 \times 7 \times 11.$$

Which of the following is equal to the **greatest common divisor** (GCD) of p and q?

Problem 4.14

x is a natural number with

$GCD(x, 36) = 9$ and $LCM(x, 36) = 108$.

Find x.

MathTopia Press

The first 4 to 40

Using each of the digits 1, 2, 3, and 4, once and only once, with the basic rules of arithmetic (+, −, times, ÷, and parentheses), express all of the integers from 1 to 25.

Answer	Solution 1	Solution 2
1	$(4 - 3) \times (2 - 1)$	$(4 - 2) \div (3 - 1)$
2		
3		
4		
5		
6		
7		
8		
9		
10		
11		
12		
13		
14		
15		
16		
17		
18		

Answer	Solution 1	Solution 2
19		
20		
21		
22		
23		
24		
25		
26		
27		
28		
29		
30		
31		
32		
33		
34		
35		
36		
37		
38		
39		
40		

MathTopia Press

1. The greatest common divisor GCD and the least common multiple LCM of 54, 72, and 90 are, respectively,

   A) 18 and 540   B) 18 and 1040

   C) 18 and 1080   D) 18 and 2160

                    E) None

2. Let A and 24 be relatively prime,

   if LCM(A,24) = 840,

   then find the sum of the digits of A?

   A) 8   B) 10   C) 12   D) 16   E) 18

3. Find the LCM(m, m + 1) for any positive integer m.

   A) m^2 B) $m^2 + 2$ C) $2m + 1$

        D) $m^2 - 1$ E) None

4. Which of 2000, 2015, 2016, or 2017 has the largest prime divisor?

   A) 2000   B) 2015   C) 2016

        D) 2017   E) 2020

5. How many integers between 2000 and 4000 have all three of the numbers 25, 30, and 45 as factors?

   A) 1   B) 2   C) 3   D) 4   E) 5

6. The least common multiple of a and b is 30, and the least common multiple of b and c is 40. What is the minimum possible value of 1 cm (a, c)?

   A) 24   B) 32   C) 36   D) 40   E) 60

MathTopia Press

7. Find the number of pairs of positive integers (a, b) such that, GCD(a, b) = 6 and a + b = 96.

   A) 5   B) 8   C) 11   D) 16   E) 20

10. If LCM(24, x, 60) = $2^3 \cdot 3 \cdot 5^2$ and
    GCD(24, x, 60) = 6.
    What is the minimum value of x?

    A) 100   B) 120   C) 150   D) 200   E) 300

8. A and B are positive integers such that
   A + B = 60 and GCD(A, B) = 6.
   Find the maximum value of A − B.

   A) 12   B) 18   C) 24   D) 36   E) 48

11. A whole number larger than 2 leaves a remainder of 4 when it divides each of the following 68, 100, and 132 numbers. What is the biggest possible whole number?

    A) 16   B) 20   C) 30   D) 32   E) 36

MathTopia Press

9. A whole number larger than 2 leaves a remainder of 3 when divided by each of the numbers 4, 5, 6, and 8. The smallest such number lies between which of two numbers.

   A) 50 and 59   B) 65 and 75   C) 115 and 225
            D) 205 and 225   E) 210 and 250

12. The gcd of two natural numbers is 180 and the lcm of the two numbers is 1800. If one of the natural numbers is 360, what is the other natural number.

    A) 300   B) 360   C) 900   D) 1800   E)None

1. What are the greatest common divisor and least common multiple, respectively, of 6, 108, and 162?

   A) 2 and 162   B) 2 and 104976

   C) 6 and 104976   D) 2 and 324

            E) None

2. How many integers between 500 and 800 have all three of the numbers 10, 15, and 25 as factors?

   A) 1   B) 2   C) 3   D) 4   E) 5

3. The product of LCM(A, B) and GCD(A, B) is 1392. One of these numbers is 24.

   What is the biggest prime factor of the second number?

   A) 3   B) 7   C) 13   D) 24   E) 29

4. x and y are two distinct whole numbers such that $x + y = 192$ and GCD(x, y) = 12. Which of the following could be $x - y$?

   A) 12   B) 48   C) 96   D) 144   E) 168

5. Suppose x and y are distinct prime numbers such that $a = x^3 y^2$ and $b = y^3 x^2$. What is $\dfrac{\text{LCM}(a, b)}{\text{GCD}(a, b)}$.

   A) $x^2 y$ B) y^2 C) x D) y E) xy

6. The dimensions of a rectangular field are 630 m and 900 m respectively. A farmer wants to plant trees around the field so that the trees are equally spaced with the greatest possible distance between two consecutive trees.

   How many trees does the farmer need?

   A) 30   B) 32   C) 34   D) 36   E) 48

MathTopia Press

7. What is the ratio of the least common multiple of 1500 and 2560 to the greatest common factor of 1500 and 2560?

   A) 1840   B) 1920   C) 2040   D) 2048   E) None

8. The least common multiple of A and B is 900. How many (A, B) positive integer pairs can be found?

   A) 27   B) 53   C) 54   D) 125   E) None

9. x, y, and y are positive integers.
   A = 3x + 1 = 4y − 2 = 5z + 8
   Find the value of y that makes A minimum.

   A) 10   B) 12   C) 15   D) 19   E) 23

10. x and y are relatively prime numbers such that

    $LCM(x, y) = 200$ and $\dfrac{100}{x} + xy + GCD(x, y) = 205$,

    What is x + y?

    A) 12   B) 18   C) 25   D) 33   E) 42

11. x, y, z are positive integers and x > 45.
    If x = 4y − 1 = 5z + 3.
    What is the minimum value of x?

    A) 54   B) 63   C) 65   D) 70   E) 83

12. The greatest common factors of two integers is 6. Which of the following cannot be the sum of those two integers?

    A) 272   B) 288   C) 306   D) 618   E) None

MathTopia Press

Problem Set 1

1. If we factorize the given numbers, we will find that
$$54 = 2 \cdot 3^3$$
$$72 = 2^3 \cdot 3^2$$
$$90 = 2 \cdot 3^2 \cdot 5$$
Hence, gcd $(54, 72, 90) = 2 \cdot 3^2 = 18$ and
lcm$(54, 72, 90) = 2^3 \cdot 3^3 \cdot 5 = 1080$.
The answer is C

2. If a and b two positive integers, then
$$\gcd(a, b) \cdot \text{lcm}(a, b) = a \cdot b$$
Because it is given that gcd $(A, 24) = 1$ and
lcm $(A, 24) = 840$,
$$24A = \gcd(A, 24) \cdot \text{lcm}(A, 24) = 840$$
$$\Rightarrow A = \frac{840}{24} = 35$$
The sum of the digits of A is $3 + 5 = 8$.
The answer is A

3. We know that two consecutive numbers are relatively prime. Therefore, gcd $(m, m + 1) = 1$. By that,
$$\text{lcm}(m, m + 1) = \gcd(m, m + 1) \cdot \text{lcm}(m, m + 1)$$
$$= m(m + 1) = m^2 + m$$
The answer is E

4. Since 2017 is prime and all other factors of given numbers are naturally smaller than 2017.
The answer is D

5. If a number is divided by some numbers, then it is also divided by their least common multiple. Hence, the numbers we are looking for must be divisible by lcm $(25, 30, 45) = 450$.
Let's say this number is 450k for $k \in \mathbb{Z}$,
$$2000 \leq 450k \leq 4000 \Rightarrow 4{,}444 \cdots \leq k \leq 8.888 \ldots$$
Therefore, k might be 5, 6, 7, 8.
The answer is D

6. If x and y are two positive integers, then both x and y divide lcm (x, y). Hence, b divides both 30 and 40, and gcd $(30, 40) = 10$. To obtain minimum value of lcm (a, c), we should choose a and c smaller as much as we can.
For $b = 10$, and $(a, c) = (3, 4)$. lcm $(a, c) = 12$
The answer is B

7. If gcd $(a, b) = 6$, then there exist m, n positive integers such that gcd $(m, n) = 1$ and $a = 6m$, and $b = 6n$. Therefore,
$$a + b = 6(m + n) = 96 \Rightarrow m + n = 16$$
(m, n) can be (1, 15), (3, 13), (5, 11), (7, 9) and their permutations. For each(m, n) pair, there exists exactly one (a, b). Therefore, there are 8 pairs.
The answer is B

8. To obtain maximum value of A − B, we should choose maximum A and minimum B. Since B is divisible by 6 and positive, B can be minimum 6. For $B = 6$, we can find that $A = 54$ and $A - B = 48$. The answer is E

9. Let the number we are looking for be n. $n − 3$ is divisible by 4, 5, 6, 8, and their least common multiple.
lcm $(4, 5, 6, 8) = 120 \Rightarrow$ min $n = 120 + 3 = 123$
The answer is C

MathTopia Press

10. It is given that x divides $2^3 \cdot 3 \cdot 5^2$. Therefore, we can think x as $2^a \cdot 3^b \cdot 5^c$ where a, b, and c are non-negative integers.

$\text{lcm}(24, x, 60) = \text{lcm}(2^3 \cdot 3, 2^a \cdot 3^b \cdot 5c, 2^2 \cdot 3 \cdot 5^2)$

$= 2^{\max(3,a,2)} \cdot 3^{\max(1,b,1)} \cdot 5^{\max(0,c,1)}$

$\gcd(24, x, 60) = \gcd(2^3 \cdot 3, 2^a \cdot 3^b \cdot 5c, 2^2 \cdot 3 \cdot 5^2)$

$= 2^{\min(3,a,2)} \cdot 3^{\min(1,b,1)} \cdot 5^{\min(0,c,1)}$

Because $\gcd(24, x, 60) = 2^1 \cdot 3^1 \cdot 5^0$ and $\text{lcm}(24, x, 60) = 2^3 \cdot 3^1 \cdot 5^2$,

$\max(0, c, 1) = \max(1, c) = 2 \Rightarrow c = 2$

$\min(3, a, 2) = \min(2, a) = 1 \Rightarrow a = 1$

$\min(1, b, 1) = \min(1, b) = 1 \Rightarrow b \geq 1$

$\max(1, b, 1) = \max(1, b) = 1 \Rightarrow b \leq 1 \Rightarrow b = 1$

Therefore, $x = 2^1 \cdot 3^1 \cdot 5^2 = 150$

The answer is C

11. Assume that the number we are looking for is n. Then, n divides $68 - 4 = 64$, $100 - 4 = 96$, and $132 - 4 = 128$, and their greatest common divisor.

$\gcd(64, 96, 128) = 32 \Rightarrow \max n = 32$

The answer is D

12. Assume that other natural number is m. Then,

$360m = \gcd(m, 360) \cdot \text{lcm}(m, 360)$

$= 180 \cdot 1800 \Rightarrow m = \dfrac{180 \cdot 1800}{360} = 900$

The answer is C

Problem Set 2

1. Let's factorize the given numbers,

$$6 = 2^1 \cdot 3^1$$
$$108 = 2^2 \cdot 3^3$$
$$162 = 2 \cdot 3^4$$

As a result, $\gcd(6, 108, 162) = 2^1 \cdot 3^1 = 6$ and $\text{lcm}(6, 108, 162) = 2^2 \cdot 3^4 = 324$.

The answer is E

2. If 10, 15, and 25 divides a number, then their least common divisor also divides.

Hence, lcm (10, 15, 25) = 150 divides those numbers. Multiples of 150 between 500 and 800 are 600 and 750. So, there are two numbers.

The answer is B

3. Assume that other number is m. Then,

$24m = \text{lcm}(24, m) \cdot \gcd(24, m) = 1392$

$\Rightarrow m = \dfrac{1392}{24} = 58$

The biggest prime divisor of 58 is 29.

The answer is E

4. Because gcd (x, y) = 12, there exist a and b whole numbers such that gcd (a, b) = 1 and x = 12a, and y = 12b. By that,

$x + y = 12(a + b) = 192 \Rightarrow a + b = 16$

(a, b) can be (15, 1), (13, 3), (11, 5), (9, 7), and their permutations. For (a, b) = (15, 1),

$x - y = 12(a - b) = 168$

Other options cannot be obtained.

The answer is E

5. By direct calculations,

$$\dfrac{\text{lcm}(a, b)}{\gcd(a, b)} = \dfrac{x^{\max(3,2)} \cdot y^{\max(2,3)}}{x^{\min(3,2)} \cdot y^{\min(2,3)}} = \dfrac{x^3 y^3}{x^2 y^2} = xy$$

The answer is E

MathTopia Press

6. Assume that distance between two consecutive trees is m meters. Because the number of trees is an integers, both $\frac{630}{m}$ and $\frac{900}{m}$ are integers. Hence, m is a rational number. Assume a and b are relatively prime two positive integers such that $m = \frac{a}{b}$. Because $\frac{630b}{a}$ and $\frac{900b}{a}$ are integers, and gcd(a, b) = 1, a divides both 630 and 900, and gcd(630, 900) = 90. Hence, a can be at most 90 and b can be at least 1. So, maximum value of m is 90.Hence, the farmer needs at least $2 \cdot \left(\frac{630}{m} + \frac{900}{m}\right) = 34$ trees.
The answer is C

7. Let's calculate directly,
$$\frac{lcm(1500, 2560)}{gcd(1500, 2560)} = \frac{lcm(2^2 \cdot 3^1 \cdot 5^3, 2^9 \cdot 5^1)}{gcd(2^2 \cdot 3^1 \cdot 5^3, 2^9 \cdot 5^1)}$$
$$= \frac{2^9 \cdot 3^1 \cdot 5^3}{22 \cdot 5} = = 2^7 \cdot 3 \cdot 5^2 = 9600$$
The answer is E

8. Because both A and B divide
lcm (A,B) = 900 = 22 · 32 · 52. So, we can think A and B as
$$A = 2^a \cdot 3^b \cdot 5^c$$
$$B = 2^x \cdot 3^y \cdot 5^z$$
Hence,
lcm(A,B) = $2^{max(a,x)} \cdot 3^{max(b,y)} \cdot 5^{max(c,z)} = 2^2 \cdot 3^2 \cdot 5^2$
Therefore, (a, x) can be (0, 2), (1, 2), (2, 2), (2, 1), (2, 0). Similarly, both (b, y) and (c, z) can be 5 different pairs.
So, there are 5 · 5 · 5 = 125-many (A,B) pairs.
The answer is D

9. If we add 2 to equations,
$$A + 2 = 3(x + 1) = 4y = 5(z + 2)$$
So, 3, 4, 5, and their least common factor divide A + 2.
lcm(3, 4, 5) = 60 ⇒ min(A + 2) = 60 ⇒ 4y = 60 ⇒ y = 15
The answer is C

10. Since x and y are relatively prime, then gcd(x, y) = 1 and lcm(x, y) = xy.
By that, xy = 200 and
$$\frac{100}{x} + xy + gcd(x, y) = \frac{100}{x} + 201 = 205$$
⇒ x = 25
Also, y = 8. Their sum is 25 + 8 = 33.
The answer is D

11. If we substract −3 from the equations,
$$x - 3 = 4(y - 1) = 5z$$
So, 4 and 5, and their least common divisor divide x − 3. Hence, 20 divides x − 3. Since x > 45, x − 3 can be at least 60. Hence x can be at least 63.
The answer is B

12. If gcd(a, b) = 6, then both a, b, and a + b is divisible to 6. However, 272 is not divisible to 6. So, it cannot be sum of those two numbers.
The answer is A

MathTopia Press

MY NOTES

MathTopia Press

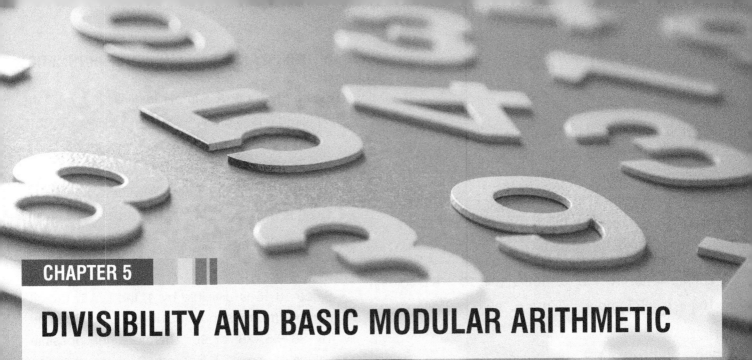

CHAPTER 5

DIVISIBILITY AND BASIC MODULAR ARITHMETIC

DIVISION ALGORITHM

Definition 5.1

Let m be a positive integer (m > 0) and let b be any integer. There is exactly one pair of integers q (called the quotient) and r (called the remainder) such that

$$b = qm + r \text{ where } 0 \leq r < m.$$

The dividend is equal to the divisor times the quotient plus the remainder.

Example 5.1

When A is divided by 6, the quotient is x + 2 and remainder is 2. What is x in terms of A?

From the division algorithm,

$A = 6(x + 2) + 2$

$A = 6x + 14$

$x = \dfrac{A - 14}{6}$

Problem 5.1

If A is divided by 5 that leaves a remainder of 3. What is the remainder when $A^2 + 3A$ is divided by 5?

Solution

We can choose 3 or 8 to solve this;

- If A = 3, $A^2 + 3A = 3^2 + 3 \cdot 3 = 18$, the remainder is 3.

- If A = 8, $A^2 + 3A = 64 + 3 \cdot 8 = 88$, the remainder is 3.

Problem 5.2

When A and B are divided by 6, the remainders are 4 and 5 respectively.
Find the remainder when A + B is divided by 6.

Solution

By using the division algorithm,

$A = 6a + 4$, $B = 6b + 5$ and

$A + B = 6(a + b) + 9 = 6(a + b + 1) + 3$.

Therefore the remainder is 3.

MathTopia Press

Problem 5.3

When the three-digit number a0b is divided by the two-digit number a0, we have

Divisor + Quotient + Remainder = 85.

What is the value of $a \times b$?

A) 35   B) 28   C) 20   D) 18

Solution

$a0b/a0 = a0 \cdot 10 + b \Rightarrow 10a + b + 10 = 85$, so $10a + b = 75$ and $a = 7$, $b = 5$. $a \cdot b = 35$.

DIVISIBILITY RULES

The divisibility rules for 2, 3, 4, 5, 6, 7, 8, 9, 11, and 13 are given below.

- **Divisibility by 2:** A number is divisible by 2 if the last digit is 0, 2, 4, 6 or 8.

- **Divisibility by 3:** A number is divisible by 3 if the sum of the digits is divisible by 3.

Since 18 is divisible by 9, 9 is a factor of 18. A divisibility test is a rule for determining whether one whole number is divisible by another. It is a quick way to find factors of large numbers.

Problem 5.4

5m3 is a three-digit number where m is a digit. If 5m3 is divisible by 3, find all the possible values of m.

Solution

Since 5m3 is divisible by 3, $5 + m + 3 = 8 + m$ must be divisible by 3.

Let us find the possible values of m.

If $8 + m = 9$, then $m = 1$.

If $8 + m = 12$, then $m = 4$.

If $8 + m = 15$, then $m = 7$.

If $8 + m = 18$, then $m = 10$.

However, this is not possible because m must be a digit. Therefore, the only possible values of m are 1, 4, and 7.

- **Divisibility by 4:** A number is divisible by 4 if the last two digits is divisible by 4.

Problem 5.5

t is a digit. Find all the possible values of t if:

- 187t6 is divisible by 4.
- 2741t is divisible by 4.

Solution

- Since 187t6 is divisible by 4, the last two-digit number (t6) must be divisible by 4, so it can be 16, 36, 56, 76, or 96. Therefore, the possible values of t are 1, 3, 5, 7, and 9.

- Since 2741t is divisible by 4, the last two-digit number (1t) must be a multiple of 4, so it can be 12 or 16. Therefore, the possible values of t are 2 and 6.

- **Divisibility by 5:** A number is divisible by 5 if the last digit is either 0 or 5.

Problem 5.6

m235m is a five-digit number where m is a digit. If m235m is divisible by 5, find all the possible values of m.

Solution

Since m235m is divisible by 5, then its last digit must be either 0 or 5. But m cannot be 0, because it is the first digit of the five-digit number. Therefore, the only possible value of m is 5.

- **Divisibility by 6:** A number is divisible by 6 if it is divisible by 2 and it is divisible by 3.

Problem 5.7

235mn is a five-digit number where m and n are digits. If 235mn is divisible by 5 and 6, find all the possible pairs of (m;n).

MathTopia Press

Solution

Since 235mn is divisible by 5, n can take the values 0 and 5. However, if 235mn is divisible by 6 then n must be even. So n must be 0. For
n = 0, 2+3+5+m+n = 2+3+5+m+0 = 10+m.
Because 235mn is divisible by 6, 10+m must be a multiple of 3. Therefore, m can be 2, 5, or 8. Hence, all the possible pairs are (2, 0), (5, 0), and (8, 0).

- **Divisibility by 8:** A number is divisible by 8 if the last three digits is divisible by 8.
- **Divisibility by 9:** A number is divisible by 9 if the sum of the digits is divisible by 9.

Problem 5.8

5m432n is a six-digit number where m and n are digits. If 5m432n is divisible by 9, find all the possible values of m+n.

Solution

Since 5m432n is divisible by 9, 5+m+4+3+2+n = 14+(m+n) must be divisible by 9.

Because m and n are digits, 0 ≤ (m+n)18.

Therefore, 14+(m+n) can be 18 or 27.

If 14+(m+n) = 18, then m+n = 4.

If 14+(m+n) = 27, then m+n = 13.

Therefore, m+n can be 4 or 13.

- **Divisibility by 11:** A natural number is divisible by 11 if the difference between the sum of the odd-numbered digits and the sum of the even-numbered digits is a multiple of 11.

Problem 5.9

34t415 is a 6-digit number where t is a digit. If 34t415 is divisible by 11, find the value of t.

Solution

Find the difference between the the sum of the odd-numbered digits and the sum of the even-numbered digits: $(3+t+1)-(4+4+5) = (4+t)-13 = t-9$.
If the number is divisible by 11 then $t-9$ must be multiple of 11. The only possible value is $t-9 = 0$, therefore $t = 9$.

- **Divisibility by 7:** Multiply the digits from right to left by the coeeficients 1, 3, 2, −1, −3, −2, ... respectively then add those numbers together. If the final answer is divisible by 7, so is the original number.

Problem 5.10

Is 9114 divisible by 7?

Solution

$1·4+3·1+2·1+(−1)·9 = 4+3+2−9 = 0$, so 9114 is divisible by 7.

Problem 5.11

If $N = 2^3 · 3^2 · 7 · n$, and N is divisible by 50, then which of the following could be the value of n?
A) 5   8) 15   C) 20   0) 40   E) 75

Solution

Since N is divisible by 50, n should be divisible by $5^2 = 25$. Therefore, the value of n could be 75. The answer is E.

Problem 5.12

For how many different values of C is 27C4 divisible by 6?
A) 0   8) 1   C) 2   0) 3   E) 4

Solution

27C4 is divisible by 6 if and only if it is divisible by 2 and 3. It is obviously divisible by 2 because it is even. It is divisible by 3 if and only if $2 + 7 + C + 4 = 13 + C$ is divisible by 3. Thus, the possible values of C are 2, 5 and 8. The answer is D.

MathTopia Press

Problem 5.13

An integer N has 10 positive divisors. If 2N has 15 positive divisors and 3N has 20 positive divisors, how many positive divisors does 4N have?

A) 12   B) 20   C) 30   D) 36   E) 40

Solution

Since the number of positive divisors of N can be represented as either 10 or $2 \cdot 5$, the integer N is represented as

$$N = p^9 \text{ or } N = p \cdot q^4$$

for some distinct primes p and q. Hence,

$$2N = \begin{cases} 2 \cdot p^9 & \text{if } p \neq 2, \\ 2^{10} & \text{if } p = 2, \end{cases} \text{ or }$$

$$2N = \begin{cases} 2 \cdot p \cdot q^4 & \text{if } p, q \neq 2, \\ 2^2 \cdot q^4 & \text{if } p = 2 \text{ and } q \neq 2, \\ p \cdot 2^5 & \text{if } p \neq 2 \text{ and } q = 2. \end{cases}$$

Among those representations, only $2N = 2^2 \cdot q^4$ has 15 positive divisors.

Therefore $N = 2 \cdot q^4$, $q \geq 3$, and hence

$$3N = \begin{cases} 2 \cdot 3 \cdot q^4 & \text{if } q > 3, \\ 2 \cdot 3^5 & \text{if } q = 3. \end{cases}$$

The only possible representation for 3N which has 20 positive divisors is $3N = 2 \cdot 3 \cdot q^4$ when $q > 3$. Finally, $4N = 2^3 \cdot q^4$ has 20 positive divisors.

The answer is B.

MODULAR ARITHMETIC & DIGIT PROBLEMS

In mathematics, modular arithmetic is a system of arithmetic for integers, where numbers "wrap around" upon reaching a certain value—the modulus (plural moduli).

Definition 5.2

Arithmetic with time is called clock arithmetic.

A familiar use of modular arithmetic is in the 12-hour clock, in which the day is divided into two 12-hour periods. If the time is 7 : 00 now, then 8 hours later it will be 3 : 00. Usual addition would suggest that the later time should be $7 + 8 = 15$, but this is not the answer because clock time "wraps around" every 12 hours. Because the hour number starts over after it reaches 12, this is arithmetic modulo 12.

Problem 5.14

Express the following times in the twelve-hour system.

- seven o'clock in the morning
- five o'clock in the afternoon
- eleven o'clock at night

Solution

- seven o'clock in the morning is 7 a.m. b.
- five o'clock in the afternoon is 5 p.m. c.
- eleven o'clock at night is 11 p.m

An ordinary clock shows the set of numbers 1, 2, 3, 4, 5, 6, 7, 8, 9, 10, 11, 12 on its face. In the twelve-hour clock arithmetic system, we use 0 instead of 12, so the set of numbers for this system is 0, 1, 2, 3, 4, 5, 6, 7, 8, 9, 10, 11.

If the time is six o'clock now, what time will it be nine hours later? To find the sum of 6 and 9 in twelve-hour clock arithmetic, we first add the numbers: $6 + 9 = 15$. But we need a number in the set 0;1; :::12, so we divide the result by 12. The remainder is 3, and this is the hour shown on the clock.

Definition 5.3

Let $a, b \in \mathbb{Z}$, $m \in \mathbb{Z}^+$ $(m > 1)$ such that $a = m \cdot b + k$ where $(0 \leq k < m)$. Then, we can write $a \equiv k \pmod{m}$ and say a is equivalent (or congruent) to k, modulo m. Often we abbreviate 'modulo0' to 'mod0'.

MathTopia Press

Problem 5.15

Find the units digit of 27^{29}

Solution

To find the units digit of 27^{29}, we have to find the remainder when it is divided by 10.

$27^1 \equiv 7 \pmod{10}$, $27^2 \equiv 9 \pmod{10}$

$\Rightarrow 27^2 \equiv 27 \cdot 27 \equiv 7 \cdot 7 \equiv 9 \pmod{10}$,

$27^3 \equiv 3 \pmod{10}$

$\Rightarrow 27^3 \equiv 27^2 \cdot 27 \equiv 9 \cdot 7 \equiv 3 \pmod{10}$,

$27^4 \equiv 1 \pmod{10}$

$\Rightarrow 27^4 \equiv 27^3 \cdot 27 \equiv 3 \cdot 7 \equiv 1 \pmod{10}$,

So $27^{29} = (27^4)^7 \cdot 27^1 \equiv 1 \cdot 27 \equiv 7 \pmod{10}$

Problem 5.16

If $7^{77} + 5^{55} \equiv x \pmod 8$, then find x.

Solution

We can solve this problem separately.

$7^1 \equiv 7 \pmod 8$　　　　$5^1 \equiv 5 \pmod 8$

$7^2 \equiv 1 \pmod 8$　　　　$5^2 \equiv 1 \pmod 8$

$7^{77} \equiv (7^2)^{38} \cdot 7^1 \equiv 1 \cdot 7 \pmod 8$

$(5^2)^{27} \cdot 5^1 \equiv 1 \cdot 5 \pmod 8$

So $7^{77} + 5^{55} \equiv 7 + 5 \equiv 4 \pmod 8$

Problem 5.17

If today is Friday, which day of the week will it be in 25 days' time?

Solution

If today is Friday, then in seven days the day will be Friday again since the names of the days repeat in seven days. So we can use modula 7 to add and subtract the days of the week. The set of remainders for modula 7 arithmetic is {0, 1, 2, 3, 4, 5, 6}. When we divide 25 by 7 the remainder is 4. $25 \equiv 4 \pmod 7$. Four days after Friday is Tuesday. So in 25 days' time it will be Tuesday.

Remark 5.1

Fundamental properties of modular arithmetic

- $a \equiv b \pmod m$ and $b \equiv c \pmod m$
  $\Rightarrow a \equiv c \pmod m$

- $a \equiv b \pmod m$ and $c \equiv d \pmod m$
  $\Rightarrow a + c \equiv b + d \pmod m$,
  $a - c \equiv b - d \pmod m$

- $a \equiv b \pmod m$ and $c \equiv d \pmod m$
  $\Rightarrow ac \equiv b \cdot d \pmod m$

- $a \equiv b \pmod m \Rightarrow$ for all $n \in \mathbb{N}$ $a^n \equiv b^n \pmod m$

- $ac \equiv b \cdot c \pmod m$ and $\gcd(c, m) = 1$
  $\Rightarrow a \equiv b \pmod m$

Problem 5.18

What is the units digit of $2^{2020} \cdot 7^{2020}$?

A) 2　　　B) 4　　　C) 6　　　D) 8　　　E) 9

Solution

Notice that $2^{2020} \cdot 7^{2020}$ is even. Therefore, the units digit is either 0, 2, 4, 6 or 8. Then it is enough to compute $(2^{2020} \cdot 7^{2020})$ mod 5 to obtain the exact units digit. Since $7 \equiv 2 \pmod 5$, we have

$(2^{2020} \cdot 7^{2020}) \equiv (2^{2020} \cdot 2^{2020}) \equiv 2^{4040} \pmod 5$.

Since $2^4 \equiv 1 \pmod 5$, we have

$2^{4040} \equiv (2^4)^{1010} \equiv 1^{1010} \equiv 1 \pmod 5$.

Thus, the units digit is 6.

The answer is C.

MathTopia Press

Problem 5.19

The number 2^{1000} is divided by 13.
What is the remainder?

Solution

Consider 2^{1000} modulo 13, because this produces the remainder. An important observation to make to simplify the process is that since $65 = 64 + 1$.

$2^6 \bmod 13 \equiv (65 - 1) \bmod 13 \equiv -1$.

So

$$2^{1000} \bmod 13 \equiv 2^{996} \cdot 2^4 \ \bmod 13$$
$$\equiv (2^6)^{166} \bmod 13 \cdot 16 \bmod 13$$
$$\equiv (2^6 \bmod 13)^{166} \cdot 16 \bmod 13$$
$$\equiv (-1)^{166} \cdot 3 = 3.$$

Problem 5.20

What is the remainder when 2^{32} is divided by 11?

Solution

11 is prime, so we can apply Fermat's little theorem:

$$2^{10} \equiv 1 \quad (\bmod 11)$$
$$\Rightarrow 2^{30} \equiv 1 \quad (\bmod 11)$$
$$\Rightarrow 2^{32} \equiv 2^2 \equiv 4 \quad (\bmod 11)$$

Problem 5.21

The four-digit number A55B is divisible by 36. What is the sum of A and B? (Source: MOEMS)

MathTopia Press

Problem 5.22

The 10-digit number abababababab is multiple of 36.
Find the sum of all possible values of a?

Problem 5.23

The number A4273B is a six-digit integer in which A and B are digits, and the number is divisible by 72. Find the value of A and the value of B.
(Source: MOEMS)

1. The 3-digit ABC is divisible by 15.

   Which of the following cannot be the value of A + B?

   A) 7   B) 8   C) 10   D) 12   E) 15

2. The 5-digit number 3A26B is multiple of 20. What is the minimum value of A+B?

   A) 0   B) 8   C) 9   D) 10   E) 11

3. The 6-digit numbers 63A2B2 and 42AB3C are each multiple of 3. Which of the following could be the value of C?

   A) 0   B) 2   C) 3   D) 5   E) 7

4. The 5-digit number AA3AB divided by 66 with the remainder of 0. What is the sum of all possible values of A?

   A) 9   B) 10   C) 11   D) 12   E) 15

5. A and B are whole numbers. When A + 10 is divided by B then quotient is 12 and remainder is 7.

   What is the remainder when A – 12 divided by 6?

   A) 1   B) 2   C) 3   D) 4   E) 5

6. When 6 divides a positive integer n, the remainder is 5.

   What is the remainder when n^2 is divided by 12?

   A) 1   B) 4   C) 6   D) 13   E) None

MathTopia Press

7. Which of the following numbers is divisible by 5?

    A) $2^{20} + 1$　　　　B) $2^{21} + 1$　　　C) $2^{22} + 1$

    　　　　D) $2^{23} + 1$　　　　E) $2^{24} + 1$

8. The number N = 3K5M is a 4-digit number. When N is divided by 10, the remainder is 2. When N divided by 11, the remainder is 10. What is K?

    A) 2　　　B) 3　　　C) 4　　　D) 5　　　E) 6

9. AB is a two-digit number such that $\frac{AB}{8} + \frac{AB}{20}$ is an integer. How many two-digit AB can be written?

    A) 2　　　B) 3　　　C) 4　　　D) 6　　　E) 8

10. Suppose that a and b are digits in a four-digit natural number 7a5b. If 7a5b is divisible by 18, how many different possible values can a have?

    A) 5　　B) 6　　C) 7　　D) 9　　E) None

11. The four digit number 53xy is divisible by 3, 4, and 5. What is the sum of all possible x values?

    A) 4　　B) 7　　C) 11　　D) 12　　E) 13

12. What is the sum of a and b such that the number a2018b is divisible by 9 and 11?

    A) 7　　B) 11　　C) 13　　D) 15　　E) 18

MathTopia Press

1. Find the remainder when 2003 − 2004 − 2005 divided by 10.

   A) 0   B) 2   C) 4   D) 6   E) 8

2. When the 5-digit number a627b is divided by 56 then it gives the remainder of 4. Find $4a + b$.

   A) 28   B) 30   C) 34   D) 36   E) 39

3. The 6-digit number 43x72y is multiple of 55. Which of the following could be the sum of the distinct values of x?

   A) 4   B) 6   C) 9   D) 10   E) 13

4. Suppose 4a2b is a 4-digit number. For how many values of a make the number can be divisible by 2 and 9?

   A) 2   B) 4   C) 5   D) 6   E) 10

5. When a^2 is divided by 9, the remainder is 7. What is the remainder when $2a^2 + a^4 + a^6$ is divided by 9?

   A) 1   B) 4   C) 5   D) 7   E) 8

6. $A = \underbrace{11 + 11 + \ldots + 11}_{11}$ and $B = \underbrace{21 + 21 + \ldots + 21}_{21}$.

   What is the remainder when A − B is divided by 10?

   A) 0   B) 2   C) 4   D) 6   E) 8

MathTopia Press

7. What is the unit digit of 17^{2017}?

   A) 1   B) 3   C) 5   D) 7   E) 9

10. Find the tens digit of 16^{2017}?

    A) 1   B) 3   C) 5   D) 7   E) 9

8. What is tens digit of $2017^{2017} - 2018$?

   A) 0   B) 1   C) 2   D) 5   E) 8

11. What is the units digit of $2^{2019} + 3^{2019} + 4^{2019}$?

    A) 3   B) 5   C) 7   D) 8   E) 9

MathTopia Press

9. What is the remainder when

   $$5^0 + 5^1 + 5^2 + 5^3 + \ldots + 5^{2017}$$

   is divided by 8?

   A) 2   B) 3   C) 5   D) 6   E) 7

12. xx, yy, and zz 2-digit whole numbers.

    If $x^2 + y^2 + z^2 = 74$ then find the number of positive divisors of $(xx)^2 + (yy)^2 + (zz)^2$?

    A) 6   B) 12   C) 24   D) 48   E) None

Problem Set 1

1. If ABC is divisible by 15, then it is divisible by 5.
   So, $C = 0$ or $C = 5$.
   If $C = 0$, then
   $$ABC \equiv A + B + C \equiv A + B \equiv 0 \ (mod3)$$
   If $C = 5$, then
   $$ABC \equiv A + B + C \equiv A + B + 5 \equiv 0 \ (mod3)$$
   $$\Rightarrow A + B \equiv 1 \ (mod3)$$
   Hence, $A + B$ cannot be 8.
   The answer is B

2. Since 20 is divisible by 10, 3A26B is also divisible by 10. So, $B = 0$. A can be at least 0, therefore, $A + B = 0$.

   The answer is A

3. Because the given numbers are multiple of 3,
   $$63A2B2 \equiv 6 + 3 + A + 2 + B + 2 \equiv A + B + 1$$
   $$\equiv 0 \ (mod3) \Rightarrow A + B \equiv 2 \ (mod3)$$
   $$42AB3C \equiv 4 + 2 + A + B + 3 + C \equiv A + B + C$$
   $$\equiv 2 + C \equiv 0 \ (mod3)$$
   Therefore, $C \equiv 1 \ (mod\ 3)$. C can be 7.
   The answer is E

4. Since $66 = 2 \cdot 3 \cdot 11$, B is even and
   $$AA3AB \equiv 3A + 3 + B \equiv B \equiv 0 \ (mod3)$$
   So, $B = 0$ or $B = 6$.
   If $B = 0$,
   $$AA3AB \equiv AA3A0 \equiv 300 + 11010A \equiv 3 - A \equiv 0$$
   $$(mod11) \Rightarrow A = 3$$
   If $B = 6$,
   $$AA3AB \equiv 306 + 11010A \equiv 9 - A \equiv 0 \ (mod11)$$
   $$\Rightarrow A = 9$$
   So, the sum of all possible values of A is
   $3 + 9 = 12$.
   The answer is D

5. By the given information,
   $$A + 10 = 12B + 7$$
   By that,
   $$A - 12 = 12B - 15 = 6(2B - 3) + 3$$
   Therefore, the remainder is 3.
   The answer is C

6. By the given information, there exists a non-negative integer k such that $n = 6k + 5$. So,
   $$n^2 = (6k + 5)^2 = 36k^2 + 60k + 25$$
   $$= 12(3k^2 + 5k + 2) + 1$$
   Therefore, the remainder is 1.
   The answer is A

7. By the Fermat's Theorem, $24 \equiv 1 \ (mod\ 5)$.
   Therefore,
   $$222 + 1 \equiv 220 \cdot 22 + 1 \equiv 22 + 1 \equiv 0 \ (mod5)$$
   Other options can be checked easily.
   The answer is C

8. The remainder when N is divided by 10 gives us the units digit. In other words, $M = 2$. Also, $N - 10 = 3K42$ is divisible by 11. Hence,
   $$3042 + 100K \equiv 6 + K \equiv 0 \ (mod11)) \ K = 5$$
   The answer is D

MathTopia Press

9. Let's organize the given sum,

$$\frac{AB}{9} + \frac{AB}{20} = \frac{7 \cdot AB}{40}$$

Since 7 and 40 are relatively prime, 40 must divide AB. So, AB can be 40 or 80.

The answer is A

10. Because $18 = 2 \cdot 9$, b is even and

$7a5b \equiv 12 + a + b \equiv 0 \ (\text{mod}9)$

$\Rightarrow a + b \equiv 6 \ (\text{mod}9)$

Therefore, $a + b = 6$ or $a + b = 15$.

(a, b) can be (6, 0), (4, 2), (2, 4), (0, 6), (9, 6), (7, 8). Hence, a can have 6 different values.

The answer is B

11. Since 53xy is divisible by 2 and 5, its units digit is 0. Also, it is divisible by 4, therefore, x0 is divisible by 4. All possible values for x are 0, 2, 4, 6, 8. However, if $x \neq 4$, 53x0 is not divisible by 3. So, x = 4.

The answer is A

12. Because a2018b is divisible by both 9 and 11,

$a2018b \equiv a + 2 + 0 + 1 + 8 + b \equiv a + b + 2$

$\equiv 0 \ (\text{mod}9) \Rightarrow a + b \equiv 7 \ (\text{mod}9)$

So, $a + b = 7$ or 16. If $a + b = 16$, then all possible pairs are (a, b) = (9, 7), (7, 9), and (8, 8). However, for none of these pairs, the number is divisible by 11. Hence, $a + b = 7$.

The answer is A

Problem Set 2

1. Let's calculate directly,

$2003 - 2004 - 2005 \equiv 3 - 4 - 5 \equiv -6 \equiv 4 \ (\text{mod}10)$

The answer is C

2. Because $56 = 8 \cdot 7$,

$a627b \equiv 10^4 a + 6270 + b \equiv 0 + 6 + b \equiv 4 \ (\text{mod}8)$

$\Rightarrow b \equiv 6 \ (\text{mod}8) \Rightarrow b = 6$

$a627b \equiv 10^4 a + 6270 + b \equiv 4a + 5 + b \equiv 4 \ (\text{mod}7)$

$\Rightarrow 4a \equiv 0 \ (\text{mod}7)$

Therefore, a = 7, and 4a + b = 34.

The answer is C

3. Because $55 = 5 \cdot 11$, y is 0 or 5, and

$43x72y \equiv 430720 + 1000x + y \equiv 4 - x + y$

$\equiv 0 \ (\text{mod}11) \Rightarrow x - y \equiv 4 \ (\text{mod}11)$

So, if y = 0, then x = 4. If y = 5, then x = 9. Therefore, the sum of the distinct values of x are 13.

The answer is E

4. Since the number is divisible by 2, b is even. Also,

$4a2b \equiv 4 + a + 2 + b \equiv 0 \ (\text{mod}9)$

$\Rightarrow a + b \equiv 3 \ (\text{mod}9)$

Hence, $a + b = 3$ or 12. So, (a, b) can be (1, 2), (3, 0), (8, 4), (6, 6), (4, 8). a can have 5 different values.

The answer is C

Box Algebra

5. By direct calculations,

$2a^2 + a^4 + a^6 \equiv 2 \cdot 7 + 7^2 + 7^3 \equiv 406 \equiv 1 \pmod 9$

The answer is A

6. Let's organize $A - B$

$A - B = \underbrace{(-10) + (-10) + \cdots + (-10)}_{\text{11-many}} +$

$\underbrace{(-21) + (-21) + \cdots + (-21)}_{\text{10-many}} = -110 - 210$

and it is clear that $A - B$ is divisible by 10.

The answer is A

7. It is clear that 17^{2017} is odd. Also,

$17^{2017} \equiv 2^{2017} \equiv (2^4)^{504} \cdot 2 \equiv 1 \cdot 2 \equiv 2 \pmod 5$

So, the units digit is 7.

The answer is D

8. The last two digits can be find by looking to remainder when divided by $100 = 4 \cdot 25$.

$2017^{2017} - 2018 \equiv 1^{2016} - 2 \equiv 3 \pmod 4$

$2017^{2017} - 2018 \equiv 17^{2017} - 18 \equiv (15 + 2)^{2017} - 18 \pmod{25}$

$\equiv 15^{2017} + \binom{2017}{1}15^{2016} \cdot 2^1 + \dots + \binom{2017}{2015}15^2 \cdot$

$2^{2015} + \binom{2017}{2016}15^1 \cdot 2^{2016} + 2^{2017} - 18 \pmod{25}$

$\equiv 2017 \cdot 15 \cdot 2^{2016} + 2^{2017} - 18 \equiv 7 \cdot 2^{2016} - 18$

$\equiv 7 \cdot 2^6 \cdot (2^{10})^{201} - 18 \pmod{25}$

$\equiv 7 \cdot 64 \cdot (-1)^{201} - 18 \equiv -466 \equiv 9 \pmod{25}$

Hence, the last two digit is 59.

The answer is D

9. If we check for small numbers,

$5^{2k} \equiv 1 \pmod 8$

$5^{2k+1} \equiv 5 \pmod 8$

Hence,

$5^0 + 5^1 + \cdots + 5^{2017}$

$\equiv \underbrace{(1 + 5) + (1 + 5) + \cdots (1 + 5)}_{\text{1009-many}}$

$\equiv 6 \cdot 1009 \equiv 6 \pmod 8$

The answer is D

10. It is obvious that 16^{2017} is divisible by 4. Also,

$16^{2017} \equiv 2^{8068} \equiv (2^{10})^{806} \cdot 256 \equiv (-1)^{806} \cdot 256 \equiv 6 \pmod{25}$

So, the last two digits of 16^{2017} is 56.

The answer is C

11. Since 2 and 4 are even and 3 is odd,

$2^{2019} + 3^{2019} + 4^{2019}$ is odd. Also,

$2^{2019} + 3^{2019} + 4^{2019} \equiv (2^4)^{504} \cdot 8 + (3^4)^{504} \cdot 27 + (4^4)^{504} \cdot 64 \equiv 8 + 27 + 64 \equiv 4 \pmod 5$

Hence, the units digit is 9.

The answer is E

12. Let's reorganize $(xx)^2 + (yy)^2 + (zz)^2$,

$(xx)^2 + (yy)^2 + (zz)^2 = 11^2(x^2 + y^2 + z^2)$

$= 11^2 \cdot 74 = 2 \cdot 11^2 \cdot 37$

The number of positive divisors is

$(1 + 1)(2 + 1)(1 + 1) = 12$.

The answer is B

MathTopia Press

MathTopia Press

CHAPTER 6

BASIC EQUATIONS & INEQUALITIES

1. EQUATIONS

Definition 6.1 — Linear Equations in One Variable

A linear equation (or first degree equation) with one unknown is an equation that can be written in the form $ax + b = 0$ where a and b are real numbers, $a \neq 0$ and x is a variable.

Remark 6.1

- If $a = b$ then $a + c = b + c$
- If $a = b$ then $a - c = b - c$
- If $a = b$ then $\frac{a}{c} = \frac{b}{c}$, where $c \neq 0$
- If $a = b$ then $a \cdot c = b \cdot c$

Solving Linear Equations

Let us begin by listing some general strategies for solving such equations.

1. Use the distributive property to remove any parentheses in the equation

2. Simplify each side of the equation.

3. Apply the addition or subtraction properties of equality to get the variables on one side of the equal sign and the constants on the other.

4. Simplify again if it is necessary.

5. Apply the multiplication or division properties of equality to isolate the variable.

6. Check the result (substitute the number for the variable in the original equation).

We can use this procedure to solve the standard linear equation of the form.

$$
\begin{aligned}
ax+b &= 0 \\
ax+b-b &= 0-b \quad \text{(subtract b from both sides)} \\
\frac{ax}{a} &= -\frac{b}{a} \quad \text{(divide both sides by a)} \\
x &= -\frac{b}{a} \quad \text{(simplify)}
\end{aligned}
$$

Example 6.1

Solve $-2x+3 \cdot (2x-4) = 8$

$$-2x+3 \cdot (2x-4) = 8 \,\text{(distributive property)}$$
$$-2x+3\cdot 2x-3\cdot 4 = 4x-12 = 8 \,\text{(combine like terms)}$$
$$x = 5$$

Definition 6.2 — Identity

An equation which is true for all possible values of the variable(s) in the equation is called an identity.

Definition 6.3 — Contradiction

An equation which is not true for any possible value of the variable(s) it contains is called a contradiction (or impossible equation).

Example 6.2

- $2x+6 = 2(x+3) \Rightarrow 2x+6 = 2 \cdot x + 2 \cdot 3$ $\Rightarrow 2x+6 = 2x+6$. We can see that $2x+6 = 2(x+3)$ is true for any value of x, because the two sides arc identical. So the solution set is the set of all real numbers, and the equation is an identity.

- Consider the equation $x+1 = x+5$. If we subtract x from both sides we get $x-x+1 = x-x+5$ $\Rightarrow 1 = 5$ which is false. So this equation is an impossible equation and the solution set is empty.

Problem 6.1

If
$$\frac{3}{4}x = \frac{2}{3}x + \frac{1}{6},$$
what is the value of x?

Solution
$$\frac{3}{4}x = \frac{2}{3}x + \frac{1}{6}$$
the least common denominator is 12.

Multiply both sides by 12 and distribute

$12 \cdot \frac{3}{4}x = 12 \cdot \frac{2}{3}x + 12 \cdot \frac{1}{6}$ cross cancel and multiply

$\quad 9x = 8x + 2$ subtract 8x

$\quad\quad x = 2$ this is the answer

Problem 6.2

Solve for x: $\frac{x}{2} - \frac{x}{3} = \frac{x}{4} + \frac{1}{2}$

MathTopia Press

Solution

The denominators are 3, 4, and 2, and the least common multiple of 3, 4, and 2 is 12.

We multiply both sides of the equation by this least common multiple, and so

$\frac{x}{2} - \frac{x}{3} = \frac{x}{4} + \frac{1}{2} \Rightarrow 12\left(\frac{x}{2} - \frac{x}{3}\right) = 12\left(\frac{x}{4} + \frac{1}{2}\right)$

$\Rightarrow 6x - 4x = 3x + 6$

$\Rightarrow 2x = 3x + 6$

$\Rightarrow 2x - 3x = 6$

$\Rightarrow -x = 6$

$\Rightarrow x = -6$

Problem 6.3

Solve for x: $\frac{2x-1}{3} = \frac{1-3x}{2}$

Solution

Cross-multiplying.

$\frac{2x-1}{3} = \frac{1-3x}{2} \Rightarrow 2(2x-1) = 3(1-3x)$

$\Rightarrow 4x - 2 = 3 - 9x$

$\Rightarrow 4x + 9x = 3 + 2$

$\Rightarrow 13x = 5$

$\Rightarrow x = \frac{5}{13}$

Problem 6.4

Solve for x: $ax - 2a = 2ab - a$

Solution

$ax - 2a = 2ab - a \Rightarrow ax = 2ab - a + 2a$

$\Rightarrow x = \frac{2ab + a}{a}$

$\Rightarrow x = 2b + 1$

Problem 6.5

Given that the equation $a(2x + 3) + 3bx = 12x + 5$ has infinitely many solutions for x. Find the values of a and b.

Solution

Change the given equation to the form $(2a + 3b - 12)x = 5 - 3a$, we have

$2a + 3b - 12 = 0$ and $5 - 3a = 0$

Therefore $a = \dfrac{5}{3}$, $b = \dfrac{12 - 2a}{3} = \dfrac{26}{9}$.

Problem 6.6

Given that the equation $2a(x + 6) = 4x + 1$ has no solution, where a is a parameter, find the value of a.

Solution

From the given equation $2a(x + 6) = 4x + 1$ we have $(2a - 4)x = 1 - 12a$.

Since it has no solution, this implies

$2a - 4 = 0$ and $1 - 12a \neq 0$,

therefore $a = 2$.

2. BASIC INEQUALITIES

Definition 6.4 — Inequalities

A statement which contains an inequality symbol between two algebraic expressions is called an inequality.

Properties of Inequalitiess

1. If $a > b$, then $a - c > b - c$
2. If $a > b$, then $a + c > b + c$
3. If $a > b$, and $c > 0$ then $a \cdot c > b \cdot c$
4. If $a > b$, and $c < 0$ then $a \cdot c < b \cdot c$
5. If $a > b$, and $c > 0$ then $\dfrac{a}{c} > \dfrac{b}{c}$
6. If $a > b$, and $c < 0$ then $\dfrac{a}{c} < \dfrac{b}{c}$

Remark 6.2

If a, b, and c are real numbers with $a < b$ and $b < c$, then $a < c$.

Solving Inequalities

1. Simplify both sides of the inequality by combining like terms and removing parentheses.
2. Add or subtract the same expression on both sides of the inequality.
3. Multiply or divide both sides of the inequality by the same positive expression (or multiply or divide both sides of the inequality by the same negative expression and reverse the inequality).

Problem 6.7

Solve $6 + 5x \geq 4 - 2x$

Solution

$6 + 5x \geq 4 - 2x \implies 5x + 2x \geq 4 - 6 \implies 7x \geq -2$

$\implies x \geq -\dfrac{2}{7}$

Problem 6.8

Solve $\dfrac{5 + 2(2 - 3x)}{3} > 9$

Solution

$\cancel{3} \cdot \dfrac{5 + 2(2 - 3x)}{\cancel{3}} > 9 \cdot 3$ (multiply both sides by 3)

$5 + 2(2 - 3x) > 27$ (remove parentheses)

$5 + 4 - 6x > 27 \implies 9 - 6x > 27$

$\implies -6x > 18$

$\dfrac{\cancel{-6}x}{\cancel{-6}} > \dfrac{18}{-6}$ (divide both sides by -6 and reverse the inequality)

$x < -3$

MathTopia Press

Problem 6.9

Solve the inequality

$$-2x - 3 \le -13$$

and graph its solution set.

Solution

Observe that

$$-2x - 3 \le -13 \Rightarrow -2x \le -13 + 3 \Rightarrow -2x \le -10$$

The next stage would be to divide by -2, which is a negative quantitiy. The sense of the inequality is reversed, and we gather

$$-2x \le -10 \Rightarrow x \ge \frac{-10}{-2} \Rightarrow x \ge 5$$

Problem 6.10

If $2x - 3 \le 3x - 1 < 2x + 5$, then find the sum of the integer values of x.

A) 4   B) 7   C) 9   D) 12   E) 14

Solution

$2x - 3 \le 3x - 1 \Rightarrow 2x - 3x \le -1 + 3 \Rightarrow -x \le 2$

$\Rightarrow x \ge -2$

$3x - 1 < 2x + 5 \Rightarrow 3x - 2x < 5 + 1 \Rightarrow x < 6$

$x \ge -2$ and $x < 6 \Rightarrow x \in \{3, 4, 5\}$

$\Rightarrow 3 + 4 + 5 = 12$ Correct answer is D.

3. ABSOLUTE VALUES

Definition 6.5 — Absolute Value of a Number

For any real number x, the absolute value of x is denoted by $|x|$. The absolute value of x is always either positive or zero, but never negative.

The absolute value $|x|$ of a real number x is the non-negative value of x without regard to its sign. Namely, $|x| = x$ for a positive x, $|x| = -x$ for a negative x in which case x is positive, and $|0| = 0$. For example, the absolute value of 3 is 3, and the absolute value of -3 is also 3. The absolute value of a number may be thought of as its distance from zero.

Properties of Absolute Value

1. Let x be real number
   (a) If $x > 0$, then $|x| = x$
   (b) If $x = 0$, then $|x| = 0$
   (c) If $x < 0$, then $|x| = -x$

2. $|x \cdot y| = |x| \cdot |y|$

3. $\left|\dfrac{x}{y}\right| = \dfrac{|x|}{|y|}$

4. $|x \pm y| \le |x| + |y|$

Example 6.3

Let's find absolute value of the given numbers.

- $|-2| = -(-2) = 2$, $|2| = 2$, $|0| = 0$

- $\left|-\dfrac{3}{2}\right| = -\left(-\dfrac{3}{2}\right) = \dfrac{3}{2}$, $\left|\dfrac{4}{7}\right| = \dfrac{4}{7}$

- If $x < y$, then $x - y < 0$,
  So $|x - y| = -(x - y) = y - x$

- If $x < y$, then $y - x > 0$, So $|y - x| = y - x$

- If $x < 0 < y$ and $|x| > y$, then $|x + y| < 0$,
  So $|x + y| = -(x + y) = -x - y$

- If $x < 0$, then $x^7 < 0$, So $|x^7| = -x^7$

- If $|x^4 + 1| = x^4 + 1$

Example 6.4

If $x < y < z < 0$, then let's find the value of

$$\frac{|x|}{x} - \frac{|y|}{y} + \frac{|z|}{z},$$

Since $x < 0$, $y < 0$ and $z < 0$ we have $|x| = -x$,

$|y| = -y$ and $|z| = -z$,

So $\dfrac{|x|}{x} - \dfrac{|y|}{y} + \dfrac{|z|}{z} = \dfrac{-x}{x} - \dfrac{-y}{y} + \dfrac{-z}{z}$

$= -1 - (-1) + (-1) = -1$

Equation with Absolute Values

1. Let $a > 0$, if $|x| = a$, then $x = a$ and $x = -a$
2. If $|x| = |y|$, then $x = y$ or $x = -y$

MathTopia Press

Example 6.5

Let's find the value of the given expression

$|x-1|+|x|-|-x|$ when $x < 0$.

Since $x < 0$ we have $|x-1|+|x|-|-x|$

$= -(x-1)+(-x)-(-x) = -x+1-x+x = -x+1$

Problem 6.11

Find the sum of all values of x which satisfy the given equation, $|2x-6| = 2001$

A) 3   B) 5   C) 6   D) 8   E) 12

Solution

$|2x-6| = 2001 \Rightarrow 2x-6 = 2001$ or $2x-6 = -2001$

that is $x = \dfrac{2007}{2}$ or $\dfrac{-1995}{2}$ then $\dfrac{2007}{2} + \dfrac{-1995}{2}$

$= \dfrac{2007-1995}{2} = \dfrac{12}{2} = 6$

Correct answer is C.

Problem 6.12

Let a,b and c are real numbers such that

$(2a+4)^2 + \left|\dfrac{b}{2}-5\right| + |c-2| = 0$.

What is the value of $a^4 + bc$?

A) 21   B) 23   C) 27   D) 36   E) 48

Solution

If $(2a+4)^2 + \left|\dfrac{b}{2}-5\right| + |c-2| = 0$

then $(2a+4)^2 = 0$, $\dfrac{b}{2} - 5 = 0$ and $c-2 = 0$,

so $a = -2$, $b = 10$ and $c = 2$.

$a^4 + bc = (-2)^4 + 10 \cdot 2 = 36$

The answer is D.

Problem 6.13

What is the sum of the values of a which satisfy the given equation, $|2a-6| = a+3$?

A) 9   B) 10   C) 11   D) 12   E) 13

Solution

$2a-6 = a+3 \Rightarrow a = 9$ and $2a-6 = -a-3$

$\Rightarrow a = 1$ that is $9 + 1 = 10$

Correct answer is B.

Problem 6.14

If $|x+1| + (y+2)^2 = 0$ and $ax - 3ay = 1$,

find the value of a.

Solution

Since $|x+1| \geq 0$ and $(y+2)^2 \geq 0$ for any real x, y,

so $x+1 = 0$ and $y+2 = 0$, i.e. $x = -1$, $y = -2$.

By substituting them into $ax - 3ay = 1$, it follows

that $-a + 6a = 1$, therefore $a = \dfrac{1}{5}$.

Problem 6.15

If $|x-2| + x - 2 = 0$ then the range of x is

A) $x > 2$,   B) $x < 2$ C) $x \geq 2$,   D) $x \leq 2$

Solution

The given equation produces $|x-2| = 2 - x$, so

$x \leq 2$ and $|x-2| = 2-x \iff x-2 = 2$ or

$x-2 = x-2 \iff x = 2$ or $x \leq 2$.

Problem 6.16

(AHSME/1990) Determine the number of real solutions of the equation $|x-2| + |x-3| = 1$

A) 0   B) 1   C) 2   D) 3   E) more than 3

Solution

There are three cases: $x \leq 2$; $2 < x \leq 3$, and $3 < x$.

(i) When $x \leq 2$,

$|x-2| + |x-3| = 1 \iff (2-x) + (3-x) = 1 \iff x = 2$;

(ii) When $2 < x \leq 3$,

$|x-2| + |x-3| = 1 \iff (x-2) + (3-x) = 1 \iff$ any

$x \in (2, 3]$ is a solution.

Thus, the answer is E.

MathTopia Press

The Four 4s Problem

Use the digit 4 exactly four times to write number sentences equivalent to the numbers from 26 to 50.

You may use any mathematical operations and symbols (e.g., 4.4, 44, 4^4, 4!, $\sqrt{4}$). Use parentheses as needed to clarify the order of operations.

Answer	Solution 1	Solution 2
26	$4 / .4 + 4 \times 4$	$4! + 4 \times .4 + .4$
27		
28		
29		
30		
31		
32		
33		
34		
35		
36		

Answer	Solution 1	Solution 2
37		
38		
39		
40		
41		
42		
43		
44		
45		
46		
47		
48		
49		
50		

MathTopia Press

1. Solve $3(x - 1) - 2x = 2x + 3$

    A) 0   B) −2   C) −4   D) −6   E) No Solution

2. Solve $x(x + 1) = (x + 2)(x - 2)$

    A) 1   B) 2   C) 4   D) −4   E) No Solution

3. Solve $\dfrac{2x}{3} + 1 = x + \dfrac{x - 1}{3}$

    A) 0   B) 2   C) −1   D) −2   E) $\dfrac{3}{2}$

4. If $\left(\dfrac{2x - 1}{4}\right)^2 + \left(\dfrac{4x - y}{3}\right)^2 = 0$, then find y

    A) 2   B) 3   C) 6   D) 8   E) 10

5. Find values of a which makes the following equation true $(96 \div 48) \times 9 = (96 \times 9) \div (a \times 9)$

    A) 96   B) 48   C) 24   D) 9   E) None

6. Which of the following sets describes all real-number values of x which makes the inequality $5(x + 1) > 5(x - 2)$ true?

    A) $x < -8$ B) $x > 0$ C) $x > \dfrac{1}{8}$

    D) $\mathbb{R}$ E) No Solution

MathTopia Press

7. Find the greatest possible integer value of x if

$$\frac{2x - 3}{5} < \frac{12 - 2x}{4}$$

A) 2   B) 3   C) 4   D) 5   E) 6

8. Find the sum of all possible integer values of x if

$$3 \le \frac{3x + 3}{2} \le 6$$

A) 6   B) 4   C) 3   D) 2   E) 1

9. How many x integers satisfy the inequality

$x + 3 \le 3x - 5 \le x + 11$?

A) 9   B) 8   C) 7   D) 6   E) 5

10. Suppose x, y, and z are integers such that

$-1 \le x < 3$, $-3 \le y < 5$, and $4 < z \le 6$.

What is the maximum possible value of

$x - 3y + 2z$?

A) 24   B) 28   C) 36   D) 48   E) None

11. If $\frac{3x - y}{4} = 7$ and $-2 < y < 5$, then

find the maximum possible integer value of x.

A) 5   B) 7   C) 10   D) 13   E) 15

12. Suppose x and y are real numbers such that
$-4 < x \le 3$ and $-4 < y \le 5$ find the maximum
value of $x^2 + y^2$

A) 29   B) 34   C) 36   D) 40   E) 41

MathTopia Press

1. Real numbers a, b, and c satisfy the following inequalities

   i) $0 < a < 1$, ii) $-1 < b < 0$, and iii) $1 < c < 2$.

   Which of the following numbers is always positive?

   A) $b+a^2$ B) $b+b^2$ C) $b+2b^2$

            D) $b+ac$ E) $b+c$

2. If $x^2 < x$ and $a = \dfrac{1}{x^2}$, $b = x^3$, and $c = x^2$, which of the following is always true?

   A) $b < c < a$ B) $b < a < c$ C) $a < b < c$

            D) $c < b < a$ E) $c < a < b$

3. I am thinking of a number, 5 more than twice my number is less than 37, but at least 1. If my number is an integer,

   How many possible values my number would be?

   A) 10   B) 12   C) 15   D) 16   E) 18

4. If $[-2, 7]$ is the largest interval value for x which satisfies the inequality of $-4 \le \dfrac{2x - a}{3} \le b$, what is $a-b$?

   A) 8   B) 6   C) 5   D) 1   E) -3

5. If $-2 < x \le 3$ and $-3 \le y < 4$, which of the following is always true?

   A) $6 < xy < 12$ B) $-8 < xy < 9$

   C) $-9 \le xy < 12$ D) $-9 \le xy \le 12$

                    E) None

6. Suppose a and b are integers such that $-4 < a \le 4$ and $-3 \le b < 7$.

   What is the minimum value of $a^2 - 2b$?

   A) -14 B) -12 C) -7 D) -3 E) 15

MathTopia Press

7. Suppose x and y are real numbers such that $-4 < x < 5$ and $-6 < y < -3$, how many integer values does $x^2 + y^2$ have?

A) 50 B) 51 C) 61 D) 69 E) 70

10. Suppose x and y are positive integers such that $x + y < 711$ and $\dfrac{5y - 8}{x - 2} = 4$ then, find the maximum value of x.

A) 280 B) 300 C) 350 D) 390 E) None

8. If $\dfrac{1}{2} < \dfrac{1}{x} < 3$ and $2 < y < 5$.

What is the sum of all possible integer values of $\dfrac{xy + 1}{y}$?

A) 2 B) 3 C) 4 D) 5 E) 8

11. Simplify $\dfrac{a + b}{ab} + \dfrac{b - c}{bc} + \dfrac{a - c}{ac}$

A) $\dfrac{2}{a}$ B) $\dfrac{2}{c}$ C) $\dfrac{2}{b}$ D) $-\dfrac{2}{a}$ E) None

9. Find x that satisfies $\dfrac{2}{2 + \dfrac{x}{x - 1}} = 6$.

A) $\dfrac{1}{2}$ B) $\dfrac{5}{2}$ C) $\dfrac{7}{2}$ D) $\dfrac{9}{2}$ E) $\dfrac{5}{8}$

12. If $5 - \dfrac{3 - \dfrac{x + 4}{2}}{6} = 5$, then what is x?

A) 1 B) 2 C) 4 D) 6 E) None

MathTopia Press

Problem Set 1

1. Let's solve the equation directly,
$$3(x - 1) - 2x = 2x + 3 \Rightarrow x - 3 = 2x + 3$$
$$\Rightarrow x = -6$$
The answer is D

2. Let's solve the equation directly,
$$x(x + 1) = (x + 2)(x - 2) \Rightarrow x^2 + x = x^2 - 4$$
$$\Rightarrow x = -4$$
The answer is D

3. Let's organize the equation to solve it,
$$\frac{2x}{3} + 1 = x + \frac{x - 1}{3} \Rightarrow 2x + 3 = 4x - 1$$
$$\Rightarrow x = 2$$
The answer is B

4. Square of a number is always positive unless it is 0. Hence, if the sum of square of some numbers is 0, then each number is 0. By that, $2x - 1 = 0$ and $4x - y = 0$. Therefore,
$$(x, y) = (\frac{1}{2}, 2)$$
The answer is A

5. Let's calculate left hand side first.
$$(96 \div 48) \times 9 = 2 \times 9 = 18$$
Right hand side is
$$(96 \times 9) \div (a \times 9) = 18 \Rightarrow 18 = \frac{96 \cdot 9}{9a} = \frac{96}{a}$$
$$\Rightarrow a = \frac{16}{3}$$
The answer is E

6. If we organize the inequality, we can find that $5 > -10$ and it is always true. So, the inequality is satisfied for every $x \in \mathbb{R}$.

The answer is D

7. Let's reorganize the inequality
$$\frac{2x - 3}{5} < \frac{12 - 2x}{4} \Rightarrow 8x - 12 < 60 - 10x$$
$$\Rightarrow 18x < 72 \Rightarrow x < 4$$
Hence, x can be 1, 2, 3.
The answer is B

8. Let's reorganize the inequality
$$3 \leq \frac{3x + 3}{2} \leq 6 \Rightarrow 1 \leq \frac{x - 1}{2} \leq 2$$
$$\Rightarrow 2 \leq x + 1 \leq 4 \Rightarrow 1 \leq x \leq 3$$
Hence, x can be 1, 2, 3, their sum is 6.
The answer is A

MathTopia Press

9. Let's reorganize the inequality

$x + 3 \leq 3x - 5 \leq x + 11 \Rightarrow 3 \leq 2x - 5 \leq 11$

$\Rightarrow 8 \leq 2x \leq 16 \Rightarrow 4 \leq x \leq 8$

Hence, x can be 4, 5, 6, 7, 8.

The answer is E

10. Let's reorganize the inequalities

$-1 \leq x < 3$

$-15 < -3y \leq 9$

$8 < 2z \leq 12$

Hence, max $x = 2$, max$(-3y) = 9$, and max$(2z) = 12$. By that,

max $(x - 3y + 2z) = 2 + 9 + 12 = 23$

The answer is E

11. Since $3x - y = 28$, $y = 3x - 28$, and

$-2 < 3x - 28 < 5 \Rightarrow 26 < 3x < 33$

$\Rightarrow \dfrac{16}{3} < x < 11$ Hence, max$(x) = 10$.

The answer is C

12. Let's reorganize the inequalities

$-4 < x \leq 3 \Rightarrow 0 \leq x^2 < 16$

$-4 < y \leq 5 \Rightarrow 0 \leq y^2 \leq 25$

Hence, $0 \leq x^2 + y^2 < 41$, and thus,

max $(x^2 + y^2) = 40$.

The answer is D

MathTopia Press

Problem Set 2

1. If we choose $a = \dfrac{1}{2}$ and $b = -\dfrac{1}{2}$, option A, B, C will not be positive.

If we choose $a = \dfrac{1}{2}$, $b = -\dfrac{7}{8}$, and $c = \dfrac{3}{2}$, option D will be negative. Also,

$$0 < b + c < 2$$

So, $b + c$ is always positive. The answer is E

2. Since $x^2 \geq 0$ for all real numbers, $x > 0$. Therefore,

$x > x^2 \Rightarrow 1 > x > 0$

$\Rightarrow x^{-2} > 1 > x^2 > x^3 \Rightarrow a > c > b$

The answer is A

3. Assume that the number is x, then

$1 \leq 2x + 5 < 37 \Rightarrow -4 \leq 2x < 32 \Rightarrow -2 \leq x < 16$

Therefore, x can be $-2, -1, 0, 1, 2, \ldots, 15$.

There are 18 possible values.

The answer is E

4. Let's organize the inequality

$-4 \leq \dfrac{2x - a}{3} \leq b \Rightarrow -12 \leq 2x - a \leq 3b$

$\Rightarrow \dfrac{a - 12}{2} \leq x \leq \dfrac{3b + a}{2}$

Hence, $\dfrac{a - 12}{2} = -2$ and $\dfrac{3b + a}{2} = 7$.

By solving these two equations, we can find that $a = 8$ and $b = 2$, and $a - b = 6$.

The answer is B

5. To obtain maximum or minimum value of xy, we should choose x and y as their boundary values. By that, we can find that
$$-9 \leq xy < 12$$
The answer is C

6. To obtain minimum value of $a^2 - 2b$, we should choose minimum value of a^2, and maximum value of b. For $a^2 = 0$ and $b = 6$, $a^2 - 2b = -12$.

The answer is B

7. Let's reorganize the inequalities
$$-4 < x < 5 \Rightarrow 0 \leq x^2 < 25$$
$$-6 < y < -3 \Rightarrow 9 < y^2 < 36$$
$$\Rightarrow 9 < x^2 + y^2 < 61$$
Therefore, $x^2 + y^2$ can be 10, 11, . . . , 60.
There are 51 possible values.

The answer is B

8. By organizing the inequalities, we can obtain that
$$\frac{1}{2} < x < 2 \text{ and } \frac{1}{5} < \frac{1}{y} < \frac{1}{2}.$$
By summing these two inequalities up,
$$\frac{8}{15} < x + \frac{1}{y} = \frac{xy + 1}{y} < \frac{5}{2}$$
Therefore, $\frac{xy + 1}{y}$ can be 1 and 2.

Their sum is 3. The answer is B

9. Let's reorganize the equation,
$$\frac{2}{2 + \frac{x}{x-1}} = 6 \Rightarrow \frac{1}{\frac{3x-2}{x-1}} = \frac{x-1}{3x-2} = 3$$
$$\Rightarrow x - 1 = 9x - 6 \Rightarrow x = \frac{5}{8}$$
The answer is E

10. Since $\frac{5y - 8}{x - 2} = 4$, $5y - 8 = 4x - 8$, and
$5y = 4x$. There exists positive integer k such that $y = 4k$ and $x = 5k$. By that,
$$x + y = 9k < 711 \Rightarrow k < 79$$
Therefore, the maximum value of
$x = 5k$ is $5 \cdot 78 = 390$.

The answer is D

11. Let's reorganize the given expression,
$$\frac{a+b}{ab} + \frac{b-c}{ab} + \frac{a-c}{ac}$$
$$= \frac{1}{b} + \frac{1}{a} + \frac{1}{c} + \frac{1}{b} + \frac{1}{c} + \frac{1}{a} = \frac{2}{c}$$
The answer is B

12. Let's reorganize the equality,
$$5 - \frac{3 - \frac{x+4}{2}}{6} = 5 \Rightarrow 3 = \frac{x+4}{2} \Rightarrow x = 2$$
The answer is B

MathTopia Press

CHAPTER 7

THE CARTESIAN COORDINATE SYSTEM

Definition 7.1

The Cartesian coordinates in the plane are specified in terms of the xx coordinates axis and the y-coordinate axis, as illustrated in the below figure. The origin is the intersection of the x and y-axes. The Cartesian coordinates of a point in the plane are written as (x,y). The point below has coordinates $(-3,2)$, as the point is three units to the left and two units up from the origin.

Definition 7.2

The intersecting x- and y-axes divide the coordinate plane into four sections. These four sections are called quadrants. Quadrants are named using the Roman numerals I, II, III, and IV beginning with the top right quadrant and moving counter clockwise.

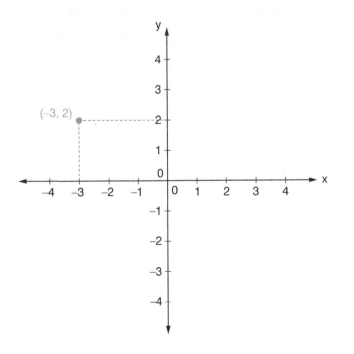

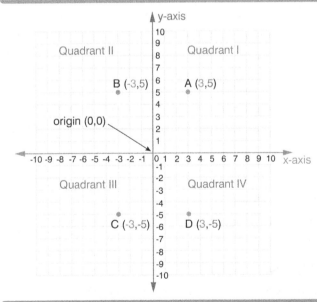

Definition 7.3

The slope of a line measures how steep it is. The slope of the line connecting two points (x_1, y_1) and (x_2, y_2) is defined as the difference in y-coordinates, divided by the difference in x-coordinates:

Finding slope using two points on the line.

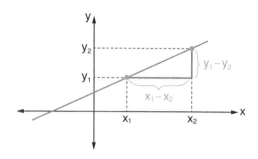

$$\text{Slope} = m = \frac{\text{Change in y}}{\text{Change in x}} = \frac{y_2 - y_1}{x_2 - x_1}$$

Problem 7.1

What is the slope of a line containing the points A(3, −5) and B(7, 2)?

Solution

$$m = \frac{y_2 - y_1}{x_2 - x_1} = \frac{2 - (-5)}{7 - 3} = \frac{7}{4}$$

Remark 7.1 — Some important facts about slope

- A positive slope means that the y-coordinate increases as x increases; a negative slope means that the y-coordinate decreases as x increases.

- A horizontal line has slope zero, and a vertical line has undefined slope.

- Two lines are parallel if they have the same slope.

- Two lines are perpendicular if one is horizontal and one is vertical, or if their slopes multiply to -1; i.e. they are negative reciprocals of each other.

Parallel Lines

Two nonvertical lines are parallel if and only if they have the same slope.

Perpendicular Lines

Two lines with slopes m_1 and m_2 are perpendicular if and only if $m_1 m_2 = -1$, that is, their slopes are negative reciprocals.

$$m_2 = -\frac{1}{m_1}$$

Also, a horizontal line (slope 0) is perpendicular to a vertical line (no slope).

MathTopia Press

Remark 7.2 — Slope-Intercept Form

Point-Slope Form Of The Equation Of A Line

An equation of the line that passes through the point (x_1, y_1) and has slope m is

$$y - y_1 = m(x - x_1)$$

Problem 7.2

A line with slope 3 intersects a line with slope 5 at point (10, 15). What is the distance between the x-intercepts of these two lines?

A) 2   B) 5   C) 7   D) 12   E) 20

Solution

Using the point-slope form, the equation of each line is

$$y - 15 = 3(x - 10) \rightarrow y = 3x - 15$$
$$y - 15 = 5(x - 10) \rightarrow y = 5x - 35$$

Substitute in y = 0 to find the x-intercepts.

$$0 = 3x - 15 \rightarrow x = 5$$
$$0 = 5x - 35 \rightarrow x = 7$$

The difference between them is 7 − 5 = (A) 2.

Remark 7.3 — Point-Slope Form

Slope-Intercept Form Of The Equation Of A Line

An equation of the line that has slope m and y-intercept b is

$$y = mx + b$$

Example 7.1

If (3, −4) is on the line given by y = 4x + b.
What is the value of b?

(3, −4) is on the line

$$y = 4x + b$$
$$\downarrow \quad\quad \downarrow$$
$$-4 = 4(3) + b \quad \text{multiply}$$
$$-4 = 12 + b \quad \text{subtract 12}$$
$$-16 = b$$

The value of b is −16.

Remark 7.4 — y–intercept

To find the y – intercept, set x = 0 and solve for y.

$y = mx + b$ $x = 0$

$y = 0x + b$ (0, b) is the y – intercept

$y = b$ ↑

                the constant term in y = mx + b

Remark 7.5 — x–intercept

To find the x – intercept, set y = 0 and solve for x.

$y = mx + b = 0$ subtract b

$mx = -b$ divide by m

$x = \dfrac{-b}{m}$ $\left(-\dfrac{b}{m}, 0\right)$ is the x – intercept

Problem 7.3

Find the slope and the y – intercept of the line given by 8x – 4y = 12.

Solution

Let's isolate y and compare the equation to

$y = mx + b$

    $8x - 4y = 12$ add $-8x$

      $-4y = -8x + 12$ divide by -4

         $y = 2x - 3$

slope = 2

y – intercept = -3

Remark 7.6 — Midpoints and Distances

The distance between the points (x_1, y_1) and (x_2, y_2) is $\sqrt{(x_2 - x_1)^2 + (y_2 - y_1)^2}$.

To see why, we can construct a right triangle whose side lengths are $|x_2 - x_1|$ and $|y_2 - y_1|$ (note that we should use absolute value signs, in case $x_2 < x_1$ or $y_2 < y_1$):

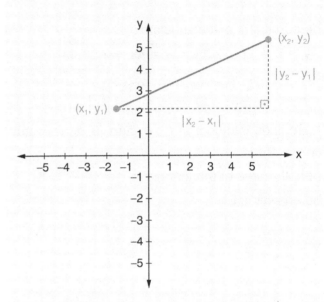

MathTopia Press

By the Pythagorean theorem, we have

$d^2 = |x_2 - x_1|^2 + |y_2 - y_1|^2 = (x_2 - x_1)^2 + (y_2 - y_1)^2,$

so $d = \sqrt{(x_2 - x_1)^2 + (y_2 - y_1)^2}$.

Again it does not matter which point is (x_1, y_1).

Example 7.2

Find the distance between the points $(-2, -3)$ and $(-4, 4)$.

$d = \sqrt{(-4 - (-2))^2 + (4 - (-3))^2}$

$= \sqrt{(-4 + 2)^2 + (4 + 3)^2} = \sqrt{(-2)^2 + (7)^2}$

$= \sqrt{4 + 49} = \sqrt{53}$

Problem 7.4

Two lines which intersect at (2, 2) have slopes -2 and $\frac{1}{2}$. What is the area of the triangle enclosed by these two lines and the line $x = 0$?

A) 4   B) 8   C) 10   D) 12

E) None of the preceding

Solution

The equations of the lines are

$$y - 2 = 2(x - 2) \Rightarrow y = 4x - 2$$

and

$$y - 2 = \frac{1}{2}(x - 2) \Rightarrow y = \frac{1}{2}x + 1.$$

Those lines intersect at (0, 6) and (0, 1) with the line $x = 0$.

Then, the area of the triangle is $\dfrac{(6 - 1) \cdot 2}{2} = 5$.

The answer is E.

Problem 7.5

What is the area of the triangle formed by the lines $y = 6 - x$, $y = 6 + x$, and $y = 2$?

A) 16   B) 18   C) 19   D) 20   E) 21

Solution

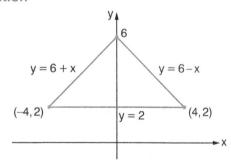

The intersection points are (2, 4), (2, −4) and (0, 6). As drawn in the figure on the right, the height is 4 and the length of the base is 8 in the triangle.

Therefore, its area is $\dfrac{4 \cdot 8}{2} = 16$.

The answer is A.

Problem 7.6

The area of triangle formed by the x-axis, and the line $2y = mx + 6$ is 36. What is $|m|$?

A) $\dfrac{1}{16}$ B) $\dfrac{1}{8}$ C) $\dfrac{1}{4}$ D) $\dfrac{3}{4}$ E) $\dfrac{4}{3}$

Solution

The x- and y-intercepts of the line $2y = mx + 6$ are $-\dfrac{6}{m}$ and 3, respectively.

Since the area of the triangle is 36, we have

$$36 = \frac{1}{2} \cdot \left(3 \cdot \frac{6}{|m|}\right) = \frac{9}{|m|}.$$

Therefore, $|m| = \dfrac{1}{4}$.

The answer is C.

Problem 7.7

Given that a can be neither 2 nor 1, lines $(a + 2)x + 2y + 4 = 0$ and $2x + (a - 1)y + 6 = 0$ are parallel to each other.

Find the possible negative value of a.

Problem 7.8

Given that a is not 0. Lines $ax + (b + 1)y - 1 = 0$ and $(b - 5)x + ay + 7 = 0$ are perpendicular to each other. Find b.

MathTopia Press

Problem 7.9

Let P be the point obtained by rotating the point (3, 4) around the point (1, −1) counterclockwise by 90°. Find the coordinates of P.

Problem 7.10

In the diagram, the equation of line AD is
$y = \sqrt{3}(x\ 1)$.

BD bisects $\angle$ADC. If the coordinates of B are (p, q), what is the value of q?

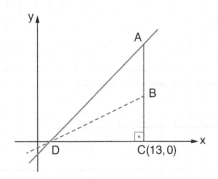

Problem 7.11

What is the shortest distance from origin to the line that contain the points (−4, 0) and (0, 3)?

MathTopia Press

Problem 7.12

What is the shortest distance from the point (1, 2) to the line 3x + 4y = 12?

Count Down Number Game

SCORING: For each of the target integers, your team will receive 10 points for reaching the exact target, or 9 points for finding an integer that is 1 away from the target, or 8 points for finding an integer that is 2 away from the target, etc. or 1 point for finding an integer that is 9 away from the target.

Using each of the given numbers exactly once, and only addition, subtraction, multiplication, division, and parenthesis, your goal is to get to the target number or an integer as close to the target number as you can

Example: If the given numbers are 1, 2, 3, 4, 10, 50 and target number is 605, then

$608 = (10 + 2) \times 50 + (1 + 3 + 4)$ would receive 7 p

Given Numbers: 2, 3, 4, 5, 10, 75	
Target Number	**Solution**
101	
121	
141	
161	
181	
201	
221	
241	
261	
281	

Given Numbers: 1, 2, 4, 5, 10, 50	
Target Number	**Solution**
541	
641	
741	
765	
777	
781	
799	
801	
811	
819	
839	
859	
899	
919	
939	
959	
979	
999	
1001	

MathTopia Press

1. For the line y = mx + b, mb < 0.

   Which of the following could be the graph of this line?

   A)   B)   C)   D)

   E) None of the preceding

2. Find the equation of a line that passes through the point (–7, 7/2) and the midpoint of (–2, 4) and (3, 4).

   A) 30y – 2x – 119 = 0   B) 2y – 30x = 0

   C) 40y – 120x – 119 = 0   D) 3y – 2x – 19 = 0

         E) 30y – 40x – 119 = 0

3. What is x?

   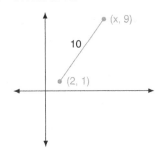

   A) 6   B) 7   C) 8   D) 9   E)

4. The equation of line ℓ is

   $$3x - 2y = 4.$$

   If line n contains the point (2, 3) and is perpendicular to line ℓ, If the equation of line l is y = mx + b, what is b?

   A) –1   B) 0   C) $\frac{11}{3}$ D) 2   E) $\frac{13}{3}$

5. Line ℓ is perpendicular to 2x + 2y = 2, and with the same y–intercept, is graphed on the coordinate plane. What is the sum of its x– and y–intercepts?

   A) 0   B) 2   C) 3   D) 4   E) 5

6. The points A(a, 1), B(9, 0) and C(–3, 4) lie on a straight line. The value of a is

   A) 3   B) $\frac{8}{3}$ C) $\frac{7}{2}$ D) 6   E) $\frac{5}{2}$

MathTopia Press

7. In the coordinate plane below, two lines are perpendicular to each other. What is x?

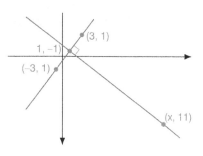

A) 10   B) 12   C) 15   D) 16   E) 17

8. Given that $a \neq 0$. Lines $ax + (b + 1)y - 1 = 0$ and $(b - 5)x + ay + 7 = 0$ are perpendicu to each other. Find b.

A) 2   B) 3   C) 4   D) 5   E) 6

9. Including the endpoints, how many points on the line segment joining $(-9, -2)$ and $(6, 8)$ have coordinates that are both integers?

A) 2   B) 7   C) 16   D) 11   E) 6

10. In the figure below, $B = (a, b)$ is the intersection point of two lines. Find $a + b$.

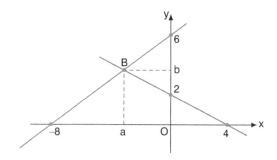

A) $\frac{2}{5}$ B) $\frac{2}{3}$ C) $\frac{3}{4}$ D) $\frac{3}{5}$ E) $\frac{4}{5}$

11.

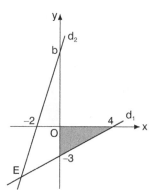

Lines d_1 and d_2 interest at point E. If two shaded areas are equal, what is the sum of coordinates of point E?

A) –8   B) –10   C) –12   D) –14   E) –16

12. The area of the triangle formed by the x-axis, y-axis, and the line $2y = mx + 6$ is 36.

What is $|m|$?

A) $\frac{1}{16}$ B) $\frac{1}{8}$ C) $\frac{1}{4}$ D) $\frac{3}{4}$ E) $\frac{4}{3}$

MathTopia Press

Problem Set 1

1. Since the slope times the y-intercept is negative, this means one of them should be negative. Therefore, the only valid option is D

2. The general line equation is:
$$y - y_0 = m(x - x_0)$$
where the slope m is given by:
$$m = \frac{y_2 - y_1}{x_2 - x_1}$$
Also, the midpoint of the two given points is (0.5,4), so the slope would be:
$$m = \frac{4 - 7/2}{0.5 - (-7)} = \frac{\frac{1}{2}}{7.5} = \frac{1}{15}$$
Plugging back in the general line equation along with the point (0.5,4):
$$y - 4 = \frac{1}{15}\left(x - \frac{1}{2}\right) \Rightarrow y = \frac{1}{15}x - \frac{119}{30}$$
$$\Rightarrow 30y - 2x - 119 = 0 \quad \text{The answer is A}$$

3. Remember the distance between two points in space equation:
$$\sqrt{(x_2 - x_1)^2 + (y_2 - y_1)^2}$$
Plugging in the numbers:
$$10 = \sqrt{(x - 2)^2 + (9 - 1)^2} \Rightarrow 100 = (x - 2)^2 + 64$$
$$\Rightarrow 36 = (x - 2)^2 \Rightarrow x - 2 = 6 \Rightarrow x = 8$$
The Answer is C

4. The slopes of two perpendicular straight lines are related by:
$$m_n = \frac{-1}{m_l}$$
Rearranging the equation of line I:
$$y = \frac{3}{2}x - 2 \Rightarrow m_l = \frac{3}{2} \Rightarrow = m_n = \frac{-2}{3}$$
Now, using the general equation of a straight line with the slope and point given:
$$y - 3 = \frac{-2}{3}(x - 2) \Rightarrow y = \frac{-2}{3}x + \frac{4}{3} + 3$$
$$= \frac{-2}{3}x + \frac{13}{3} \quad \text{The Answer is E}$$

5. The slopes of two perpendicular straight lines are related by:
$$m_l = \frac{-1}{3}$$
Rearranging the equation of the line:
$$y = -x - 1 \Rightarrow m = -1 \Rightarrow m_l = 1 \text{ and } h = 1$$
Therefore the equation of line I is:
$$y = x + 1 \Rightarrow 0 = x + 1 \Rightarrow x = -1 \text{ is the x intercept}$$
Therefore the sum is: $-1 + 1 = 0$
The answer is A

6. Since the three points lie on the same line, we can use points B and C to get the equation of the line such that:
$$m = \frac{4 - 0}{-3 - 9} = \frac{-1}{3} \Rightarrow y - 0 = \frac{-1}{3}(x - 9)$$
$$\Rightarrow y = \frac{-1}{3}x + 3$$
plugging in point A:
$$1 = \frac{-1}{3}x + 3 \Rightarrow x = 6$$
The answer is D

7. The two lines are perpendicular. Therefore:
$$m_1 = \frac{-1}{m_2}$$
let's call the line with the two known points (line 1), So:
$$m_1 = \frac{-1 - 3}{3 - (-1)} = -1 \Rightarrow m_2 = 1$$
So the equation of line (2):
$$y - (-1) = 1(x - 1) \Rightarrow y = x - 2$$
plugging in y = 11:
$$11 = x - 2 \Rightarrow x = 13$$
The Answer is B

MathTopia Press

8. Rearranging both equations:

$$ax + (b + 1)y - 1 = 0 \Rightarrow y = \frac{-a}{b + 1}x + \frac{1}{a}$$

$$(b - 5)x + ay + 7 = 0 \Rightarrow y = \frac{-(b - 5)}{a}x - \frac{7}{a}$$

Since the lines are perpendicular, their slopes (the coefficient of x) are related as follows:

$$\frac{-a}{b + 1} = \frac{a}{b - 5} \Rightarrow 5 - b = b + 1 \Rightarrow b = 3$$

The answer is B

9. Let's find the equation of the line connecting both points:

$$m = \frac{8 - (-2)}{6 - (-9)} = \frac{10}{15} = \frac{2}{3}$$

$$y - 8 = \frac{2}{3}(x - 6) \Rightarrow y = \frac{2}{3}x + 4$$

Looking at the line equation, both coordinates are integers only when x is 3, −3, 0 and their multiples. Therefore, within the range [−9, 6] there are 6 points including the end points.

The answer is E

10. To find the point of intersection of 2 lines, we must equate their line equations. Let's find their equations:

$$m_1 = \frac{2 - 0}{0 - 4} = \frac{-1}{2}; \quad m_2 = \frac{6 - 0}{0 - (-8)} = \frac{3}{4}$$

Line 1:

$$y - 2 = \frac{-1}{2}x \Rightarrow y = \frac{-1}{2}x + 2$$

Line 2:

$$y - 6 = \frac{3}{4}x \Rightarrow y = \frac{3}{4}x + 6$$

Equating both equations:

$$\frac{3}{4}x + 6 = \frac{-1}{2}x + 2 \Rightarrow a = \frac{-16}{5} \Rightarrow b = \frac{18}{5}$$

$$\Rightarrow a + b = \frac{2}{5}$$

The answer is A

11. The shaded areas are right triangles. Therefore:

$$A_{yellow} = A_{blue} \Rightarrow \frac{2b}{2} = \frac{3 \times 4}{2} \Rightarrow b = 6$$

Now, we should find the equations of the lines, then equate them:

$$m_y = \frac{6 - 0}{0 - (-2)} = 3; \quad m_b = \frac{-3 - 0}{0 - 4} = \frac{3}{4}$$

Yellow line:

$$y - 0 = 3(x - (-2)) \Rightarrow y = 3x + 6$$

Blue line:

$$y - 0 = \frac{3}{4}(x - 4) \Rightarrow y = \frac{3}{4}x - 3$$

Equating:

$$3x - 6 = \frac{3}{4}x - 3 \Rightarrow x = -4 \Rightarrow y = -6 \Rightarrow x + y = -10$$

The answer is B

12. Rearranging the line equation to make it of the form (y = mx + h):

$$y = \frac{m}{2}x + 3$$

Thus, the y-intercept is 3, and the x-intercept is:

$$0 = \frac{m}{2}x + 3 \Rightarrow x = \frac{-6}{m}$$

Therefore, the area of the triangle is:

$$\frac{3 \times \frac{-6}{m}}{2} = 36 \Rightarrow \frac{-6}{m} = 24 \Rightarrow m = \frac{-1}{4}$$

The answer is C

MathTopia Press

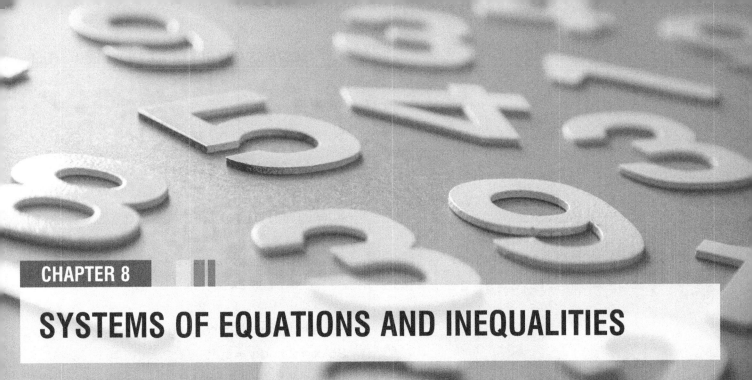

CHAPTER 8

SYSTEMS OF EQUATIONS AND INEQUALITIES

Definition 8.1 — System of Linear Equations

System of linear equations (or linear system) is a collection of one or more linear equations involving the same set of variables. A solution of a system is an assignment of values for the variables that makes each equation in the system true.

In general, systems of linear equations in two variables, consist of two equations that contain two different variables.

$a_1x + b_1y = c_1$

$a_2x + b_2y = c_2$

- When $\dfrac{a_1}{a_2} \neq \dfrac{b_1}{b_2}$, then the system has unique solution.

- When $\dfrac{a_1}{a_2} = \dfrac{b_1}{b_2} = \dfrac{c_1}{c_2}$, then the system has two same

  equations, so it has infinitely many solutions.

- When $\dfrac{a_1}{a_2} = \dfrac{b_1}{b_2} \neq \dfrac{c_1}{c_2}$, then the system has no solution.

This is example of a system of linear equations in two variables.

$2x - y = 5$

$x + 4y = 7$

We can check that x = 3 and y = 1 is a solution of this system.

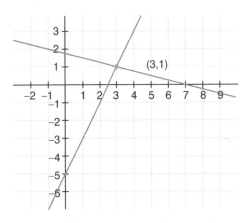

Note that the graphs of Equations 1 and 2 are lines. Since the solution satisfies each equation, the point lies on each line. So it is the point of intersection of the two lines.

Example 8.1

$2x + y = 15$

$x - y = 3$

is a system of linear equations. Its solution is an ordered pair (x, y) that simultaneously satisfies both equations.

Problem 8.1

If the system of equations $3x + 2y - 8 = 0$,

$(a - 2)x + 4y - 3 = 0$ has a unique solution, which of the following values can not be equal to a?

A) 11　　B) 10　　C) 9　　D) 8　　E) 7

Solution

If this system has only one solution, then

$$\frac{3}{a-2} \neq \frac{2}{4} \Rightarrow 12 \neq 2(a - 2) \Rightarrow 6 \neq a - 2 \Rightarrow a \neq 8$$

Problem 8.2

Solve the system of equations

$x + y = 3$, $y + z = 4$, $x + z = 5$.

Solution

Let's add two equations together to find one of the variables.

We get $2x + 2y + 2z = 12 \Rightarrow x + y + z = 6$.

After submitting $x + y = 3$ into the derived equantion, we get $3 + z = 6 \Rightarrow z = 3$,

therefore $y = 1$ and $x = 2$.

A linear equation with n variables is an equation of the form $a_1x_1 + a_2x_2 + \cdots a_nx_n = c$, where $a_1a_2, \cdots ,a_n$, c_n are constants and $x_1, x_2, \ldots , x_n$ are variables. When $n \leq 3$, we usually use the letters x, y and z for variables.

Solving Systems of Linear Equations.

There are two methods for solving systems of equations- Substitutions and elimination. The substitution method works best when at least one of the equations in the system is of the $y =$ form.

1. Substitution

The method of solution by substitution is used when at least one equation is given with either 2 or y as the subject of the formula, or if it is easy to make x or y the subject

MathTopia Press

Example 8.2

Solve by substitution: $\begin{cases} y = 3 + x \\ 2x - 4y = -16 \end{cases}$

$$y = 3 + x \quad \ldots. (1)$$
$$2x - 4y = -16 \quad \ldots. (2)$$

Substituting (1) into (2) gives

$$2x - 4(3 + x) = -16$$
$$\therefore \ 2x - 12 - 4x = -16$$
$$\therefore \ -2x = -4$$
$$\therefore \ x = 2$$

Substituting $x = 2$ into (1) gives $y = 3 + 2 = 5$

So, $x = 2$ and $y = 5$.

Check: $2 \times 2 - 4 \times 5 = 4 - 20 = -16$

Problem 8.3

Solve the system:　$y = 2x + 25$

$5x - 3y = 13$

Solution

Substitute $2x + 25$ for y in the second equation to get: $5x - 3(2x + 25) = 13$

Distribute: $5x - 6x - 75 = 13$

Gather like terms: $-1x = 88$

Solve for x: $x = -88$

Use the $y = 2x + 25$ equation to find y:

$$y = 2(-88) + 25 = -151$$

The solution to this system is the ordered pair $(-88, -151)$.

2 Elimination

In problems where each equation has the from $ax + by = c$, elimination of one of the variables is preferred.

In this method, we multiply each equation by a constant so that the coefficients of either x or y are the same size but opposite in sign. We then add the equations to eliminate one variable.

Problem 8.4

Solve the system: $3x - 4y = 37$
$2x + 5y = -29$

Solution

The coefficients of the y variables are already opposite in sign. Multiplying both sides of the first equation by 5 and both sides of the second equation by 4 will allow us to cancel y so that we can solve for x and the for y.

$5(3x - 4y = 37)$

$4(2x + 5y = -29)$

$15x - 20y = 185$

$8x + 20y = -116$

Add the two equations:

$23x = 69$

Solve for x:

$x = 3$

Solve for y:

$2(3) + 5y = -29$

$6 + 5y = -29$

$5y = -35$

$y = -7$

The solution to this system is the ordered pair $(3, -7)$

Problem 8.5

The difference of two numbers is 7. Their sum is 23. Find the product of the numbers.

Solution

Let the numbers be x and y $(x > y)$

$x - y = 7$

$+ \quad x + y = 23$

$2x = 30 \Rightarrow x = 15 \rightarrow$ substitute this into the second equation

$x + y = 23 \Rightarrow 15 + y = 23 \Rightarrow y = 8$

The numbers are 15 and 8, and 15 x 8 is equal to 120. The answer is 120.

Problem 8.6

Solve by elimination: $\begin{cases} 2x - 3y = 4 \\ 3x + 2y = 19 \end{cases}$

Solution

$2x - 3y = 4$ .... (1)

$3x + 2y = 19$ .... (2)

We multiply each equation by a constant so the coefficients of y will be the same size but opposite in sign.

$4x - 6y = 8$ $\{2 \times (1)\}$

$9x + 6y = 57$ $\{3 \times (2)\}$

Adding, $13x \quad = 65$

$\therefore \ x = 5$

Substituting x = 5 into (1),

$2 \times 5 - 3y = 4$

$\therefore \ 10 - 3y = 4$

$\therefore \ 6 = 3y$

$\therefore \ 2 = y$

So, x = 5 and y = 2.

Check: $3x + 2y = 3 \times 5 + 2 \times 2 = 15 + 4 = 19$

Problem 8.7

There are a total of 555 students in a school. For the next term, the number of girls decreases by 17 and the number of boys increases by $\frac{1}{12}$ of the original number of boys. The total number of students decreases by 11. How many girls are in the school in the new term?

Solution

Let the number of girls be g and the number of boys be b and we can obtain 2 equations:

$\begin{cases} g + b = 555 \\ g - 17 + \frac{13}{12}b = 555 - 11 \end{cases}$

Solving for the equation we get that

$\begin{cases} g = 483 \\ b = 72 \end{cases}$

and we get the number of girls in the new term is $g - 17 = 466$. g = 483.

MathTopia Press

Remark 8.1 — Graphical Method to Solve

Use graphical methods to solve $\begin{cases} y = 3x - 2 \\ 2x + y = 13 \end{cases}$

We rearrange the second equation so the system is $\begin{cases} y = 3x - 2 \\ y = -2x + 13 \end{cases}$

We graph $Y_1 = 3X - 2$ and $Y_2 = -2X + 13$, and find the intersection point.

Casio fx-CG20

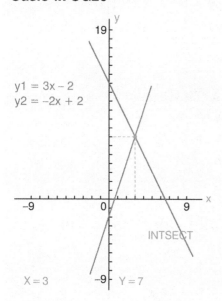

$y1 = 3x - 2$
$y2 = -2x + 2$

INTSECT

$X = 3$ $Y = 7$

TI-nspire

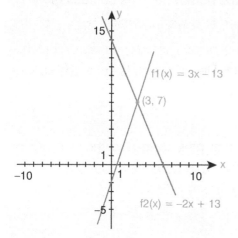

$f1(x) = 3x - 13$

$(3, 7)$

$f2(x) = -2x + 13$

So, the solution is $x = 3$, $y = 7$.

Problem 8.8 (2002 AMC 8 #17)

In a mathematics contest with ten problems, a student gains 5 points for a correct answer and loses 2 points for an incorrect answer. If Olivia answered every problem and her score was 29, how many correct answers did she have?

A) 5   B) 6   C) 7   D) 8   E) 9

Solution

Let a be the number of problems she answers correctly and b be the number she answered incorrectly. Because she answers all of the questions $a + b = 10$.

Her score is equal to $5a - 2b = 29$.

Use substitution.

$$b = 10 - a$$
$$5a - 2(10 - a) = 29$$
$$5a - 20 + 2a = 29$$
$$7a = 49$$
$$a = 7 \qquad \text{The answer is C.}$$

Problem 8.9

The hundreds digit of a three-digit number is more than the units digit. The digits of the three-digit number are reversed, and the result is subtracted from the original three-digit number. What is the units digit of the result?

A) 0   B) 2   C) 4   D) 6   E) 8

Problem 8.10 (UK-JMC-2007-3)

In my town some of the animals are really strange. Ten percent of the dogs think that they are cats and ten percent of the cats think they are dogs. All the other cats and dogs are perfectly normal. One day I tested all the cats and dogs in the town and found that 20% of them thought that they were cats.

What percentage of all cats and dogs really were cats?

MathTopia Press

1. $x = 2y + 3$

   $y = 3x + 6$

   If (x, y) is the solution to the system given above, what is the value of x + y?

   A) –3   B) –6   C) 3   D) 6   E) 9

2. A group of children riding on bicycles and tricycles rode past Billy Bob's house. Billy Bob counted 7 children and 19 wheels. How many tricycles were there?

   A) 2   B) 4   C) 5   D) 6   E) 7

3. The admission fee at a book fair is $2.50 for children an $4 for adults. On Monday, 2000 people entered the fair and $6200 was collected.

   How many childen visited the fair?

   A) 800   B) 900   C) 1000   D) 1200

   E) None of the preceding

4. The system $ax + 3y = 5$

   $4x – 6y = b$

   has infinitely many solutions

   Find the sum of a and b.

   A) –12   B) –8   C) 0   D) 8   E) 10

5. The system of equations given below has no solutions.

   $6x + ny = 10$

   $x – y = 3$

   What is the value of n?

   A) –6   B) –4   C) 1   D) 2   E) 4

6. Which of the following ordered pairs (x, y) satisfy the system of inequalities shown below?

   $x + y \leq 4$

   $-2x – y \geq 5$

   A) (3, 5)   B) (2, 4)   C) (3, –11)   D) (–3, 11)

   E) None of the preceding

7. The system shown below has exactly one solution. Which of the following could not be the value of n?

$$nx + 4y = 14$$
$$2x + 6y = 3$$

A) $\frac{1}{8}$ B) $\frac{1}{6}$ C) $\frac{1}{4}$ D) $\frac{1}{2}$ E) $\frac{4}{3}$

8. For all real numbers a and b the mathematical operations are defined as

$$a * b = (a \triangle b) - ab$$
$$a \triangle b = 2(a * b) - 4$$

Find $2 * 3$.

A) 8   B) 9   C) 10   D) 12   E) 16

9. (UNB-2008-Gr 9-7)

Marina has a bank containing only pennies and nickels. If the pennies were nickels and the nickels were pennies, she would have exactly $1.00 more.

If the total value of the money in her bank is $1.75, how many pennies does Marina have?

A) 25   B) 30   C) 40   D) 50
E) Not enough information

10. How many distinct integers x satisfy

$$2 < \frac{\sqrt{x} + 10}{\sqrt{x} + 1} < 3?$$

A) 47   B) 48   C) 49   D) 50   E) 51

11. (UK- JMC-2007 -3)

In my town some of the animals are really strange. Ten percent of the dogs think that they are cats and ten percent of the cats think they are dogs. All the other cats and dogs are perfectly normal. One day I tested all the cats and dogs in the town and found that 20% of them thought that they were cats. What percentage of all cats and dogs really were cats?

A) 12.5   B) 18   C) 20   D) 22
E) None of the preceding

12. (UNB-2010-Gr 9-21)

Farmer Fred said to Farmer John: \If you sell me 45 hectares of land, I will have twice as much land as you." Then Farmer John said to Farmer Fred: \If you sell me 45 hectares of land, I will have just as much land as you." How many hectares of land does farmer Fred have?

A) 135   B) 180   C) 225   D) 270   E) 315

MathTopia Press

Problem Set 1

1. Plugging in the first equation into the other:

    $y = 3x + 6 = 6y + 9 + 6 \Rightarrow y = -3 \Rightarrow x = -3$

    The answer is B

2. Assuming a bicycle has two wheels and a tricycle has 3 wheels, given that the number of wheels, bicycles, and tricycles are integers, the only choice that satisfies that is 5 tricycles and 2 bicycles for a total of 19 wheels, which is choice C

    OR

    Denote the number of Tricycles as y and the number of bicycles as x, we have:

    $2x + 3y = 19 \; ; \; x + y = 7$

    Substituting $x = 7 - y$ into the first equation:

    $14 - 2y + 3y = 19 \Rightarrow y = 5$

    The answer is C

3. Denoting x as the children number and y as the adult number, we have:

    $x + y = 2000$ and $2.5x + 4y = 6200$

    Plugging in $x = 2000 - y$ to the 2nd equation:

    $2.5x + 4y = 6200 = 5000 - 2.5y + 4y = 6200$

    $\Rightarrow y = \dfrac{1200}{1.5} = 800 \Rightarrow x = 1200$

    The answer is D

4. Since the system has infinitely many solutions, we know that the two equations are identical. Thus:

    $a = \dfrac{4}{-2} \; ; \; 5 = \dfrac{b}{-2} \Rightarrow a = -2 \; ; \; b = -10$

    The answer is A

5. Since the system has no solutions, we know that the two lines are parallel, meaning their slopes are identical, rearranging:

    $y = \dfrac{-6}{n}x + \dfrac{10}{n} \; ; \; y = x - 3 \Rightarrow \dfrac{-6}{n} = 1 \Rightarrow n = -6$

    The answer is A

6. Rearranging the equations:

    $-y \geq x - 4 \; ; \; -y \geq 5 + 2x$

    $\Rightarrow y \leq -x + 4 ; \; y \leq -5 - 2x$

    Immediately, we can see that the only choice that satisfies both equations is C

7. The only value of n that is not valid is the value that makes both lines parallel (i.e., slopes are equal). Rearranging:

    $y = \dfrac{-nx}{4} + \dfrac{14}{4}$ and $y = \dfrac{-2x}{6} + \dfrac{3}{6}$

    $\Rightarrow \dfrac{-n}{4} = \dfrac{-2}{6} \Rightarrow n = \dfrac{8}{6} = \dfrac{4}{6}$

    The answer is E

8. Plugging in the first equation in the second one:

$a \triangle b = 2(a \triangle b) - 2ab - 4 \Rightarrow a \triangle b = 2ab + 4$

Plugging back:

$a \star b = 2ab + 4 - ab = ab + 4$

$\Rightarrow 2 \star 3 = 2 \times 3 + 4 = 10$

The answer is C

9. Knowing that a penny is one cent, a nickel is 5 cents, and a dollar is 100 cents; let us denote pennies as p and nickels as n, we have:

$5n + p = 175$ and $n + 5p = 275$

substituting $p = 175 - 5n$ into the second equation:

$n + 875 - 25n = 275 \Rightarrow n = \dfrac{600}{24} = 25$

$\Rightarrow p = 50$

The answer is D

10. Rearranging:

$2 < \dfrac{\sqrt{x} + 10}{\sqrt{3} + 1} < 3 \Rightarrow 2 < \dfrac{\sqrt{x} + 1 + 9}{\sqrt{x} + 1} < 3$

$\Rightarrow 2 < 1 + \dfrac{9}{\sqrt{x} + 1} < 3$

$1 < \dfrac{9}{\sqrt{x} + 1} < 2 \Rightarrow 1 > \dfrac{\sqrt{x} + 1}{9} > \dfrac{1}{2}$

$\Rightarrow 9 > \sqrt{x} + 1 > \dfrac{9}{2}$

$\Rightarrow 8 > \sqrt{x} > \dfrac{7}{2} \Rightarrow 64 > x > \dfrac{49}{4}$

The number of distinct integers is

$64 - 13 - 1 = 50$

The answer is D

11. Denoting cats as C and dogs as D. Also, assuming that 90% of cats and 10% of dogs think they are cats, we get:

$\dfrac{0.9C + 0.1D}{C + D} = 0.2 \Rightarrow \dfrac{0.9C}{C + D} + \dfrac{0.1D}{C + D} = 0.2$

Let

$Z = \dfrac{C}{C + D} \Rightarrow 1 - Z = \dfrac{D}{C + D}$

Plugging back:

$0.9Z + 0.1(1 - Z) = 0.2 \Rightarrow 0.9Z - 0.1Z = 0.2 - 0.1$

$\Rightarrow Z = \dfrac{0.1}{0.8} = 0.125$

The answer is A

12. Looking at the first sentence:

$F + 45 = 2(J - 45)$

The second one says:

$J + 45 = F - 45 \Rightarrow F = J + 90$

Plugging back:

$J + 135 = 2J - 90 \Rightarrow J = 225 \Rightarrow F = 315$

The answer is E

WORD PROBLEMS

After completing this section, you will be able to solve problems involving numbers, fractions, ages, work, percentages, interest, mixtures and rates.

9.1 BASIC WORD PROBLEMS

In working with word problems, there are some words or phrases that give clues as to how the problem should be solved. The most common words or phrases are as follows.

ADD

- Sum: The sum of two consecutive integers is 15.
- Total: as in the total number of marbles.
- Addition : as in a recipe calls for the addition of five pints.
- Plus: as in three liters plus two liters .
- Increase: as in her pay was increased by $15 .
- More than: as in this week the enrollment was eight more than last week.
- Added to : as in if you added $3 to the cost .

SUBTRACT

- Difference : as in what is the difference between.
- Fewer : as in there were fifteen fewer men than women.

- Remainder : as in how many are left or what quantity remains.
- Less than : as in a number is five less than another number.
- Reduced : as in the budget was reduced by $5.
- Decreased : as in if he decreased the speed of his car by ten miles per hour.
- Minus : as in some number minus 9 is.

MULTIPLY

- Product : as in the product of 8 and 5 is.
- Of : as in one-half of the group.
- Times : as in five times as many girls as boys.
- At : as in the cost of ten yards of material at 70cent a yard is.
- Total : as in if you spend $15 a week on gas, what is the total for a three-week period.
- Twice: as in twice the value of some number.

DIVIDE

- Quotient : as in the final quotient is.
- Divided : as in some number divided by 12 is.
- Ratio : as in what is the ratio of.
- Half : as in half the profits are (dividing by 2).

MathTopia Press

9.2 NUMBER AND FRACTION PROBLEMS

Problem 9.1

The sum of two numbers is 96. The bigger number is twice as large as the smaller number. Find the numbers.

Solution

Let us write the problem algebraically: where the 1st number is x and the second one is

2x, x+2x = 96 $\Rightarrow$ 3x = 96 $\Rightarrow$ x = 32,

So, the numbers are 32 and 2 · 32 = 64

Problem 9.2

The sum of three consecutive integers is 126. Find the numbers.

Solution

Let a be the smallest number, then

a+(a+1)+(a+2) = 126 $\Rightarrow$ a = 41,

So, the integers are 41, 42, and 43.

Problem 9.3

The sum of three numbers is 87. The third number is twice as large as the second. The second number is one more than twice the first number. Find the numbers.

Solution

1st	2nd	3rd
x	2x + 1	2(2x + 1)

x+(2x+1)+2(2x+1) = 87 $\Rightarrow$ 7x+3 = 87 $\Rightarrow$ x = 12.

Therefore, the numbers are 12, 25 and 50.

Problem 9.4

The sum of the denominator and the numerator of a fraction is 47. If 2 is subtracted from the denominator and 5 is added to the numerator, the value of the fraction is $\frac{2}{3}$. Find the fraction.

Solution

Let the fraction be $\frac{x}{y}$. Then x+y = 47 $\Rightarrow$ y = 47−x

$\Rightarrow \frac{x}{y} = \frac{x}{47-x}$. Also,

$\frac{x+5}{47-x-2} = \frac{2}{3} \Rightarrow \frac{x+5}{45-x} = \frac{2}{3} \Rightarrow 3(x+5) = 2(45-x)$

$\Rightarrow 3x+15 = 90-2x \Rightarrow 3x+2x = 90-15$

$\Rightarrow 5x = 75 \Rightarrow x = 15$

$\Rightarrow \frac{x}{y} = \frac{x}{47-x} = \frac{15}{47-15} = \frac{15}{32}$

So, the fraction is $\frac{15}{32}$

Problem 9.5

The sum of half of a number and one-third of another number is 22. The difference of half of the second number and one sixth of the first number is 11. Find the numbers.

Solution

Let the first number be x and the second number be y.

If $\frac{x}{2} + \frac{y}{3} = 22 \Rightarrow 3x+2y = 132$, and $\frac{y}{2} + \frac{x}{6} = 11$

$\Rightarrow 3y-x = 66$, then we find from the equations

$\left. \begin{array}{l} 3x+2y = 132 \\ 3y-x = 66 \end{array} \right\} \Rightarrow \left. \begin{array}{l} 3x+2y = 132 \\ 9y-3x = 198 \end{array} \right\} \Rightarrow y = 30, x = 24$

9.3 AGE PROBLEMS

We can use algebra to solve problems about people's ages. When solving problems like this, it is useful to remember the following things:

MathTopia Press

- In t years, everyone will be t years older.
- t years ago, everyone was t years younger.
- The difference between the ages of two people is always constant.
- The sum of the ages of n people will increase by nt years in t years.

For example, Rick is 13 and his younger brother Alex is 8 years old.

1. In three years, Rick will be 13 + 3 years old, and Alex will be 8 + 3 years old.
2. Two years ago, Rick was 13 − 2 years old, and Alex was 8 − 2 years old
3. The difference between the brothers' ages now is 13 − 8 = 5 years. In twenty years the difference will be 33 − 28 = 5 years: the difference does not change.
4. The sum of the brothers' ages is 13 + 8 = 21. In twenty years the sum will be 33 + 28 = 61. This is the same as
$21 + nt = 21 + (2 \cdot 20) = 21 + 40 = 61.$

Problem 9.6

A mother is 38 years old and her daughter is 13 years old. In how many years will the mother be twice as old as her daughter?

Solution

	mother	daughter
now	38	13
x years later	38 + x	13 + x

Let the number of years be x:

$38 + x = 2(13 + x) \Rightarrow 38 + x = 26 + 2x$

$\Rightarrow 38 - 26 = 2x - x \Rightarrow x = 12$ years later.

So the answer is in 12 years.

Problem 9.7

The sum of the ages of three children is 27. In how many years will the sum of their ages be 63?

Solution

	child 1	child 2	child 3
now	x	y	z
t years later	x + t	y + t	z + t

$x+y+z = 27 \Rightarrow (x+t) + (y+t) + (z+t) = 63$

$\Rightarrow \underbrace{x+y+z+3t}_{27} = 63 \Rightarrow 27+3t = 63 \Rightarrow t = 12.$

Problem 9.8

A mother has three children. The middle child is two years older than the youngest child, and the oldest child is two years older than the middle child. The mother's age now is twice the sum of the ages of her children. If the mother is 30 years old now, find her age when her oldest child was born.

Solution

child 1	child 2	child 3
x − 4	x − 2	x

$2(x+x-2+x-4) = 30 \Rightarrow 2(3x-6) = 30$

$\Rightarrow 3x-6 = 15 \Rightarrow x = 7$

9.4 WORK PROBLEMS

We can use algebra to calculate how long it takes for a number of workers to complete a particular job. For example, we might want to know how long it will take for six men to build a wall. In problems like this, we suppose that each man works at the same speed or rate, for example, that each man alone can build 5m² of wall in one day. We will use the formula

(work rate) · (working time) = (amount of work done)
or r · t = w

For example, in the problem above, the formula for six men would use

$r = 5m^2 \cdot 6 = 30m^2$ of wall, t = number of days, and w = area of wall produced

The following calculations are useful for solving work problems.

1. If a number of workers can complete a job in t hours, then the same number of workers can complete $\frac{1}{t}$ of the job in one hour.

2. Suppose two workers can complete a job in x and y hours respectively. If they work together, they will complete the job in t hours, where t is given by $\frac{1}{x} + \frac{1}{y} + \frac{1}{t}$

Problem 9.9

Andrew can wash the family car in 45 minutes. Mike can wash it in 30 minutes. How long will it take them to wash the car if they work together?

Solution

	rate	time	work
Andrew	$\frac{1}{45}$	t	$\frac{1}{45} \cdot t$
Mike	$\frac{1}{30}$	t	$\frac{1}{30} \cdot t$

$\frac{1}{45} \cdot t + \frac{1}{30} \cdot t = 1 \Rightarrow \frac{2t+3t}{90} \Rightarrow 5t = 90$

$\Rightarrow t = 18$

We can also write:

$\frac{1}{45} + \frac{1}{30} = \frac{1}{t} \Rightarrow \frac{5}{90} = \frac{1}{t} \Rightarrow t = 18$

Problem 9.10

Two pipes A and B can fill a storage tank in four and six hours respectively. A drain C can empty the full tank in three hours. How long will it take to fill the tank if both pipes and the drain are open?

Solution

$\frac{1}{4} + \frac{1}{6} + \frac{1}{3} = \frac{1}{x} \Rightarrow \frac{3+2-4}{12} = \frac{1}{x} \Rightarrow \frac{1}{12} = \frac{1}{x}$

(3)   (2)   (4)

$\Rightarrow x = 12$

Problem 9.11

Two pipes A and B can fill an empty pool in six and eight hours respectively. A drain C can empty the full pool in twelve hours. For two hours, the pipes and the drain are left open. Then pipe A and pipe B are closed. How long will it take the drain C to empty the water in the pool?

Solution

$\frac{1}{6} \cdot 2 + \frac{1}{8} \cdot 2 - \frac{1}{12} \cdot 2 = \frac{1}{3} + \frac{1}{4} + \frac{1}{6}$

                      (4)   (3)   (2)

$= \frac{4+3-2}{12} = \frac{5}{12}$

of the pool will be filled in two hours.

After this, $r \cdot t = w \Rightarrow \frac{1}{12} \cdot t = \frac{5}{12} \Rightarrow t = 5$

So, it will take drain C five hours to empty the pool.

9.5 PERCENTAGE PROBLEMS

The following calculations are useful for solving percentage problems.

1. $b\% = \frac{b}{100}$

2. $b\%$ of a number is $x \cdot \frac{b}{100}$

3. If we increase a number x by $b\%$, the result is

$x + x \cdot \frac{b}{100} = x \cdot \frac{100+b}{100}$

4. If we decrease a number x by $b\%$, the result is

$x - x \cdot \frac{b}{100} = x \cdot \frac{100-b}{100}$

MathTopia Press

Example 9.1

35% of 600 is $x = 600 \cdot (35\%) = 600 \cdot \dfrac{35}{100} = 210$

Example 9.2

If $x\%$ of 40 is 8, then $8 = 40 \cdot (x\%) = 40 \cdot \dfrac{x}{100}$

$\Rightarrow x = \dfrac{80}{4} = 20$

Problem 9.12

The number of workers in a factory increases from 525 to 550. Find the percentage increase in the number of workers.

Solution

The increase is $550 - 525 = 25$ workers.

So the problem is: what percent of 525 is 25?

$25 = 525 \cdot \dfrac{x}{100} \Rightarrow x = \dfrac{100}{21} \cong 4.76.$

So the answer is approximately 4.76%.

Problem 9.13

The price of a car goes up by $\%3$, which is $420. What is the new price of the car?

Solution

Let x be the old price. $420 = x \cdot \dfrac{3}{100}$

$\Rightarrow x = \dfrac{420 \cdot 100}{3} = 14000$

So the new price is $14000 + $420 = $14420.

Problem 9.14

80% of the students in a class pass a math exam. If six students failed the exam, find the number of students in the class.

Solution

If 80% pass, then 20% fail. $x \cdot \dfrac{20}{100} = 6 \Rightarrow x = 30$

So there are 30 students.

Problem 9.15

A shopkeeper bought a jacket and a suit from a wholesaler. He then sold the jacket for $55, which was 25% more than the wholesale price. He sold the suit for $64, which was 20% less than the wholesale price. How much money did the shopkeeper lose or earn?

Solution

Let x be the wholesale price of the jacket. Then

$x \cdot \dfrac{125}{100} = 55 \Rightarrow x = 44,$

so the shopkeeper bought the jacket for $44 and earned $11. However, the wholesale price of the suit was

$x \cdot \dfrac{80}{100} = 64 \Rightarrow x = 80.$

Therefore the shopkeeper lost $80 - 64 = $16.
In total, he lost $16 - $11 = $5.

9.6 RATE& DISTANCE PROBLEMS

If an object does not change its speed during motion, then it is said to be in uniform motion. Uniform motion problems are sometimes given in math and physics. Drawing a simple sketch and making a table are used for solving uniform motion problems. We use the formula

$$\textit{distance} = \textit{rate} \cdot \textit{time} \quad (d = r \cdot t)$$

Problem 9.16

A bus leaves a city travelling at a speed of 60km/h. Two hours later, a second bus leaves from the same place, and drives along the same road at 90km/h. How long will it take for the second bus to catch up with the first bus?

MathTopia Press

Solution

In two hours, the first bus will have traveled

$d_1 = r_1 \cdot t_1 \Rightarrow d_1 = 60 \cdot 2 = 120$km.

When the second bus meets the first bus, the first bus will have traveled $(d_1 + d_2)$km..

$120 + r1 \cdot t = r_2 \cdot t \Rightarrow 120 + 60 \cdot t = 90 \cdot t$

$\Rightarrow 120 = 30t \Rightarrow t = 4$

So the buses will meet after four hours.

Second Way:

	rate	time	distance
first bus	60km/h	t + 2	60 · (t + 2)
second bus	90km/h	t	90 · t

$60 \cdot (t + 2) = 90 \cdot t \Rightarrow 60t + 120 = 90t$

$\Rightarrow 120 = 30t \Rightarrow t = 4$ hours.

Problem 9.17

Hayley walks 3 km/h faster than Elan. They leave school walking in opposite directions. After 2.5 hours, they are 30 km apart. How fast do Hayley and Elan walk?

Solution

Since they walk in opposite directions, 30 km is the sum of the distances they cover in 2.5 hours.

	rate	time	distance
Hayley	r + 3	2.5	2.5 · (r + 3)
Elan	r	2.5	2.5 · r

So $(2.5) \cdot (r + 3) + (2.5) \cdot r = 30$

$\Rightarrow (2.5) \cdot [r + 3 + r] = 30$

$\Rightarrow (2.5) \cdot (2r + 3) = 30 \Rightarrow 2r + 3 = \dfrac{30}{2.5}$

$\Rightarrow 2r + 3 = \dfrac{300}{25} = 12$

$\Rightarrow 2r + 3 = 12 \Rightarrow 2r = 9 \Rightarrow r = \dfrac{9}{2} = 4.5$km/h.

Therefore, Hayley walks at 4.5 + 3 = 7.5km/h, and Elan walks at 4.5km/h.

Problem 9.18

Martha rode her bike to Aunt Rebecca's place against a strong headwind. She covered the distance in 20 minutes. After a short time at Aunt Rebecca's place she rode back home, this time with a lovely tail wind (the tail wind strength was exactly the same as before). Her return journey took just 8 minutes. How long would it take Marcia to ride to Aunt Rebecca's if there was no wind?

Solution

Let actual speed (without wind) be n mph

Let the wind speed be x mph

Going to Aunt Rebecca's

$\text{Speed} = \dfrac{\text{Distance}}{\text{Time}}$

$n - x = \dfrac{d}{\frac{1}{3}} = 3d$

On the way back from Aunt Rebecca's

This time you add wind speed beacuse it is "pushing" Martha

$\therefore n + x = \dfrac{d}{\frac{2}{15}} = \dfrac{15d}{2}$

We want to find $\dfrac{d}{n}$ because we are trying to find the speed

$n - x = 3d$ (Equation 1)

$n + x = \dfrac{15d}{2}$ (Equation 2)

Equation 1 + Equation 2 gives

$21d = 4n$

Divide both sides by n $\dfrac{21d}{n} = 4$

$\dfrac{d}{n} = \dfrac{4}{21}$ (hours)

$= \dfrac{80}{7}$ minutes (to convert hours into minutes)

$= 11\dfrac{3}{7}$ minutes

So it would take $11\dfrac{3}{7}$ minutes to go one way if there was no wind.

Problem 9.19

A cyclist cycled from Town A to Town B at an average speed of 20 mph, and then turned around immediately and cycled back to where she had started. If her average overall speed for the journey was 24 mph, what was her average speed on the way back (from Town B to Town A)?

Problem 9.21

Three halls contained 252 chairs altogether. One-fifth of the chairs were transferred from the first hall to the second hall. Then, one-third of the chairs were transferred from the second hall to the third hall and the number of chairs in the third hall doubled. In the end, the number of chairs in the three halls became the same.

How many chairs were in the second hall at first?

MathTopia Press

Problem 9.20

Four numbers add up to 58. The following amounts are all equal to one another: the first number plus 1; the second number minus 2; the third number multiplied by 3; and the fourth number divided by 4.

If the largest of the four numbers is X and the second largest is Y, what is the value of X+Y?

Problem 9.22

Hakan travels 20 miles in 3 hours, partly on foot and partly on by bike. He walks at 3 mph and cycles 9 mph.

How far does he cycle?

1.

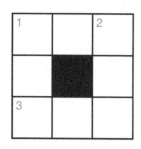

Complete this crossnumber using eight different non-zero digits.

Across

1. A square
3. A cube

Down

1. A prime
2. A prime

2. Complete this crossnumber.

Across

1. A prime number
3. The square of a square

Down

1. The square of a square
2. A prime

3. (UK Junior Mathematical Challenge, 2001)

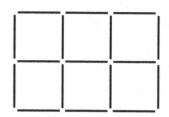

The diagram shows six small squares made from matches.

What is the smallest number of matches you need to remove to leave just three small squares?

4.

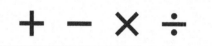

$9 \div (8 - 7) + 6 - 5 \times (4 - 3 + 2) + 1 = 1.$

Can you make

2020

using just the digits 9, 8, 7, 6, 5, 4, 3, 2, 1 in this order and the symbols $+ - \times \div$ ( ) ?

MathTopia Press

1. The sum of three consecutive integers is 102. Find the smallest number.

   A) 33   B) 34   C) 35   D) 36   E) 37

4. The value of a fraction is $\frac{1}{3}$. When 5 is subtracted from both numerator and the denominator, its value is $\frac{1}{13}$.
   Find the value of the denominator.

   A) 7   B) 11   C) 13   D) 15   E) 18

2. A father is three times as old as his son, and the sum of their ages is 76 years. How old is the son?

   A) 19   B) 21   C) 25   D) 31   E) 33

5. Three pipes can fill a pool in twelve hours. A drain can empty the full pool in eighteen hours.
   How many hours will it take to fill a quarter of the pool if the three pipes and the drain are open the same time?

   A) 9   B) $\frac{15}{2}$ C) $\frac{1}{9}$ D) $\frac{1}{6}$ E) $\frac{1}{2}$

3. 47 is divided into three numbers. The second number is 8 more than the first number and 10 less than the third number. Find the first number.

   A) 3   B) 5   C) 7   D) 8   E) 9

6. Anna can work three times as fast as Zach. Working alone, Zach can do a job in 36 days. How many days would it take Anna to do one-third of the job alone?

   A) 12   B) 10   C) 9   D) 4   E) 3

MathTopia Press

7. Mike and Zheng can do a job together in ten days. Mike can do it alone in fifteen days. How many days would it take Zheng to do the job alone?

    A) 30   B) 20   C) 15   D) $\dfrac{1}{30}$ E) $\dfrac{1}{15}$

8. It takes Lisa five hours to travel from city A to city B at a constant speed of 80 km/h.

    How many hours will it take Lisa to complete the same journey if he drives at 50 km/h?

    A) 16   B) 12   C) 10   D) 8   E) 6

9. It takes Sage six hours to drive from city A to city B at a constant speed of (V +10) km/h. She can cover the same distance driving at a speed of (2V −6) km/h in four hours. Find v.

    A) 32   B) 36   C) 38   D) 40   E) 42

10. Two cities A and B are connected by a road. A car leaves city A and begins traveling towards city B at (V +20) km/h. At the same time, another car leaves city B and begins traveling towards city A at (V −5) km/h. The cars pass each other after eight hours. Four hours after passing each other, the cars are 260km apart.

    How long is the road from A to B?

    A) 260   B) 360   C) 450   D) 520   E) 720

11. John is 24 years younger than his dad and John's mom is twice as old as John. 5 years ago, John's age was equal to the $\dfrac{1}{6}$ of times the sum his mother's and father's current ages.

    How old is John today?

    A) 21   B) 20   C) 19   D) 18   E) 17

12. In an online math practice test, John attempts to solve $\dfrac{3}{4}$ of the problems and answers $\dfrac{5}{8}$ of those questions correctly.

    When he submits the test, he finds that he answered 105 math questions right. How many math questions are in this test?

    A) 248   B) 243   C) 224   D) 220   E) 218

MathTopia Press

1. Pipe A can fill the first pool by itself in 15 hours and Pipe B can empty the second pool in 10 hours alone. In how many hours will the height of water in both pools be the same?

    A) 4   B) 5   C) 6   D) 8   E) 9

2. With all her money, Karen can buy only "b" pounds of cherries or "c" pounds of strawberries. If Karen has "A" dollars in her wallet, how much more is the price of one pound of strawberries than one pound of cherries?

    A) $\dfrac{A}{b-c}$ B) $\dfrac{A(b-c)}{b \cdot c}$ C) $\dfrac{b+c}{A}$

    D) $\dfrac{b+c}{2A}$ E) $\dfrac{A \cdot b \cdot c}{b-c}$

3. After 30% price reduction, the discount price of the shirt in a store is x dollars. How much profit would the seller have made if he had sold the shirt at 3x dollars?

    A) 110   B) 100   C) 90   D) 80   E) 70

4. Marcy is 12 and Karen is x years old. How old will Marcy be when Karen becomes 3x + 10 years old?

    A) x + 10   B) x + 24   C) 2x + 22
       D) 2x + 12   E) 2x + 24

5. A string is feet long. When two other strings, one of which is twice as long and the other three times as long, are connected to the original string at the right and the left ends respectively, the midpoint of these three strings altogether is 6 feet to the left of the original string.

    Which is the value of ?

    A) 12   B) 15   C) 18   D) 21   E) 24

6. A school is selling tickets to a talent show performance. On the first day of ticket sales the school sold 6 senior citizen tickets and 2 child tickets for a total of $76. The school took in $52 on the second day by selling 3 senior citizen tickets and 2 child tickets.

    What is the price of a child ticket?

    A) 10   B) 12   C) 14   D) 16   E) 18

MathTopia Press

7. Mariah solves all practice questions on her ACT test practice book in 20 days. She solves 200 practice questions per day to complete $\frac{3}{4}$th of the ACT book. She solves 100 practice questions to complete the remainder of the book.

How many questions are there in the ACT practice book?

A) 3,200   B) 2,400   C) 1,600

          D) 1,200   E) 1,000

8. During the school year, John was given an award of 25 cents for each math test he passed and was fined 50 cents otherwise. At the end of the school year, John had passed 7 times as many math tests as he had failed and made 3.75.

How many tests did John fail?

A) 3   B) 4   C) 7   D) 15   E) 21

9. A grandfather's age is 23 times the difference of the ages of his grandson's which have a sum of 15. If in 3 years the grandfather's age will be 24 times the age difference of his grandson's, what is the age the older grandson today?

A) 5   B) 6   C) 7   D) 8   E) 9

10. A worker can complete a job in 14 days. If this worker works for 4 days and rest for 1 day he will complete half of the job in x days, and the whole job in y days. What is y – x?

A) 7   B) 8   C) 9   D) 10   E) 11

11. A soccer team receives 3 points for every win, 1 point for every draw and 0 points for every loss. At the end of the 34-game season, they finished with 75 points. What is the minimum number of games they could have won?

A) 18   B) 19   C) 20   D) 21   E) 22

12. Hose "A" can fill a water tank in 8 minutes, However, a drain at the bottom of the tank can empty the tank in 24 minutes. When the tank is empty, how long after opening hose"A", would you need to open drain"B" so that the tank fills up in 9 minutes?

A) 7   B) 6.5   C) 6   D) 5.5   E) 5

MathTopia Press

Problem Set 1

1. Assume that the smallest number is a, then others are a + 1 and a + 2, their sum is
a + (a + 1) + (a + 2) = 3a + 3 = 102
$\Rightarrow$ 3a = 99 $\Rightarrow$ a = 33
The answer is A

2. Let x be the age of the son, then father's age will be 3x. Their sum is 4x = 76, and by that, x = 19.
The answer is A

3. Assume that the first number is x. It is given that the second one is x + 8 and the third one is x + 18. Their sum is
x + (x + 8) + (x + 18) = 3x + 26 = 47 $\Rightarrow$ x = 7
The answer is C

4. Let the fraction be $\frac{a}{3a}$, then it is given that
$\frac{a - 5}{3a - 5} = \frac{1}{13}$ $\Rightarrow$ 13a − 65 = 3a − 5
$\Rightarrow$ 10a = 60 $\Rightarrow$ a = 6
Therefore, the denominator is 3a = 18.
The answer is E

5. If three pies can fill a pool in 12 hours, then they can fill a quarter of the pool in 3 hours. Also, the drain can empty the quarter of the pool in $\frac{18}{4} = \frac{9}{2}$ hours.
If they are active at the same time,
$\frac{1}{t} = \frac{1}{3} - \frac{2}{9} = \frac{1}{9}$ $\Rightarrow$ t = 9
They will fill a quarter of the pool in 9 hours.
The answer is A

6. Zach can do one-third of the job in 12 days. Because Anna is 3 times as fast as Zach, she can do one-third of the job in 4 days.
The answer is D

7. Assume that Zheng do the job in Z days. Then
$\frac{1}{15} + \frac{1}{Z} = \frac{1}{10}$ $\Rightarrow$ $\frac{1}{Z} = \frac{15 - 10}{150} = \frac{1}{30}$ $\Rightarrow$ Z = 30
The answer is A

8. The distance between city A and city B is 5 · 80 = 400 km. If he drives at 50 km/h, he will arrive in $\frac{400}{50} = 8$ hours.
The answer is D

MathTopia Press

9. The distance betweeen cities is

$4(2V - 6) = 6(V + 10) \Rightarrow 2V = 84 \Rightarrow V = 42$

The answer is E

10. Assume that the road is x km. The distance cars totally make until they pass each other is x. Hence,

$x = 8(V + 20) + 8(V - 5)$ and

$260 = 4(V + 20) + 8(V - 5)$

It can be seen that $260 = \dfrac{x}{2}$. Therefore, x = 520.

The answer is D

11. Assume that John is x years old. Then, his mother is 2x, his father is x + 24 years old. Therefore,

$x - 5 = \dfrac{2x + (x + 24)}{6} \Rightarrow 6x - 30 = 3x + 24$

$\Rightarrow x = 18$

The answer is D

12. Let the number of the questions in the test be 32x. Then, John will attempts to solve

$32x\dfrac{3}{4} = 24x$ questions. He will solve $24x\dfrac{5}{8} = 15x$

questions correctly. Therefore,

$15x = 105 \Rightarrow x = 7 \Rightarrow 32x = 224$

The answer is C

Problem Set 2

1. Assume that the height of the pool is h and Pipe A fill h_1 meters in t hours, and Pipe B empty $h - h_1$ meters in t hours. After t hours, the height of both pools will be h_1.

$\dfrac{h_1}{h} = \dfrac{t}{15}$ and $\dfrac{h - h_1}{h} = \dfrac{t}{10}$

$\Rightarrow 1 = \dfrac{h_1}{h} + \dfrac{h - h_1}{h} = \dfrac{t}{15} + \dfrac{t}{10} = \dfrac{5t}{30}$

$\Rightarrow t = 6$

The answer is C

2. 1 pound of cherries is $\dfrac{A}{b}$ dollars and 1 pound of strawberries is $\dfrac{A}{c}$ dollars. Hence, one pound strawberries is $\dfrac{A}{c} - \dfrac{A}{b} = \dfrac{A(b - c)}{bc}$ dollars expensive than one pound cherries.

The answer is B

3. Let the cost price is y. With 30% discount, the price will be $\dfrac{7y}{10} = x$, therefore, $y = \dfrac{10x}{7}$

If the seller had sold the shirt at 3x dollars, his profit would be $3x - \dfrac{10x}{7} = \dfrac{11x}{7}$.

The profit is $\dfrac{\frac{11x}{7}}{\frac{10x}{7}} = \dfrac{11}{10} = 110\%$

The answer is A

4. The time should be passed is

$3x + 10 - x = 2x + 10$. After 2x + 10 years, Marcy will be 12 + 2x + 10 = 2x + 22 years old.

The answer is C

5. Other strings are 2x and 3x feet long. If we add them to ends of the first string, the midpoint will be the end point because $x + 2x = 3x$.

Hence, midpoint will change $\dfrac{x}{2} = 6$ feet.

Therefore, x = 12 feet.

The answer is A

6. Let the senior ticket is s dollars and children ticket is c dollars. Then,

$6s + 2c = 76 \Rightarrow 3s + c = 38$

$3s + 2c = 52$ So,

$c = (3s + 2c) - (3s + c) = 52 - 38 = 14$ dollars.

The answer is C

7. Assume that there are 4x questions in the book, then Mariah will solve 3x questions by solving 200 questions per day. She will solve x questions by solving 100 questions per day. The book will be completed in 20 days.

$20 = \dfrac{3x}{200} + \dfrac{x}{100} = \dfrac{5x}{200} + \dfrac{x}{40} \Rightarrow x = 800$

There exist 4x = 3200 questions.

The answer is A

8. Assume that John fails x tests and passes 7x tests.

Then $7x \cdot 0.25 - x \cdot 0.5 = \dfrac{7x}{4} - \dfrac{x}{2} = \dfrac{5x}{4} = 3.75$

$\Rightarrow 5x = 15 \Rightarrow x = 3$

The answer is A

9. Let the older grandson's age be x and younger grandson's age be y. Grandfather's age is $23(x - y)$. It is given that $x + y = 15$.

After 3 years, the difference between ages of grandsons will not change but grandfather's age will be $24(x - y)$.

Therefore, $24(x - y) - 23(x - y) = 3$. Hence, $x - y = 3$ and $x + y = 15 \Rightarrow 2x = 18 \Rightarrow x = 9$

The answer is E

10. This worker is working after 4 days work. Because $\dfrac{14}{4} = 3.5$, he will rest 3 days.

The job will be completed in y = 14+3 = 17 days.

Also, because $\dfrac{7}{4} = 1.75$, he will rest 1 day until completing the half of the job.

Hence, x = 7+1 = 8 days. y − x = 17 − 8 = 9.

The answer is C

11. Assume that the team won x games, draw y games, and lost z games.

Then, $x + y + z = 34$ and $3x + y = 75$.

Because $z \geq 0$, $x + y \leq 34$,

$75 = 3x + y \leq 2x + 34 \Rightarrow 41 \leq 2x \Rightarrow 21 \leq x$

x can be minimum 21.

Example is (x, y, z) = (21, 12, 1).

The answer is D

12. Assume that volume of the pool is 24 L. Therefore, hose A fills 3 L/min and drain B empty 1 L/min. Now assume that we need to open hose A after t minutes. Then,

$3t + (9 - t)(3 - 1) = 18 + t = 24 \Rightarrow t = 6$

The answer is C

MathTopia Press

MY NOTES

MathTopia Press

CHAPTER 10

RATIOS AND PROPORTIONS

Definition 10.1 — RATIO.

The ratio of two quantities, a and b, is their quotient $\frac{a}{b}$. This ratio can be expressed $\frac{a}{b}$, a : b, a to b, percent, or as a decimal. Ratios are mostly linked to fractions (equivalently) by way of unit rates. We usually use fraction notation for ratios but when we compare more than two quantities we use the colon notation. For example, "The ratios of pennies to dimes to quarters is 8 : 6 : 2." This tells us that for every 8 pennies we have 6 dimes and 2 quarters.

Example 10.1

If one store has 150 items and another store has 100 of the same items, we can express the ratio of the items as $\frac{150}{100}$, 150 : 100 or 150 to 100.
Ratios are usually written in lowest terms; so, the above ratios would reduce $\frac{150}{100} = \frac{15}{10} = \frac{3}{2}$

Problem 10.1

The ratio of boys to girls in a class is 4 : 3. The class has 28 students. How many boys and girls are in the class?

MathTopia Press

Solution

The ratio 4 : 3 is equivalent to the ratio 4x : 3x where 4x represents the number of boys and 3x represents the number of girls.

$4x+3x = 28 \Rightarrow 7x = 28 \Rightarrow x = 4$ Therefore, the number of boys is 4x = 4 · 4 = 16 and the number of girls is 3x = 3 · 4 = 12.

Problem 10.2

There are 25 more boys than girls in the Junior Pi school of 325 students. Find the ratio of number of boys to the number of girls in the school.

Solution

We can set up an equation with x being the number of girls in the school. The number of boys is equal to x+25. Total is

$x+x+25 = 325 \Rightarrow 2x+25 = 325 \Rightarrow 2x = 300 \Rightarrow x = 150.$

The number of boys is x+25 = 175 and the number of girls is x = 150. The ratio of number of boys to the number of girls is $\frac{175}{150} = \frac{7}{6}$.

Problem 10.3

A rectangular box has integer side lengths in the ratio of 1 : 2 : 3. Which of the following could be the volume of the box?

A) 48 B) 56 C) 64 D) 96 E) 98

Solution

We can represent the lengths of the box as x, 2x, 3x. The volume of the box is $x \cdot 2x \cdot 3x = 6x^3$.

Since the sides have to be integers value, then we divide choices by 6. So, the result has to a cube number. The choice A, 48, is the only option that satisfies the given conditions.

The correct answer is A.

Problem 10.4

The top of the highest building in City A is 77 feet higher than the top of the highest building in City B. The heights of the two buildings are in the ratio of 2 : 9. In feet, how tall is the smaller building?

Solution

Let the height of the smaller building be h and the height of the taller building be h+77.

From the given ratio; $\dfrac{h}{h+77} = 29$.

Solving h gives us h = 22.

Problem 10.5

If $\dfrac{a}{7} = \dfrac{b}{6} = \dfrac{c}{2}$ and a+2b−3c = 52, find the value of c.

Solution

From the ratios, we can express that
a = 7k, b = 6k, and c = 2k.

Then, substitute the values into the given equation
$7k+2(6k)-3(2k) = 52 \Rightarrow 7k+12k-6k = 52$
$\Rightarrow 13k = 52$ and k = 4.

Therefore, the value of c = 2k = 2(4) = 8.

Problem 10.6

Find the ratio of x to y if $\dfrac{5x+3y}{9x+2y} = \dfrac{2}{3}$

Solution

To find x : y, we first simplify the given equation by cross-multiplying to get rid of the fractions:
$3(5x+3y) = 2(9x+2y) \Rightarrow 15x+9y = 18x+4y$
$\Rightarrow 5y = 3x. \Rightarrow \dfrac{x}{y} = \dfrac{5}{3}$

Problem 10.7

If a : b = 3/4 and b : c = 3/5, then what is a : c?

Solution

We need to make an equal value of both ratios by expanding them. Since LCM(3,4) = 12

- $\dfrac{a}{b} = \dfrac{3}{4} = \dfrac{9}{12}$

- $\dfrac{b}{c} = \dfrac{3}{5} = \dfrac{12}{20}$

a = 9k, b = 12k, and c = 15k.

Therefore, the ratio of a : c = 9k/20k = 9/20

Definition 10.2 — PROPORTION.

A proportion is a statement that gives the equality of two ratios, denoted as $\dfrac{a}{b} = \dfrac{a}{b}$.
We also say two quantities are in direct proportion.

Example 10.2

If x and y are directly proportional and x = 3 when y = 7, then what is x when y is 21?

Since x and y are directly proportional, the ratio x : y is constant. So, $\dfrac{x}{y} = \dfrac{3}{7} = \dfrac{x}{21}$.

Solving this equation for x, we find x = 9

MathTopia Press

Remark 10.1

if $\dfrac{a}{b} = \dfrac{c}{d} = \dfrac{e}{f} = k$, then $\dfrac{a+c+e}{b+d+f} = k$

Remark 10.2

If x and y are inversely proportional, then the product xy is constant.

We can also write this as $x = \dfrac{k}{y}$

Example 10.3

If x and y are inversely directly proportional and if x = 4 when y = 15, then what is x when y is 12?

Since xy is constant, $4 \times 15 = x \times 12$.

Therefore, x = 5

Problem 10.8

Dr. Kanbir's car can go 32 miles on a gallon of gas, and costs 2.5 dollars per gallon. How many miles can Dr. Kanbir drive on 20 dollars worth of gas?

Solution

Dr.Kanbir can get (20/2.5) = 8 gallons.
He can go $32 \times 8 = 256$ miles.

Problem 10.9

Tim was assessed property taxes of $2400 on a house valued at $108000. What is the assessment amount on a $140000 house?

Solution

We use the ratio of taxes to value and let N represents taxes on a $144000 house.

$$\frac{2400}{108000} = \frac{N}{144000} = \frac{2400}{108} = \frac{N}{144} \Rightarrow \frac{2400}{3} = \frac{N}{4}$$

$\Rightarrow$ N = 3200

Problem 10.10

The interior angles of a triangle are in 1:3:5. Find the measure of each angle in the triangle.

Solution

Let us express the angle measures as x, 3x, and 5x. We know that the sum of the interior angles of a triangle is 180 degrees, so

$x+3x+5x = 180 \Rightarrow x = 20$.

Therefore, the angle measures are 20°, 60°, and 100°.

Problem 10.11

A father and his son are 32 and 8 years old, respectively. In how many years will their ages be in the ratio of 5:2?

Solution

Let x be the number of years. The father's age will be 32+x in x years. The son's age will be 8+x in x years.

$$\frac{32+x}{8+x} = \frac{5}{2} \Rightarrow 2(32+x) = 5(8+x)$$

$\Rightarrow 64+2x = 40+5x \Rightarrow 24 = 3x$ and x = 8

Problem 10.12

$\dfrac{x}{y} = \dfrac{z}{t} = \dfrac{m}{n} = \dfrac{2}{3}$ if given.

Find the ratio of $\dfrac{2x-3z+6m}{2y-3t+6n}$

Solution

We can represent
x = z = m = 2k and y = t = n = 3k
by substituting into the given expression

$$\frac{2(2k)-3(2k)+6(2k)}{2(3k)-3(3k)+6(3k)} = \frac{10k}{15k} = \frac{2}{3}$$

Problem 10.13

On a long straight road, Car A, which is traveling at 60 mph, is 5 miles behind Car B, which is traveling at 40 mph. Assuming that they continue to travel at those speeds, how long will it take for Car A to catch Car B?

Problem 10.15

If all cows produce milk at the same rate, and 5 cows can produce 5 gallons of milk in 5 days, how many days will it take 10 cows to produce 10 gallons of milk?

MathTopia Press

Problem 10.14

x and y are directly proportional.

If x is 6 when y is 10, what is y when x is 12?

Problem 10.16

If $\dfrac{2a + b}{a} = \dfrac{2c + d}{c} = k,$

What is the value of $\dfrac{a + c}{b + d} = ?$

1. If $\dfrac{a}{b} = \dfrac{b}{c} = \dfrac{3}{2}$, calculate the value of $\left(\dfrac{a+b}{b}\right)\left(\dfrac{c}{b+c}\right)$.

   A) 1   B) 2   C) $\dfrac{1}{2}$ D) $\dfrac{2}{3}$ E) None

2. If $\dfrac{a+b}{a} = 3$, what is the value of $\dfrac{a+b}{b}$?

   A) $\dfrac{2}{3}$ B) $\dfrac{2}{5}$ C) $\dfrac{3}{2}$ D) $\dfrac{5}{4}$ E) $\dfrac{5}{6}$

3. If $\dfrac{a}{7} = \dfrac{b}{6} = \dfrac{c}{2}$ and $a + 2b - 3c = 13$, find the value of a?

   A) 6   B) 7   C) 12   D) 15   E) 20

4. What number must be added to both numerator and the denominator of $\dfrac{1}{3}$ to make the value of the resulting fraction $\dfrac{2}{3}$?

   A) 1   B) 2   C) 3   D) 4   E) 5

5. If $\dfrac{x}{y} = \dfrac{2}{3}$, which of the following is **not** correct?

   A) $\dfrac{x+y}{y} = \dfrac{5}{3}$ B) $\dfrac{y-x}{y} = \dfrac{1}{3}$ C) $\dfrac{x+1}{x+1} = \dfrac{3}{4}$

   D) $\dfrac{x^2}{y^2} = \dfrac{4}{9}$ E) None

6. The incredible growing plant doubles every day in height. If the plant reaches to 200 feet in 10 days, how long does it take it to reach up to 50 feet?

   A) 5   B) 7   C) 8   D) 9   E) 10

MathTopia Press

7. On a map, a 8-centimeter length represents 48 kilometers. How many kilometers does a 20-centimeter length represent?

   A) 21   B) 96   C) 100   D) 120   E) 384

10. If $a : b = \frac{3}{4}$ and $b : \frac{3}{5}$, then what is $a : c$?

   A) $\frac{1}{5}$ B) $\frac{3}{5}$ C) $\frac{4}{5}$ D) $\frac{6}{5}$

   E) None of the preseding

8. It is given that 8 is 10% of P and 20 is 50% of Q. What is the value of $\frac{P}{Q}$?

   A) $\frac{2}{25}$ B) $\frac{1}{2}$ C) $\frac{4}{5}$ D) 2   E) 8

11. x and y are directly proportional.

   If x is 3 when y is 7, what is y when x is 7?

   A) $\frac{21}{6}$ B) 3   C) $\frac{7}{3}$ D) $\frac{49}{3}$ E) 17

MathTopia Press

9. The ratio of the corresponding side lengths of two similar triangles is 5 : 4, and the perimeter of the larger triangle is 30 cm. What is length the of the shortest side of the smaller triangle, if its side lengths are consecutive even numbers?

   A) 10 cm   B) 8 cm   C) 6 cm   D) 4 cm   E) 2 cm

12. On a farm

   the number of cows and the number of sheep are in the ratio 6 : 5

   the number of sheep and the number of pigs are in the ratio 2 : 1

   The total number of cows, sheep and pigs on the farm is 189

   How many sheep are there on the farm?

   A) 70   B) 77   C) 81   D) 89   E) 91

1. If $\frac{x}{a} = \frac{y}{b} = 4$, what is the value of $\frac{a^2 + b^2}{x^2 - y^2}$?

   A) $\frac{1}{16}$ B) $\frac{1}{8}$ C) $\frac{1}{2}$ D) $\frac{1}{4}$ E) $\frac{3}{2}$

4. If $\frac{b}{a} = \frac{3e}{2d}$ and $\frac{a}{b} = \frac{c}{d} = \frac{e}{f} = \frac{4}{3}$.

   Find the ratio of $\frac{f}{c}$.

   A) $\frac{3}{4}$ B) $\frac{2}{3}$ C) $\frac{1}{2}$ D) $\frac{9}{16}$ E) $\frac{9}{32}$

2. $\frac{a - b + 2}{a + b + 3} = \frac{2}{3}$, find $\frac{a}{b}$

   A) 5   B) 4   C) 3   D) 2   E) 1

5. If $\frac{a}{xy} = \frac{b}{xz} = \frac{c}{yz} = 2$ and

   $a + b + c = \frac{2}{x} + \frac{2}{y} + \frac{2}{z}$.

   What is by?

   A) 1   B) 2   C) 3   D) 4   E) 5

3. Amy rode her bike for a total of 6 hours yesterday during training. She first rode miles in four hours, and at the same rate she rode another 9 miles. How many miles did she ride her bike in the first four hours?

   A) 18   B) 16   C) 14   D) 12   E) 10

6. If $\frac{a}{b} = \frac{b}{c} = \frac{c}{d} = 2$,

   which of the following is equal to $\frac{a^2 + b^2 + c^2}{b^2 + c^2 + d^2}$?

   A) 1   B) 2   C) 3   D) 4   E) 5

MathTopia Press

7. A rectangular box has integer side lengths in the ratio $\dfrac{1:3}{2:2}$.

   Which of the following could be the volume of the box?

   A) 136   B) 148   C) 184   D) 192   E) 204

8. Four-fifth of the people in a room are seated in five-sixth of the chairs. The rest of the people are standing. If there are 5 empty chairs, how many people are in the room?

   A) 15   B) 18   C) 20   D) 25   E) 30

9. If $\dfrac{3x + y}{x} = \dfrac{3z + t}{z} = \dfrac{1}{k}$,

   what is the value of $\dfrac{x + z}{y + t}$?

   A) $\dfrac{k}{1-3k}$ B) $\dfrac{3}{k}$ C) $\dfrac{k+1}{3k}$ D) $\dfrac{k}{3k+1}$ E) None

10. If $\dfrac{a}{3} = \dfrac{b}{4} = \dfrac{c}{5} = \dfrac{2a + 3b + kc}{6}$.

    What is k?

    A) 1.6   B) 2.4   C) 3.2   D) 3.6   E) 4.2

11. If a, b and c are positive integers such that $\dfrac{a}{b} = 5$ and $\dfrac{b}{c} = \dfrac{2}{3}$, then which of the following is the smallest value a + b + c can take?

    A) 10   B) 12   C) 14   D) 15   E) 16

12. Suppose that x, y, and z are real number such that

    $$\dfrac{xy}{x + y} = 2, \quad \dfrac{xz}{x + z} = 3, \quad \dfrac{yz}{y + z} = 4$$

    what is x?

    A) $\dfrac{1}{2}$ B) $\dfrac{11}{23}$ C) $\dfrac{17}{27}$ D) $\dfrac{24}{7}$ E) $\dfrac{4}{5}$

MathTopia Press

Problem Set 1

1. Rearranging the expression:

$$\left(\frac{a+b}{b} + \frac{c}{b+c}\right) = \left(\frac{a}{b} + 1\right)\left(\frac{c}{b} + 1\right)$$

$$= \left(\frac{3}{2} + 1\right)\left(\frac{2}{3} + 1\right) = \frac{25}{6}$$

The answer is E

2. Rearranging the given expression:

$$\frac{a+b}{a} = 1 + \frac{b}{a} = 3 \Rightarrow \frac{b}{a} = 2$$

Rearranging the requested expression:

$$\frac{a+b}{b} = \frac{a}{b} + 1 = \frac{1}{2} + 1 = \frac{3}{2}$$

The answer is C

3. From the first equation:

$$2a = 7c \Rightarrow c = \frac{2a}{7} \, ; \; 7b = 6a \Rightarrow b = \frac{6a}{7}$$

Substituting in the second equation:

$$a + \frac{12a}{7} - \frac{6a}{7} = 13 \Rightarrow \frac{13a}{7} = 13 \Rightarrow a = 7$$

The answer is B

4. Since the resulting fraction's denominator is also 3, the answer must be a factor of 3, Therefore, the answer is C

5. Looking at the choices, we can directly deduce that the incorrect answer is C because $\frac{x+1}{x+1}$

6. Since the plant reaches 200 feet in 10 days, and doubles in height everyday, one can conclude that it reached 50 feet two days prior to reaching 200 feet, since $50 \times 2 = 100$ and $100 \times 2 = 200$ Therefore, the answer is C

7. If 8 centimeters represent 48 kilometers, then assuming the ratio is the same, one can write:

$$\frac{8}{20} = \frac{48}{x} \Rightarrow x = \frac{48+20}{8} = 120$$

The answer is D

8. From the given information:

$$0.1P = 8 \Rightarrow P = 80 \, ; \; 0.5Q = 20 \Rightarrow Q = 40$$

$$\Rightarrow \frac{P}{Q} = \frac{80}{40} = 2$$

The answer is D

9. Using the similarity ratio, we can write:

$$\frac{30}{x} = \frac{5}{4} \Rightarrow x = \frac{30 \times 4}{5} = 24$$

Where x is the perimeter of the smaller triangle. Moreover, since the side lengths are consecutive even numbers, then the shortest side length that satisfies x = 24

The answer is C

10. If

$$\frac{a}{b} = \frac{3}{4} \text{ and } \frac{b}{c} = \frac{3}{5}$$

Then:

$$\frac{a}{c} = \frac{a}{b} \times \frac{b}{c} = \frac{3}{4} \times \frac{3}{5} = \frac{9}{20}$$

The answer is E

MathTopia Press

11. Since x and y are directly proportional:

$$\frac{3}{7} = \frac{7}{y} \Rightarrow y = \frac{7 \times 7}{3} = \frac{49}{3}$$

The answer is D

12. Denoting cows as C, sheep as S, pigs as P, we have:

$$\frac{C}{S} = \frac{6}{5} \Rightarrow C = \frac{6S}{5}$$

$$\frac{S}{P} = \frac{2}{1} \Rightarrow P = \frac{S}{2}$$

$$C + S + P = 189 \Rightarrow \frac{6S}{5} + \frac{S}{5} + S = 189$$

$$\Rightarrow \frac{27}{10}S = 189 \Rightarrow S = \frac{189 \times 10}{27} = 70$$

The answer is A

Problem Set 2

1. From the given equation:

$$x = 4a \; ; \; y = 4b$$

Plugging back:

$$\frac{a^2 + b^2}{x^2 - y^2} = \frac{a^2 + b^2}{16(a^2 + b^2)} = \frac{1}{16}$$

The answer is A

2. $3a - 3b + 6 = 2a + 2b + 6 \Rightarrow a - 5b = 0$

$\Rightarrow a = 5b \Rightarrow \frac{a}{b} = 5$

The answer is A

3. From the given information, one can deduce that Amy rode 9 miles in two hours. Therefore:

$$\frac{9}{x} = \frac{2}{4} \Rightarrow x = \frac{9 \times 4}{2} = 18$$

The answer is A

4. Substituting the first equation in the second:

$$\frac{2d}{3e} = \frac{c}{d} = \frac{e}{f} = \frac{4}{3}$$

$$\frac{2d}{3e} = \frac{4}{3} \Rightarrow d = 2e$$

$$\frac{c}{d} = \frac{4}{3} \Rightarrow 3c = 4d$$

$$\frac{e}{f} = \frac{4}{3} \Rightarrow 3e = 4f$$

$$\Rightarrow \frac{4f}{3c} = \frac{3e}{4d} = \frac{3e}{8e} = \frac{3}{8}$$

$$\Rightarrow \frac{f}{c} = \frac{3 \times 3}{8 \times 4} = \frac{9}{32}$$

The answer is E

5. By multiplying the first port xyz. We get

$$\frac{a + b + c}{\frac{1}{z} + \frac{1}{y} + \frac{1}{z}} = 2 \, xyz$$

from the secon information

$$\frac{a + b + c}{\frac{1}{x} + \frac{1}{y} + \frac{1}{z}} = 2 \Rightarrow \text{Therefore } xyz = 1$$

The answer is A

6. Assuming the ratios are all equal to 2

$$\frac{a}{b} = \frac{b}{c} = \frac{c}{d} = 2$$

We have:

$$a = 2b; \; b = 2c; \; c = 2d$$

Substituting in the requested expression:

$$\frac{a^2 + b^2 + c^2}{b^2 + c^2 + d^2} = \frac{(2b)^2 + (2c)^2 + (2d)^2}{b^2 + c^2 + d^2} = 4$$

The answer is D

MathTopia Press

7. From the ratio of the side lengths one can deduce that:

$$\frac{1:3}{2:2} \Rightarrow 3L = W = H \Rightarrow V = 3L^3$$

Excluding the answers that aren't factors of 3, only D and E are left. Looking at D:

$$192 = 3L^3 \Rightarrow L^3 = 64 \Rightarrow L = 4$$

As for E:

$$204 = 3L^3 \Rightarrow L^3 = 68$$

Clearly, the answer is D

8. Denoting total number of people as P and chairs as C, we have:

$$\frac{5}{6}C + 5 = C \Rightarrow \frac{1}{6}C = 5 \Rightarrow C = 30$$

If 5 empty chair then 25 people in the room.
The Answer is D

9. From the given equation:

$$\frac{3x + y}{x} = \frac{3z + t}{z} \Rightarrow 3xz + yz = 3xt + xt$$

$$\Rightarrow yz = xt$$

$$\Rightarrow \frac{y}{x} = \frac{t}{z} = \frac{1}{k}$$

$$x = yk \; ; z = tk$$

Substituting:

$$\frac{x + z}{y + t} = \frac{yk + tk}{y + t} = k$$

The answer is E

10. From the given equation:

$$5a = 3c \Rightarrow a = \frac{3c}{5} \; ; 5b = 4c \Rightarrow b = \frac{4c}{5}$$

$$\frac{2a + 3b + kc}{6} = \frac{\frac{6c}{5} + \frac{12c}{5} + kc}{6} = \frac{c}{5}$$

$$6c = 18c + 5kc \Rightarrow 18 + 5k = 6$$

$$\Rightarrow k = \frac{-12}{5} = -2.4$$

The answer is B

11. $a = 5b \; ; 3b = 2c \Rightarrow c = \frac{3b}{2}$

Substituting in $a + b + c$:

$$a + b + c = 5b + \frac{3b}{2} + b = \frac{15b}{2}$$

The smallest value that makes the aforementioned expression an integer is $b = 2 \Rightarrow a = 10 \Rightarrow c = 3$

The answer is D

12. Reversing the given equations:

$$\frac{x + y}{xy} = \frac{1}{2} \Rightarrow \frac{1}{x} + \frac{1}{y} = \frac{1}{2}$$

Similarly:

$$\frac{1}{x} + \frac{1}{z} = \frac{1}{3}$$

$$\frac{1}{y} + \frac{1}{z} = \frac{1}{4}$$

Subtracting equation 3 from equation 2:

$$\frac{1}{x} + \frac{1}{y} = \frac{1}{12}$$

Adding the first equation:

$$\frac{1}{x} + \frac{1}{y} - \frac{1}{y} + \frac{1}{x} = \frac{1}{2} + \frac{1}{12}$$

$$\Rightarrow \frac{1}{x} + \frac{7}{24} \Rightarrow x = \frac{24}{7}$$

The answer is D

MY NOTES

MathTopia Press

CHAPTER 11

STATISTICS & DATA

Definition 11.1 — MEAN.

The mean of a set of data is the arithmetic average of the set of data. In other words, the mean of a set of data is the sum of all the values, divided by the number of values in the set.

$$\text{Mean} = \frac{\text{Sum of the values}}{\text{Number of values}}$$

Example 11.1

For example, consider the set of data 13, 15, 19, 23, 16, 14, 21, 17, 12, 10. There are ten values. To find the mean, we add all the values and divide by the number of values.

$$\text{Mean} = \frac{13+15+19+23+16+14+21+17+12+10}{10}$$

$$= \frac{160}{10} = 16$$

Definition 11.2 — MEDIAN.

When we arrange the values in a set of data in either ascending or descending order, the middle value is called the median.

Remark 11.1

To find the median of a set of data, follow the steps:
Definition

1. Arrange the values in numerical order (from the smallest to largest)

2. If there is an odd number of values, the median is the middle value

3. If there is an even number of values, the median is the mean of the two middle values.

Problem 11.1

Find the median of each list of values.

a. 5, 7, 8, 6, 3, 5, 9, 11, 13, 5, 10

b. 6, 9, 13, 15, 17, 21, 19, 18

Solution

a. First we write the values in ascending order: 3, 5, 5, 5, 6, , 8, 9, 10, 11, 13. The median is 7 because 7 is the middle value.

b. In ascending order, the values are: 6, 9, 13, , , 18, 19, 21 Since there is an even number of values, the median is $\frac{15+17}{2} = 16$

MathTopia Press

Definition 11.3 — MODE.

The mode of a set of data values is the value in the set that appears most frequently. To find the mode, you can order the values and count each one. The most frequently occurring value is the mode. If there is only one mode for a data set, it is called unique mode.

Problem 11.2

Find the mode of each list of values.

a. 11, 17, 13, 15, 16, 14, 11, 17, 14, 11

b. 63, 65, 67, 64, 63, 45, 47, 56, 63, 67, 65, 65

c. 3, 5, 7, 9, 16, 21, 13

Solution

a. Let us order the numbers. 11,11 ,11, 13, 14, 14, 15, 16, 17, 17 The mode is 11. It appears three times.

b. 45, 47, 56,63,63 ,63 , 64, 65,65 ,65 , 67, 67 There are two modes: 63 and 65. Because there are two modes, we say that this data set is bimodal.

c. Each number appears only once. There is no mode.

Definition 11.4 — RANGE.

The difference between the largest and the smallest value in a set of data is called the range of the data set.

Example 11.2

Find the range for the given data. 3, 4, 8, 4, 8, 7, 16, 10, 2, 6, 1, 15, 6.To find the range we subtract the smallest value from the largest value in the set of data. The largest value is 16 and the smallest value is 1. So 16 − 1 = 15, and the range is 15.

Problem 11.3

The arithmetic mean of two numbers a and b is 17, and a is four more than as twice as the value of b. Find a.

Solution

The arithmetic mean of a and b is 17 and a = 2b+4.

If we substitute 2b+4 for a in the first equation and solve for b we get:

$(2b+4)+b = 34 \Rightarrow 3b+4 = 30 \Rightarrow 3b = 30$
$\Rightarrow b = 10$

from there $a+b = 34 \Rightarrow a+10 = 34 \Rightarrow a = 24$.

Problem 11.4

The average(mean) of 25 numbers is 32, and the average of 15 other numbers is 20. What is the average of all 40 numbers?

Solution

The sum of all 40 numbers is

$25 \cdot 32+15 \cdot 20 = 1100$.

So their average is $\frac{1100}{40} = 27.5$

Problem 11.5

Four students take an exam. Three of their scores are 65, 75, and 80. If the average of their four scores is 75. What is the remaining score?

Solution

We can call the unknown score r.

We can set up an equation as $\frac{65+75+80+r}{4} = 75$.

Solve for r: $\frac{220+r}{4} = 75 \Rightarrow 220+r = 300 \Rightarrow r = 80$

MathTopia Press

Problem 11.6

The average age of 16 people in a room is 30 years. A 60-year-old person leaves the room.

What is the average age of the 15 remaining people?

Solution

Let x be the average of the remaining 15 people.

The equation we get is $\frac{15x+60}{16} = 30$

$\Rightarrow 15x+60 = 480 \Rightarrow 15x = 420 \Rightarrow x = 28$

Problem 11.7

The mean age of Sam's 4 friends is 9, and their median age is 8. What is the sum of the ages of Sam's youngest and oldest friends?

Solution

Since we have four numbers, the median score of ages is the average of the middle two. The sum of the two middle number is 16. The sum of all four numbers is 36. Then, the sum of the youngest and oldest is 36–16 = 20

Problem 11.8

Three positive consecutive integers starting with a have average b. What is the average of 5 consecutive integers that start with b?

Solution

The average of three consecutive numbers is $\frac{a+(a+1)+(a+2)}{3} = \frac{3a+3}{3} = a+1$, so b = a+1

The average of five consecutive numbers starting with b = a+1 is

$\frac{(a+1)+(a+2)+(a+3)+(a+4)+(a+5)}{5}$

$= \frac{5a+15}{3} = a+3$

Problem 11.9

The mean, median, and mode of the 7 data values 8; 10; m; 3; 4; 6; 5 are all equal to m.

What is the value of m?

Solution

If the mean of the 7 data values is m, the sum of those 7 data values is 7m. Then, 36+m = 7m

$\Rightarrow$ 6m = 36. Therefore, m = 6.

Problem 11.10

The average value of all the pennies, nickels, dimes, and quarters in Michelle's purse is 20 cents. If she had 4 more quarters then the average value would be 22 cents. How many coins does she have in her purse?

Solution

Let N be the number of her coins. She has 20N cents. If she had 4 quarters then she would have an average value of

$\frac{20N+100}{N+4} = 22$. Solving this gives N = 6.

Problem 11.11

The average of five numbers is 320. The average of the three greatest numbers is 489, and the average of the three least numbers is 200. What is the value of the middle number?

Solution

Let x_1, x_2, x_3, x_4, x_5 are five numbers arranged in increasing order. Notice that

$x_1+x_2+x_3+x_4+x_5 = 5\times320 = 1600$

$x_1+x_2+x_3 = 3\times200 = 600$

$x_3+x_4+x_5 = 3\times489 = 1467$.

After adding the first and the second equation and subtracting the third equation, we get the middle number, $x_3 = (600+1467)-1600 = 467$.

MathTopia Press

Problem 11.12

What value of x makes the mean of the first three numbers in this list equal to the mean of the last four?

| 15 | 5 | x | 7 | 9 | 17 |

Solution

The mean of the first three numbers in the list is $\frac{1}{3}(15+5+x)$ and the mean of the last four is

$\frac{1}{4}(x+7+9+17)$. Now,

$$\frac{1}{3}(15+5+x) = \frac{1}{4}(x+7+9+17)$$

$$\Longleftrightarrow 4(15+5+x) = 3(x+7+9+17)$$

$$\Longleftrightarrow 80+4x = 3x+99$$

$$\Longleftrightarrow x = 19$$

Problem 11.13 (AMC 8-2011 #21)

The mean of a set of five different positive integers is 15. The median is 18. The maximum possible value of the largest of these five integers is

A) 19   B) 24   C) 32   D) 35   E) 40

Problem 11.14 (AMC 8-2012 #22)

Let R be a set of nine distinct integers. Six of the elements are 2, 3, 4, 6, 9, and 14. What is the number of possible values of the median of R ?

Problem 11.15 (AMC 8-2015 #18)

An arithmetic sequence is a sequence in which each term after the first is obtained by adding a constant to the previous term. For example, 2, 5, 8, 11, 14 is an arithmetic sequence with five term, in which the first term is 2 and the constant added is 3. Each row and each column in this 5 × 5 array is an arithmetic sequence with five terms. What is the value of X?

1				25
		X		
17				81

A) 21   B) 31   C) 36   D) 40   E) 42

MathTopia Press

1. Five students take an exam. Four of their scores are 75, 80, 85, and 90. If the average of their five scores is 80, then what is the remaining score?

    A) 60   B) 65   C) 70   D) 75   E) 85

2. The average of six weights is 15 grams. This set of six weights then increased by another weight of 8 grams.

    What is the average of the seven weights?

    A) 13   B) 14   C) 15   D) 16   E) 18

3. The average of ten numbers is 20. Subtract 20 from nine of these numbers. After this subtraction, what is the average of ten numbers?

    A) 0   B) 1   C) 2   D) 3   E) 5

4. If a 4-student group averaged 75 on the math test, and a 6-student group averaged 90, what is the average for all 10 students?

    A) 84   B) 85   C) 86   D) 87   E) 90

5. The arithmetic mean of X and Y is 12, the arithmetic mean of X and Z is 6, and the arithmetic mean of Y and Z is 4.

    Which of the following is equal to Z?

    A) −5   B) −2   C) 6   D) 10   E) 12

6. In his Geometry course, Michael scored a 91 on his last test, which weighs twice as much as other tests, and an 85 on each of the other tests. Michael's test average for the course is 88 where each test, except the last one, is weighted equally.

    How many math tests in total has Michael taken in Geometry?

    A) 3   B) 4   C) 5   D) 6   E) None

MathTopia Press

7.　If the mean weight of seven people is 230lb and the mean weight of the four others is 190 lb.

What is the mean weight of the 11-people?

A) 195　　B) 200　　C) 205　　D) 210　　E) 215

8.　To receive an A is a math class, Bill needs at least a mean of 90 of five exams. Bill's grades on the first four exams were 82, 84, 93, and 96.

What minimum score does he need on the fifth exam to receive an A in the class?

A) 85　　B) 90　　C) 91　　D) 92　　E) 95

9.　The table below shows the average number of math practice questions students solve per day. If the average number of questions solved by one student in one day is 90, how many students solved 80 questions.

Average Number of Math Questions	100	150	80	50	200
Number of Students	3	2	x	8	2

A) 5　　B) 4　　C) 3　　D) 2　　E) 1

10.　The arithmetic mean of two numbers is 120, and one of these numbers is equal to 3 times the other number.

Which of the following is the difference of these two numbers?

A) 100　　B) 110　　C) 120　　D) 150　　E) None

11.　The mean, median, and unique mode of the positive integers 5, 6, 7, 8, 8, 9, and x are all equal. What is the value of x?

A) 7　　B) 8　　C) 11　　D) 13　　E) 14

12.　The average of 4 numbers is 9. What is the fourth number if three of the numbers are 6, 7, 13?

A) 6　　B) 8　　C) 9　　D) 10　　E) 12

MathTopia Press

1. Azar has five cards with dots on them. Card 1 had 2 dots and card 5 has 8 dots. The mean of the five cards' dots is 5 and the mode is 4.

   What is the median number of dots?

   A) 20   B) 25   C) 28   D) 32

   E) None of the preceding

2. The mean of a set of seven positive integer is 7, the median is 8, and the mode is 9. What is the largest possible range for this set of numbers?

   A) 10   B) 12   C) 16   D) 18   E) 19

3. The average (arithmetic mean) of 10 different positive numbers is 10.

   What is the product of the smallest and the largest value of these number set?

   A) 50   B) 55   C) 90   D) 120   E) 180

4. A fifth number, x, is added to the set 4, 6, 8, 10 to make the mean of the set of five numbers equal to its median.

   What is the number of possible value of x?

   A) 1   B) 2   C) 3   D) 4   E) More than 4

5. Which of the following cannot equal 51 consecutive integers?

   A) −255   B) −102   C) 0   D) 850   E) 5100

6. Which of the following sets of whole numbers has the largest average?

   A) Multiples of 2 between 1 and 51

   B) Multiples of 3 between 1 and 51

   C) Multiples of 4 between 1 and 51

   D) Multiples of 5 between 1 and 51

   E) Multiples of 6 between 1 and 51

MathTopia Press

7. The average weight of 6 high schoolers 150 pounds and the average weight of 4 middle schoolers is 120 pounds.

   What is the average weight of these 10 students?

   A) 130   B) 135   C) 138   D) 145   E) 138

8. Five test scores have a mean of 80, a median of 81, and a mode of 84. What is the sum of two lowest scores?

   A) 150   B) 151   C) 156   D) 166   E) None

9. In a special competition, Bob swam 2 miles in 25 minutes, biked 20 miles in 45 minutes, and then ran 4 miles in 40 minutes. What was his "average" speed for this competition? (Round your answer to the nearest whole number.)

   A) 10   B) 11   C) 12   D) 13   E) 14

10. (PiMC-2018-Final Round-Individual-24)

    Starting with any positive integer, we create a sequence as follows: Each term after the first one is the sum of the squares of the digits of the previous term. For example, starting with 2, we get the following sequence:

    2, 4, 16, 37, 58, 89, 145, 42, 20, 4, 16, ... Those starting numbers for which the sequence contains 1 are called happy numbers. For example, 1 is a happy number

    What is the next smallest happy number?

    A) 5   B) 6   C) 7   D) 9   E) 11

11. Four different positive integers are to be chosen so that they have a mean of 2021.

    What is the smallest possible range of the chosen integers?

    A) 3   B) 4   C) 5   D) 6   E) 7

12. Hazel writes on a board the positive integers from 1 to 8 inclusive, once each. She then writes x additional fives and y additional sevens on the board. The mean of all the numbers on the board is 6.5.

    What is the smallest possible value of y?

    A) 17   B) 19   C) 23   D) 25   E) 35

MathTopia Press

Problem Set 1

1. Denoting the 5th score as x, we have:

$$\frac{75 + 80 + 85 + 90 + x}{5} = 80$$

$$\Rightarrow x = 400 - 330 = 70$$

The answer is C

2. The average of the six weights is:

$$\frac{a + b + c + d + e + f}{6} = 15$$

$$\Rightarrow a + b + c + d + e + f = 90$$

Adding another 8 grams weight:

$$\frac{a + b + c + d + e + f + 80}{7} = \frac{90 + 8}{7} = 14$$

The answer is B

3. Denoting the sum of the ten numbers as x, we have:

$$\frac{x}{10} = 20 \Rightarrow x = 200$$

Subtracting 20 from 9 numbers:

$$x - 9 \times 20 = 20 \Rightarrow \frac{20}{10} = 2$$

The answer is C

4. Denoting the sum of the 4-student group grades as A, and the 6-student group as B, we have:

$$\frac{A}{4} = 75 \Rightarrow A = 300 \; ; \; \frac{B}{6} = 90 \Rightarrow B = 540$$

Then the average for all is:

$$\frac{300 + 540}{10} = 84$$

The answer is A

5. Knowing that:

$$\frac{X + Y}{2} = 12 \Rightarrow X + Y = 24$$

$$\frac{X + Z}{2} = 6 \Rightarrow X + Z = 12$$

$$\frac{Y + Z}{2} = 4 \Rightarrow Y + Z = 8$$

Subtracting the first equation from the second:

$$Z - Y = -12$$

Adding the third:

$$Z - Y + Y + Z = -4 \Rightarrow Z = -2$$

The answer is B

6. Denoting the total number of math tests as x, the average score is:

$$\frac{182 + (x - 1) \times 85}{x} = 88 \Rightarrow 88x = 97 + 85x$$

$$\Rightarrow 3x = 97 \Rightarrow x = \frac{97}{3}$$

The answer is E

7. Denoting the total weight of the 7 people as A, and the other 4 as B, we have:

$$\frac{A}{7} = 230 \Rightarrow A = 1610$$

$$\frac{B}{4} = 190 \Rightarrow B = 760$$

$$\frac{1610 + 760}{11} = 215.45$$

The answer is E

8. Denoting the 5th exam's score as x:

$$\frac{82 + 84 + 93 + 96 + x}{5} = 90$$

$$\Rightarrow x = 450 - 355 = 95$$

The answer is E

MathTopia Press

9. $$\frac{100 \times 3 + 150 \times 2 + 80x + 50 \times 8 + 200 \times 2}{15 + x} = 90$$

$\Rightarrow 1400 + 80x = 1350 + 90x \Rightarrow x = \frac{50}{10} = 5$

The answer is A

10. Knowing that:

$\frac{a + b}{2} = 120 \Rightarrow a + b = 240$

$a = 3b \Rightarrow 4b = 240 \Rightarrow b = 60 \Rightarrow a = 180$

$\Rightarrow b - a = 120$

The answer is C

11. Since the mean is equal to the median, and all the choices for x are 7 and above, then clearly, the median and mean are either 7 or 8, and since the unique mode is equal to the mean and median, then 7 is not correct.

$\frac{5 + 6 + 7 + 8 + 8 + 9 + x}{7} = 8 \Rightarrow x = 13$

The answer is D

12. $\frac{6 + 7 + 13 + x}{4} = 9 \Rightarrow x = 36 - 26 = 10$

The answer is D

Problem Set 2

1. From the given information, the cards can be written (in increasing order):

2, x, y, z, 8

Since the mode is 4, we can calculate the remaining number from the mean equation:

$\frac{2 + 4 + 4 + x + 8}{5} = 5 \Rightarrow x = 25 - 18 = 7$

So the list is:

2, 4, 4, 7, 8

The Median is 4.

The answer is E

2. Since the mean is 7, the sum of the numbers is 49. Moreover, since the mode is 9, we can assume we have two 9s with a median of 8, the list can be:

x, y, z, 8, 9, 9, s

From the mean equation:

$\frac{x + y + z + s + 8 + 18}{7} = 7$

$\Rightarrow x + y + z + s = 49 - 26 = 23$

For the largest possible range, we can take x,y,z as the lowest possible values: 1,2,3. Therefore:

$s = 23 - 1 - 2 - 3 = 17$

So the largest possible range is $17 - 1 = 16$.

The answer is C

3. Since the average is 10, their sum is 100. The summation of numbers from 1 to 9 is 45. Therefore, the largest possible number is:

$100 - 45 = 55$

With the smallest possible number being 1.

The answer is B

4. Looking at the sequence we have, we can add the numbers 7,9 or numbers less than 4, or numbers more than 10. the number 7 satisfies our condition, and from the set of numbers less than 4 there is only number 2 that satisfies our condition, as for the last set, only 12 satisfies the condition.

The Answer is C

5. Let 51 consecutive integers be

$n - 25, n - 24, \ldots, n, \ldots, n + 24, n + 25.$

The sum of all numbers is 51n. The total has to be multiple of 51.

Therefore 850 is not a multiple of 51.

The answer is D

MathTopia Press

6. From 1 to 51, there are 25 multiples of 2, their mean is:

$$\frac{2 \times 1 + 2 \times 2 + 2 \times 3 + ... + 2 \times 25}{25}$$

$$= \frac{2(1 + 2 + 3 + ... + 25)}{25}$$

$$= \frac{2 + \frac{25 \times 26}{2}}{25} = \frac{2 \times 26}{2} = 26$$

Applying the same method, we can find the average for the multiples of 3,4,5 and 6 to be:

$$\frac{3 \times \frac{17 \times 18}{2}}{17} = 27$$

$$\frac{4 \times \frac{12 \times 13}{2}}{12} = 26$$

$$\frac{5 \times \frac{10 \times 11}{2}}{10} = 27.5$$

$$\frac{6 \times \frac{8 \times 9}{2}}{8} = 27$$

Therefore, the highest average is the multiples of 5.

The answer is D

7. Denoting the total weight of the high-schoolers as A, and the other as B, we have:

$$\frac{A}{6} = 150 \Rightarrow A = 900$$

$$\frac{B}{4} = 120 \Rightarrow B = 480$$

$$\frac{900 + 480}{10} = 138$$

The answer is C

8. From the given information, the set of scores is:

x, y, 81, 84, 84

Since the mean is 80:

$$\frac{x + y + 81 + 84 + 84}{5} = 80$$

$$\Rightarrow x + y = 400 - 249 = 151$$

The Answer is B

9. The average speed is given by the total distance divided by the total time. Therefore:

$$\frac{2 + 20 + 4}{25 + 45 + 40} = \frac{26}{110} = 0.236 \text{ miles per minute}$$

$$\approx 14 \text{ miles persecond}$$

The answer is E

10. let's look at the first 6 iterations of every sequence starting by 3, 4, 5, 6, 7:

3, 9, 81, 65, 61, 37

4, 16, 37, 58, 89, 145

5, 25, 29, 85, 89, 145

6, 36, 45, 41, 17, 50

7, 49, 97, 130, 10, 1

The next smallest happy number is 7.

The Answer is C

11. Since the mean is 2021, the sum of the four numbers must be:

$$2021 \times 4 = 8084$$

for the range to be as small as possible, let's try to pick the four positive integers as consecutive numbers. A good starting point would be numbers close to 2021. picking 2019 as the smallest nubmer:

$$2019 + 2020 + 2021 + 2022 = 8082$$

Adding one to the last two terms:

$$2019 + 2020 + 2022 + 2023 = 8084$$

Therefore, the smallest possible range is B) 4

12. Since we're adding x additional fives and y additional sevens:

$$\frac{36 + 5x + 7y}{8 + x + y} = 6.5 \Rightarrow 52 + 6.5x + 6.5y$$

$$= 36 + 5x + 7y$$

$$\Rightarrow 0.5y = 16 + 1.5x \Rightarrow y = 32 + 3x$$

Therefore, the smallest possible y is 35.

The answer is E

MathTopia Press

MathTopia Press

EXPONENTS

Definition 12.1

If a is a real number and if n is a natural number then

$$a^n = \underbrace{a \cdot a \cdots a},_{n\ a's}$$

with the interpretation that $a^0 = 1$ if a $6 \neq 0$.

Suppose we wanted to compute a^2a^3.

We proceed, using the fact that $a^2 = aa$ and that $a^3 = aaa$:

$(a^2)(a^3) = (aa)(aaa) = aaaaa = a^5$.

Since the penultimate expression consists of seven a's, we have the following.

Definition 12.2

If a $\in \mathbb{R}$, and m and n are integers, then

$$a^m \cdot a^n = a^{m+n}$$

Example 12.1

- $5^3 \cdot 5^2 = 5^{3+2} = 5^5$
- $4^3 \cdot 4 = 4^{3+1} = 4^4$
- $(-3)^2 \cdot (-3)^3 = (-3)^{2+3} = (-3)^5 = -243$
- $x^3 \cdot x^2 \cdot x^5 = x^{3+2+5} = x^{10}$

Definition 12.3

If a, b $\in \mathbb{R}$, and n is an integer, then

$$(a \cdot b)^m = a^m \cdot b^m$$

Example 12.2

- $(3 \cdot 5)^3 = 3^3 5^3 = 27 \cdot 125 = 3375$
- $2^4 \cdot 3^4 = (2 \cdot 3)^4 = 6^4 = 1296$
- $(3a)^2 \cdot (-2a)^3 = 3^2 \cdot a^2 \cdot (-2)^2 \cdot a^2$
  $= 9 \cdot a^2 \cdot (-8) \cdot a^3 = -72a^2a^3 = -72a^5$

MathTopia Press

Definition 12.4

If a $\in \mathbb{R}$ and m and n are integers, then

$$(a^m)^n = a^{m \cdot n}$$

Example 12.3

- $(2^3)^2 = 2^{3 \cdot 2} = 2^6 = 64$
- $((-3)^4)^2 = (-3)^{4 \cdot 2} = (-3)^8 = 3^8$
- $\left[(-2 \cdot a \cdot b)^2\right]^3 = (-2 \cdot a \cdot b)^6 = (-2)^6 a^6 b^6$
  $= 64a^6b^6$

Definition 12.5

If $a, b \in \mathbb{R}$ and n is an integer, then
$$\left(\frac{a}{b}\right)^n = \frac{a^n}{b^n}, \ (b \neq 0)$$

Example 12.4

- $\left(\frac{4}{5}\right)^3 = \frac{4^3}{5^3}$
- $\left(\frac{x}{y^3}\right)^4 = \frac{x^4}{(y^3)^4} = \frac{x^4}{y^{12}}$

Remark 2.1

- $\underbrace{a \cdot a \cdot a \cdots a}_{n} = a^n$
- $\underbrace{a + a + a + \cdots a}_{n} = n \cdot a$
- $a^0 = 1 \ (a \neq 0)$ and 0^0 is undefined
- $a^{-n} = \frac{1}{a^n}, \ \left(\frac{a}{b}\right)^{-n} = \left(\frac{b}{a}\right)^n$
- $x \cdot a^n + y \cdot a^n - z \cdot a^n = (x + y - z) \cdot a^n$

Problem 12.1
$$\left(\frac{a^x}{b^y}\right)^m \cdot \left(\frac{b^y}{a^x}\right)^m = ?$$

A) ax−y   B) ax+y   C) bx   D) by   E) 1

Solution
$$\left(\frac{a^x}{b^y}\right)^m \cdot \left(\frac{b^y}{a^x}\right)^m = \frac{a^{x \cdot m}}{b^{y \cdot m}} \cdot \frac{a^{y \cdot m}}{b^{x \cdot m}} = 1$$
The answer is E.

Problem 12.2
$(2^6 + 2^6 + 2^6 + 2^6)^2 \cdot (25)^8 = ?$

A) 10^{14} B) 10^{15} C) 10^{16} D) 10^{17} E) 10^{18}

Solution
$(2^6 + 2^6 + 2^6 + 2^6)^2 \cdot (25)^8 = (4 \cdot 2^6)^2 \cdot (5^2)^8$
$= (2^2 \cdot 2^6)^2 \cdot 5^{16} = 2^{16} \cdot 5^{16} = (2 \cdot 5)^{16} = 10^{16}$
The answer is C.

Problem 12.3
Which of the following equals 5^{55} divided by 25^{25}?

A) 5^2 B) 25^2 C) 2^5 D) 2^{25} E) 5^5

Solution
$$\frac{5^{55}}{25^{25}} = \frac{5^{55}}{(5^2)^{25}} = \frac{5^{55}}{5^{50}} = 5^{55-50} = 5^5$$
The answer is E.

Problem 12.4
For what value of y is $(5^y \cdot 5)^2 = 25^{-2}$?

Solution
$(5^{y+1})^2 = (5^2)^{-2}$
$5^{5y+2} = 5^{-4}$
$5y+2 = -4$
$y = -\frac{6}{5}$

Problem 12.5
The number $\dfrac{9^{2022} + 9^{2022} + 9^{2022}}{3^{2022}}$

equal to 3^x for some number x.
What is x?

Solution
We have $9^{2022} = (3^2)^{2022} = 3^{4044}$,
So the numerator equals $3^1 \times 3^{4044} = 3^{4045}$
The expression equals $\dfrac{3^{4045}}{3^{2022}} = 3^{2020}$ so
$x = 2020$

Problem 12.6
$$\frac{3^{1+x} + 5 \cdot 3^x}{3^{2+x} - 3^x} = ?$$

Solution
$$\frac{3^{1+x} + 5 \cdot 3^x}{3^{2+x} - 3^x} = \frac{3 \cdot 3^x + 5 \cdot 3^x}{3^2 \cdot 3^x - 3^x} = \frac{3^x(3+5)}{3^x(9-1)} = \frac{8}{8} = 1$$

MathTopia Press

Problem 12.7

If $2^{x-2} = 3$, then $4^{x-1} = ?$

A) 12   B) 18   C) 24   D) 32   E) 36

Solution

$2^{x-2} = 3 \Rightarrow \dfrac{2^x}{2^2} = 3 \Rightarrow 2^x = 12,$

So $4^{x-1} = \dfrac{4^x}{4} = \dfrac{(2^2)^x}{4} = \dfrac{(2^x)^2}{4} = \dfrac{(12)^2}{4} = 36$

The answer is E.

Problem 12.8

Suppose $6^n = 4$, what is the value of $\dfrac{3^{n-1}}{2^{1-n}}$.

A) $\dfrac{1}{6}$ B) $\dfrac{1}{3}$ C) $\dfrac{1}{2}$ D) $\dfrac{2}{3}$ E) $\dfrac{4}{9}$

Solution

$\dfrac{3^{n-1}}{2^{1-n}} = \dfrac{3^n \cdot 3^{-1}}{2^1 \cdot 2^{-n}} = 3^n \cdot 2^n \cdot \dfrac{1}{2 \cdot 3} = 6^n \cdot \dfrac{1}{6} = \dfrac{4}{6} = \dfrac{2}{3}$

The answer is D.

Problem 12.9

If x and y are integers such that $3^{x+4} = 7^{x+y+6}$, then find the value of $x \cdot y$.

A) 4   B) 8   C) 10   D) 12   E) 16

Solution

3^0 and 7^0 make only this equation true.
Then $x+4 = 0$ and $x+y+6 = 0$, i.e. $x = -4$ and $y = -2$. Therefore $xy = (-4)(-2) = 8$.
The answer is B.

Problem 12.10

Simplify using positive exponents only:
$\left(\dfrac{x^{-6}}{y^9}\right)^{-3} \cdot \left(\dfrac{x^{-1}}{x^{-2}}\right)^2$.

Solution

We have,
$$\left(\dfrac{x^{-6}}{y^9}\right)^{-3} \cdot \left(\dfrac{x^{-1}}{x^{-2}}\right)^2 = \dfrac{x^{18}}{y^{-27}} \cdot \dfrac{y^{-2}}{x^{-4}} = x^{18-(-4)}y^{-2-(-27)} = x^{22}y^{25}.$$

Problem 12.11

The positive integers m and n are such that
$10 \times 2^m = 2^n + 2^{n+2}$.
What is the different between m and n?

A) 1   B) 2   C) 3   D) 4   E) 5

Solution

We have $10 \times 2^m = 5 \times 2 \times 2^m = 5 \times 2^{m+1}$ and
$2^n + 2^{n+2} = 2^n(1+2^2) = 2^n \times 5.$

Therefore the equation $10 \times 2^m = 2^n + 2^{n+2}$ may be written as $5 \times 2^{m+1} = 2^n \times 5$.

It follows that $2^{m+1} = 2^n$ and hence $m + 1 = n$.

Therefore $n - m = 1$

The answer is A.

Problem 12.12

How many digits are there in the number $125^4 \cdot 64^2$, when expressed as a base-10 integer?

Solution

$125^4 = (5^3)^4 = 5^{12}$ and $64^2 = (2^6)^2 = 2^{12}$

$125^4 \cdot 64^2 = 5^{12} \cdot 2^{12} = 10^{12}.$

Therefore, the number has 13 digits.

MathTopia Press

Problem 12.13

If $100^x \times 10000^{2x} = 100{,}000^{10}$, then what is the value of x?

Solution

We can write all bases in terms of 10.

$(10^2)^x \cdot (10^4)^{2x} = (10^5)^{10} \Rightarrow 10^{2x} \cdot 10^{8x} = 10^{50}$

$= 10^{10x} = 10^{50} \Rightarrow 10x = 50 \Rightarrow x = 5$

Problem 12.14

Which of these numbers is the largest?

A) 2^{5000} B) 3^{4000} C) 4^{3000} D) 5^{2000} E) 6^{1000}

Solution

We have

$$2^{5000} = (2^5)^{1000} = 32^{1000},$$

$$3^{4000} = (3^4)^{1000} = 81^{1000},$$

$$4^{3000} = (4^3)^{1000} = 64^{1000}.$$

and

$$5^{2000} = (5^2)^{1000} = 25^{1000}.$$

Since $6 < 25 < 32 < 64 < 81$, it follows that

$6^{1000} < 25^{1000} < 32^{1000} < 64^{1000} < 81^{1000}$

Therefore $6^{1000} < 5^{2000} < 2^{5000} < 4^{3000} < 3^{4000}$

Hence, 3^{4000} is the largest.

Problem 12.15

If $2^y = 3$, then what is the value of $16^y + 2^{y+2}$?

Solution

$16^y + 2^{y+2} = 2^{4y} + 2^y \cdot 2^2 = (2^y)^4 + 2^y \cdot 4$

By subsituting 3 for 2^y, we get

$= (3)^4 + 3 \times 4 = 81 + 12 = 93.$

Problem 12.16

Which of the following is correct if $a = (8^4)^7$, $b = (4^5)^8$, and $c = 2(3^4)$?

A) $c < a < b$ B) $c < b < a$ C) $a < c < b$
D) $b < c < a$ E) None of the preceding

Solution

$a = ((2^3)^4)^7 = 2^{84}$, $b = ((2^2)^5)^8 = 2^{80}$, on $C = 2(3^4) = 2^{81}$

Therefore, $b < c < a$.

The answer is D.

Problem 12.17

Find the sum of all possible x values such that $(x + 5)^{x+2} = 1$.

A) -15 B) -12 C) -10 D) -8 E) -6

Solution

We can solve that problem in three cases such that,

Case 1: Exponent is 0 while base is not zero:

$x+2 = 0$ and $x+5 \neq 0$

$\Rightarrow x = -2$ and $x \neq -5$.

Case 2: Base is 1: $x+5 = 1 \Rightarrow x = -4$.

Case 3: Base is -1 and exponent is even:

$x+5 = -1$ and $x+2$ is even, i.e $x = -6$.

Thus the sum of all possible x values is

$(-2)+(-4)+(-6) = -12$

Correct answer is B.

Problem 12.18

If $10x = 64$, then find the value of $10^{\frac{x}{2}+1}$.

MathTopia Press

Problem 12.19

Which of these numbers is the largest?

(a) 2^{7000},   (b) 3^{6000},   (c) 4^{5000},   (d) 5^{4000},   (e) 6^{3000}.

Problem 12.21

X is a real number satisfying $(x+3)^{2x+6} = 1$.

What is the sum of all possible values of x?

Problem 12.20

If $3^n = 2$ then

what is $2^{\frac{1+n}{n}} + 9n$?

Problem 12.22

If $6^m = 12$ and $6^n = 18$

What is m in term of n?

MathTopia Press

1. Each box contains a digit so that when the numbers in each row or column are read from left-to-right or top-to-bottom, they fit the clues below. Can you solve?

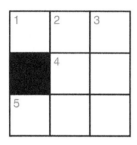

Across

1. $5^{(3)}$
4. A multiple of 9
5. Smallest three-digit number in the grid

Down

2. A multiple of 7
3. A power of 2

2. Copy these 10 digits down as shown:

1 2 3 4 5 6 7 8 9 0 = 100

Put "+" and "−" signs in to make the sum correct. Do not change the order of the numbers.

3. Using a 5 liter and a liter bottle and no other measuring device, explain how it is possible to measure out exactly 4 liters of water from a well.

4. In a magic square each row, each column, and the two main diagonals have the same total sums. Complete the partially filled in magic square shown.

	1	
5		
7		3

MathTopia Press

1. $12^{12} + 5 \cdot 12^{12} + 6 \cdot 12^{12} = ?$

    A) 12^{12}　　　　B) $2 \cdot 12^{12}$　　　　C) 12^{13}

    　　　　D) $3 \cdot 12^{13}$　　　　E) $4 \cdot 12^{13}$

2. Find the value of x for which

    $100^{x} \times 1000^{2x} = 10000^{10}$

    A) 3　　B) 4　　C) 5　　D) 6　　E) 10

3. $\dfrac{4^{50} - 4^{48}}{2^{96}} = ?$

    A) 4　B) 16　C) 448　D) 450　E) None

4. If $(3^{3x})(9) = 3^{n}$, where n and x are integers, what is the value of n in terms of x?

    A) $3x + 1$　　　　B) $3x + 2$　　　　C) $3x + 3$

    　　　　D) $6x$　　　　E) $6x + 2$

5. If $4^{a}3^{b} = 108$ and $2^{b}9^{a} = 72$, then find $2a + b$.

    A) 1　　B) 2　　C) 3　　D) 4　　E) 5

6. What is the smallest integer n such that

    $\dfrac{1}{2^{n}} < 0.001$?

    A) 9　B) 10　C) 500　D) 501　E) None

MathTopia Press

7. Find one quarter of the number 16^{160}.

   A) 4^{160} B) 16^{40} C) 8^{78} D) 2^{138} E) 2^{638}

10. What is the value of $\dfrac{2^{2019} + 2^{2017}}{2^{2019} - 2^{2017}}$?

    A) -1 B) -2 C) 2019 D) 2^{4026} E) None

8. Suppose that x is an integer and $16y = 32^x$, what is y in terms of x?

   A) 2^{5x+2} B) 2^{2x-5} C) 2^{5x-4} D) $2^{5x/2}$ E) None

11. Suppose $A = 3^y$ and $B = 2^x$.

    Which of the following is equal to 24^{xy} in terms of A and B?

    A) $A^{2xy}B$ B) AB^{2x} C) $A^{2x}B^{2y}$ D) $A^x B^{3y}$ E) None

9. If $a = (1001)^{1003} - (1001)^{1002}$ and $b = (1001)^{1001}$, then find $\dfrac{a}{b}$.

   A) 1002001   B) 1001000   C) 1000001
           D) 2002000   E) 2001000

12. Suppose a and b are real numbers greater than 1 such that $a^3 b^2 = 1$ and $a^{4x} = b^{3y}$ what is $8x + 9y$?

    A) -1 B) 0 C) 1 D) 2 E) 17

1. If $x = 3^{48}$, $y = 4^{36}$ and $z = 5^{24}$, then which of the following is correct?

   A) $x > y > z$ B) $z > x > y$ C) $z > y > x$

   D) $x > z > y$ E) None

4. If $2^{x-4} = 11$, then which of the following interval includes x?

   A) $2 < x < 3$ B) $5 < x < 5$ C) $6 < x < 7$

   D) $7 < x < 8$ E) None

2. How many integer values for n make $n^{18/n}$ have an integer value?

   A) 6   B) 7   C) 8   D) 9   E) 12

5. If $14^{x+y} = a$, then find $4^{x+y} \cdot 7^{2x+2y}$ in terms of a.

   A) $\dfrac{1}{a}$ B) a^2 C) 2a   D) a^3 E) a^4

MathTopia Press

6. If $a = 2 + 3^x$ and $b = 2 + 4 \times 3^{-x}$, then find b in terms of a.

   A) $\dfrac{a}{a-1}$ B) $\dfrac{2a}{a-2}$ C) $\dfrac{a+1}{a-2}$ D) $\dfrac{a}{a+2}$ E) None

3. If $3^{x-2} = 6^{x-1}$, then find 2^x.

   A) $\dfrac{2}{3}$ B) $\dfrac{1}{3}$ C) $-\dfrac{2}{3}$ D) $-\dfrac{1}{3}$ E) 2

7. Given that a and b are integers, what is the value of a+b, if $5^a + 7^b = -6(5^a - 7^b)$.

   A) 0   B) 1   C) 2   D) 3   E) 4

8. If $18^k = 30$, then find $2^{k+1}3^{2k-1}$.

   A) 10   B) 12   C) 16   D) 18   E) 20

9. Given that

   $6^x = 18$

   $12^y = 3$

   which of the following equals x.

   A) $\dfrac{y+1}{y-2}$ B) $\dfrac{3y-1}{y-1}$ C) $\dfrac{3y+2}{y-2}$

        D) $\dfrac{4y+1}{y+1}$ E) $\dfrac{y-1}{y+2}$

10. Find the sum of all solutions of the equation

    $(x - 3)^{(x^2-9)} = 1$.

    A) 1   B) 3   C) 4   D) 7   E) 9

11. Suppose x is a real number such that

    $3^{x+2} - 15 \cdot 3^{-x} = 6$.

    What is 3^{x+1}?

    A) 4   B) 5   C) 6   D) 7   E) 8

12. What is the minimum value of $x + y + z$, where x, y, and z are positive integers satisfying

    $2^{3x} + 2^{4y} = 2^{7z}$?

    A) 14   B) 21   C) 29   D) 35

    E) None of the preceding

MathTopia Press

Problem Set 1

1. Taking 12^{12} as a common factor:

   $12^{12}(1 + 5 + 6) = 12^{12} \times 12 = 12^{13}$

   The answer is C

2. Simplifying the equation:

   $100^x = 10^{2x}$; $1000^{2x} = 10^{3 \times 2x}$; $10000^{10} = 10^{4 \times 10}$

   $\Rightarrow 10^{2x} \times 10^{6x} = 10^{40} \Rightarrow 8x = 40 \Rightarrow x = \dfrac{40}{8} = 5$

   The answer is C

3. Taking 4^{48} as a common factor from the numerator:

   $\dfrac{4^{48}(4^2 - 1)}{2^{96}} = \dfrac{2^{2 \times 48}(4^2 - 1)}{2^{96}} = 16 - 1 = 15$

   The answer is E

4. Knowing that $9 = 3^2$, we have:

   $3^{3x} \times 3^2 = 3^n \Rightarrow 3^{3x+2} = 3^n \Rightarrow n = 3x + 2$

   The answer is B

5. Knowing that $4 = 2^2$ and $9 = 3^2$, we have:

   $2^{2a}3^b = 108$; $2^b 3^{2a} = 72$

   Recall that $72 = 8 \times 9 = 2^3 \times 3^2$, then:

   $2^3 \times 3^2 = 2^b 3^{2a} \Rightarrow a = 1; b = 3 \Rightarrow 2a + b = 5$

   The answer is E

6. Rewriting the equation:

   $\dfrac{1}{2^n} < \dfrac{1}{1000}$

   The smallest integer where 2^n is more than 1000 is B)10

7. Knowing that $16 = 2^4$, we have:

   $\dfrac{2^{4 \times 160}}{2^2} = 2^{640-2} = 2^{638}$

   The answer is E

8. Recall that $32 = 2^5$ and $16 = 2^4$, we have:

   $2^4 y = 2^{5x} \Rightarrow y = \dfrac{2^{5x}}{2^4} = 2^{5x-4}$

   The answer is C

9. Plugging in the values of a and b:

   $\dfrac{a}{b} = \dfrac{(1001)^{1003} - (1001)^{1002}}{(1001)^{1001}}$

   $\Rightarrow \dfrac{(1001)^{1001}(1001^2 - 1)}{(1001)^{1001}} = 1001^2 - 1$

   $\dfrac{a}{b} = 1002001 - 1 = 1002000$

   The answer is A

10. Taking 2^{2017} as a common factor:

    $\dfrac{2^{2019} + 2^{2017}}{2^{2019} - 2^{2017}} = \dfrac{2^{2017}(2^2 + 1)}{2^{2017}(2^2 - 1)} = \dfrac{2^2 + 1)}{2^2 - 1)} = \dfrac{5}{8}$

    The answer is E

11. Knowing that $24 = 3 \times 2^3$, we have:

    $24^{xy} = 3^{xy} \times 2^{3xy} = A^x B^{3y}$

    The answer is D

12. Taking the second equation to the power of $\dfrac{1}{3y}$:

    $a^{\frac{4x}{3y}} = b$

    Substituting back in the first equation:

    $a^3 a^{\frac{8x}{3y}} = 1 \Rightarrow a^{3 + \frac{8x}{3y}} = 1 \Rightarrow 3 + \dfrac{8x}{3y} = 0$

    $\Rightarrow 8x = -9y \Rightarrow 8x + 9y = 0$

    The answer is B

Problem Set 2

1. Taking the sixth root of each number, we have:
$\sqrt[6]{3^{48}} = 3^8 = 6561$; $\sqrt[6]{4^{36}} = 4^6 = 4096$;
$\sqrt[6]{5^{24}} = 5^4 = 625$
$\Rightarrow z < y < x$
The answer is A

2. Recall that the factors of 18 are: $\{9, 6, 3, 2, 1, 18\}$
Therefore there are only 6 numbers that make the expression an integer.
The Answer is A

3. Rewriting the equation:
$3^{x-2} = 3^{x-1} \times 2^{x-1} \Rightarrow 2^{x-1} = \frac{3^{x-2}}{3^{x-1}} = 3^{-1}$
$\Rightarrow 2^x = \frac{2}{3}$
The answer is A

4. Recall that:
$2^3 = 8; 2^4 = 16$
and $8 < 11 < 16$. Therefore:
$3 < x - 4 < 4 \Rightarrow 7 < x < 8$
The answer is D

5. Knowing that $14 = 7 \times 2$, we have:
$14^{x+y} = 7^{x+y} \times 2^{x+y} = a$
Manipulating the requested expression:
$4^{x+y} \times 7^{2x+2y} = 2^{2x+2y} \times 7^{2x+2y} = a^2$
The answer is B

6. Rearranging the equation of b:
$b = 2 + \frac{4}{3^x} = \frac{2 \times 3^x + 4}{3^x} = \frac{2(3^x + 2)}{3^x} = \frac{2a}{a-2}$
The answer is B

7. Expanding the right hand side:
$5^a + 7^b = -6 \times 5^a + 6 \times 7^b \Rightarrow 7 \times 5^a = 5 \times 7^b$
$a = b = 1 \Rightarrow a + b = 2$
The answer is C

8. Rewriting the equation:
$18^k = 30 \Rightarrow 2^k \times 3^{2k} = 2 \times 3 \times 5$
$\Rightarrow 5 = \frac{2^k \times 3^{2k}}{2 \times 3}$
$5 = 2^{k-1} \times 3^{2k-1} \Rightarrow 20 = 2^{k+1} \times 3^{2k-1}$
The answer is E

9. Breaking down and rewriting given expressions
$3^{x-2} = 2^{1-x}$ and $2^{2y} = 3^{1-y} \Rightarrow 3 = 2^{\frac{2y}{1-y}}$
By replacing $2^{\left(\frac{2y}{1-y}\right)x-2} = 2^{1-x} \Rightarrow \frac{2y}{2-3} = \frac{1-x}{2-3}$
isolating x gives $\frac{4y+1}{y+1}$.
The answer is D

10. Since $(x-3)^{x^2-9} = 1$, there are three cases:
1) $x - 3 = 1$, 2) $x^2 - 9 = 0$ but $x - 3 \neq 0$, and
3) $x - 3 = -1$ but $x^2 - 9$ is even.
Then the possible are $x = 4$ and $x = -3$.
Thus $4 + (-3) = 1$.
The answer is A

11. Let 3^x be t. Then equation becomes
$9t^2 - 6t - 15 = 0 \Rightarrow (3t+5)(3t-5) = 0$
Solving them we get $t = \frac{5}{3}$.
By replacing $3^x \cdot 3^1 = \frac{5}{3} \cdot 3 = 5$
The answer is B

12. Lcm(3, 4) = 12 One less than multiple of 7 and multiple of Lcm(3, 4) is 48.
So, $2^{48} + 3^{48} = 2^{49}$ (minimum values)
Therefore, $3x = 48$, $4y = 48$, and $7z = 49$
$x + y + z = 16 + 12 + 7 = 35$.
The answer is D

RADICALS & ROOTS

Definition 13.1

If $a^2 = b$ then a is the square root of b ($a \geq 0, b \geq 0$). We use the symbol $\sqrt{}$ to donate the square root of a number. $\sqrt{b}$ is read as "the square root of b". So if $a^2 = b$ then $a = \sqrt{b}$ ($a \geq 0$, $b \geq 0$)

Here are the square roots of all the perfect squares from 1 to 100.

$1^2 = 1 \Rightarrow \sqrt{1} = 1$ $6^2 = 36 \Rightarrow \sqrt{36} = 6$

$2^2 = 4 \Rightarrow \sqrt{4} = 2$ $7^2 = 49 \Rightarrow \sqrt{49} = 7$

$3^2 = 9 \Rightarrow \sqrt{9} = 3$ $8^2 = 64 \Rightarrow \sqrt{64} = 8$

$4^2 = 16 \Rightarrow \sqrt{16} = 4$ $9^2 = 81 \Rightarrow \sqrt{81} = 9$

$5^2 = 25 \Rightarrow \sqrt{25} = 5$ $10^2 = 100 \Rightarrow \sqrt{100} = 10$

Remark 13.1

If $x \in \mathbb{R}$, then $\sqrt{x^2} = |x|$;

- in other words, if x is a non-negative real number, then $\sqrt{x^2} = x$ and if x is a negative real number, then $\sqrt{x^2} = -x$

Definition 13.2

For any real number a and b, where $a \geq 0$, and $b \geq 0$,

$$\sqrt{a} \cdot \sqrt{b} = \sqrt{a \cdot b}$$

Example 13.1

- $\sqrt{50}\sqrt{2} = \sqrt{100} = 10$
- $\sqrt{10}\sqrt{90} = \sqrt{900} = 30$
- $\sqrt{576} = \sqrt{36 \cdot 16} = \sqrt{36}\sqrt{16} = 6 \cdot 4 = 24$

Definition 13.3

For any real number a and b, where $a \geq 0$, and $b > 0$,

$$\frac{\sqrt{a}}{\sqrt{b}} > \sqrt{\frac{a}{b}}$$

Example 13.2

- $\sqrt{\dfrac{25}{9}} = \dfrac{\sqrt{25}}{\sqrt{9}} = \dfrac{5}{3}$

- $\dfrac{\sqrt{x \cdot y}}{\sqrt{x^3 \cdot y^3}} = \sqrt{\dfrac{x \cdot y}{x^3 \cdot y^3}} = \sqrt{\dfrac{1}{x^2 \cdot y^2}} = \dfrac{\sqrt{1}}{\sqrt{x^2}\sqrt{y^2}} = \dfrac{1}{xy}$

Definition 13.4

For any real number and x positive integer n,
$$x^n = a \iff x = \sqrt[n]{a}$$
$x = \sqrt[n]{a}$ is called nth root of a.

MathTopia Press

Remark 13.2

Let a be a real number and n be a positive integer. Then there is no real number x such that $x = \sqrt[n]{a}$ if and only if n is even and a is negative.

Example 13.4

$$\frac{\sqrt{1.6} + \sqrt{0.4}}{\sqrt{0.1}} = \frac{\sqrt{\frac{16}{10}} + \sqrt{\frac{4}{10}}}{\sqrt{\frac{1}{10}}} = \frac{\frac{4}{\sqrt{10}} + \frac{2}{\sqrt{10}}}{\frac{1}{\sqrt{10}}}$$

$$= \frac{\frac{6}{\sqrt{10}}}{\frac{1}{\sqrt{10}}} = 6$$

Example 13.3

• $\sqrt[4]{-16} \notin \mathbb{R}$ but $\sqrt[3]{-8} \in \mathbb{R}$

Problem 13.1

How many integer values of x makes A a real number,

$$A = \frac{\sqrt[3]{x} + \sqrt[4]{x-3}}{1 + \sqrt{5-x}}.$$

A) 1 B) 2 C) 3 D) 4 E) 5

Solution

Since the roots of $\sqrt[4]{x-3}$ and $\sqrt[2]{5-x}$ are even, then $x-3 \geq 0$ and $5-x \geq 0$ that is $x \geq 5$ and $5 \geq x$

$\Rightarrow 3 \leq x \leq 5$, $x \in \{3,4,5\}$

Correct answer is C.

Properties of Radicals

• $\sqrt[n]{a^m} = a^{\frac{m}{n}}$

• $(\sqrt[n]{a})^m = \sqrt[n]{a^m}$

• If n is odd, then $\sqrt[n]{a^n} = a$ and If n is even, then $\sqrt[n]{a^n} = |a|$

• $\frac{a}{c} \cdot \sqrt[n]{b} = \sqrt[n]{\frac{a^n \cdot b}{c^n}}$

• $\sqrt[m]{a^n} = \sqrt[m \cdot k]{a^{n \cdot k}} = \sqrt[\frac{m}{k}]{a^{\frac{n}{k}}}$

• $x\sqrt[n]{a} + y\sqrt[n]{a} - z\sqrt[n]{a} = (x + y - z)\sqrt[n]{a}$

• $\sqrt[n]{a} \cdot \sqrt[n]{b} = \sqrt[n]{a \cdot b}$

• $\frac{\sqrt[n]{a}}{\sqrt[n]{b}} = \sqrt[n]{\frac{a}{b}}$

Problem 13.2

Compute $(\sqrt{12} + \sqrt{27} + \sqrt{75})^2$.

Solution

$\sqrt{12} = \sqrt{4 \cdot 3} = 2\sqrt{3}$

$\sqrt{27} = \sqrt{9 \cdot 3} = 3\sqrt{3}$

$\sqrt{75} = \sqrt{25 \cdot 3} = 5\sqrt{3}$

Adding them up

$2\sqrt{3} + 3\sqrt{3} + 5\sqrt{3} = 10\sqrt{3}$

Squaring the result

$(10\sqrt{3})^2 = 100 \cdot 3 = 300$

Example 13.5

• $2\sqrt[5]{3} + 7\sqrt[5]{3} - 5\sqrt[5]{3} = (2 + 7 - 5)\sqrt[5]{3} = 4\sqrt[5]{3}$.

• $\sqrt[3]{81} = \sqrt[3]{3^4} = \sqrt[3]{3^3 \cdot 3^1} = \sqrt[3]{3^3} \cdot \sqrt[3]{3^1} = 3\sqrt[3]{3^1}$.

Problem 13.3

Simplify $\sqrt{50} - \sqrt{18} - \sqrt{8})$.

Solution

We start by simplifying the square roots.

$\sqrt{50} = \sqrt{25 \cdot 2} = 5\sqrt{2}$,

$\sqrt{18} = \sqrt{9 \cdot 2} = 3\sqrt{2}$,

$\sqrt{8} = \sqrt{4 \cdot 2} = 2\sqrt{2}$,

$\sqrt{50} - \sqrt{18} - \sqrt{8} = 5\sqrt{2} - 3\sqrt{2} - 2\sqrt{2}$

$(5 - 3 - 2)\sqrt{2} = 0 \cdot \sqrt{2} = 0$

MathTopia Press

Problem 13.4

Find the value of x if

$$\sqrt{x} + \sqrt{x} + \sqrt{x} + \sqrt{x} + \sqrt{x} = \sqrt{200}$$

A) 8   B) 12   C) 40   D) 80

Solution

$5\sqrt{x} = \sqrt{200}$

$5\sqrt{x} = \sqrt{25 \cdot 8}$

$5\sqrt{x} = 5\sqrt{8}$ so x = 8

Alternate:

$5\sqrt{x} = \sqrt{200}$ we take square of both sides

$(5\sqrt{x})^2 = (\sqrt{200})^2 \Rightarrow 25 \cdot x = 200 \Rightarrow x = \dfrac{200}{25} = 8$

The answer is A.

Example 13.6

$(5 + \sqrt{3})(5 - \sqrt{3}) = 25 - 5\sqrt{3} + 5\sqrt{3} - 3$

$= 25 - 3 = 22.$

Example 13.7

a) $\sqrt[3]{x^4} = x^{\frac{4}{3}}$ c) $\sqrt{6^7} = 6^{\frac{7}{2}}$

b) $\sqrt[3]{5^2} = 5^{\frac{2}{3}}$ d) $\sqrt{x} = x^{\frac{1}{2}}$

Problem 13.5

Evaluate $\sqrt{2^4\sqrt{2^5\sqrt{2^6}}}$

Solution

So the expression we are evaluating is $\sqrt{2^4\sqrt{2^5\sqrt{2^6}}}$

$\sqrt{2^4\sqrt{2^5\sqrt{2^6}}} = \sqrt{2^4\sqrt{2^5 \times 2^3}}$

$= \sqrt{2^4\sqrt{2^8}}$

$= \sqrt{2^4 \times 2^4}$

$= \sqrt{2^8}$

$= 2^4$

$= 16$

Remark 13.3 — Find nth Roots

If x > 0, then $\sqrt[n]{x}$ is the positive number such that $(\sqrt[n]{x})^n = x.$

If x = 0, then $\sqrt[n]{x} = 0$

If x < 0 $\begin{cases} \text{and n is odd, then } \sqrt[n]{x} \text{ is the negative} \\ \text{number such that } (\sqrt[n]{x})^n = x. \\ \text{and n is even, then } \sqrt[n]{x} \text{ is not a real number.} \end{cases}$

Problem 13.6

Simplify,

$\sqrt{\sqrt{2} \cdot \sqrt[3]{2}}$

Solution

$\sqrt{\sqrt{2} \cdot \sqrt[3]{2}} = (2^{\frac{1}{2}} \cdot 2^{\frac{1}{3}})^{\frac{1}{2}}$

$= (2^{\frac{5}{6}})^{\frac{1}{2}}$

$= 2^{\frac{5}{12}}$

$= \sqrt[12]{2^5}$

Problem 13.7

If $\sqrt[4]{\left(\dfrac{3}{20}\right)^{3x+1}} = \dfrac{400}{9}$, then find x

A) −4   B) −3   C) 0   D) 3   E) 4

Solution

$\sqrt[4]{\left(\dfrac{3}{20}\right)^{3x+1}} = \dfrac{400}{9} \Rightarrow \left(\dfrac{3}{20}\right)^{\frac{3x+1}{4}} = \left(\dfrac{20}{3}\right)^2 = \left(\dfrac{3}{20}\right)^{-2}$

$\Rightarrow \dfrac{3x+1}{4} = -2 \Rightarrow x = -3$

Correct answer is B.

MathTopia Press

Problem 13.8

$$\frac{\sqrt[4]{243}}{\sqrt[4]{0.0048}} = ?$$

A) 1   B) 5   C) 10   D) 15   E) 20

Solution

$$\frac{\sqrt[4]{243}}{\sqrt[4]{0.0048}} = \frac{\sqrt[4]{3 \cdot 3^4}}{\sqrt[4]{48 \cdot 10^{-4}}} = \frac{3\sqrt[4]{3}}{\sqrt[4]{3 \cdot 2^4 \cdot (10^{-1})^4}}$$

$$= \frac{3\sqrt[4]{3}}{2 \cdot 10^{-1} \cdot \sqrt[4]{3}} = \frac{3 \cdot 10}{2} = 15$$

Correct answer is D.

Problem 13.9

$$(\sqrt{5} - 3)\sqrt{7 + 3\sqrt{5}} = ?$$

A) $-2\sqrt{2}$ B) $2\sqrt{2}$ C) -3 D) 3   E) 4

Solution

$$\sqrt{5} - 3 < 0 \Rightarrow (\sqrt{5} - 3)\sqrt{7 + 3\sqrt{5}}$$

$$= -(3 - \sqrt{5})\sqrt{7 + 3\sqrt{5}} = -\sqrt{(3 - \sqrt{5})^2 (7 + 3\sqrt{5})}$$

$$= -\sqrt{(14 - 6\sqrt{5})(7 + 3\sqrt{5})} = \sqrt{2(7 - 3\sqrt{5})(7 + 3\sqrt{5})}$$

$$= \sqrt{2(7^2 - (3\sqrt{5})^2)} = -\sqrt{2 \cdot 4} = -2\sqrt{2}$$

Correct answer is A.

Remark 13.4

For integers m, n > 0,

$$\sqrt{(m + n) \pm 2\sqrt{mn}} = \sqrt{m} \pm \sqrt{n}$$

Example 13.8

$$\sqrt{10 + 2\sqrt{21}} = \sqrt{7} + \sqrt{3}$$

$$\sqrt{12 - 2\sqrt{35}} = \sqrt{7} - \sqrt{5}$$

Problem 13.10

If m and n are positive integers, and

$$\sqrt{7 + \sqrt{48}} = m + \sqrt{n}.$$

then, what is the value of $m^2 + n^2$?

Solution

Note that $\sqrt{m + 2\sqrt{n}} = \sqrt{a} + \sqrt{b}$

if $n = a \times b$ and $m = a + b$.

By rewriting $\sqrt{7 + \sqrt{48}} = \sqrt{7 + \sqrt{4 \cdot 12}} = \sqrt{7 + 2\sqrt{12}}$

allows us to see $= \sqrt{7 + 2\sqrt{12}} = \sqrt{4} + \sqrt{3} = 2 + \sqrt{3}$

Therefore, $a = 2$ and $b = 3$.

So, $a^2 + b^2 = 2^2 + 3^2 = 13$.

Problem 13.11

Given that a > 0, b > 0, and $\sqrt{ab} = 4$ evaluate

$$\frac{1}{b}\sqrt{\frac{b}{a}} - \frac{3}{a}\sqrt{\frac{a}{b}}.$$

Solution

$$\frac{1}{b}\frac{\sqrt{b}}{\sqrt{a}} - \frac{3\sqrt{a}}{a\sqrt{b}}$$

when we rationalize the denominators we obtain

$$\frac{\sqrt{ab}}{ba} - \frac{3\sqrt{ab}}{ab} = \frac{-2\sqrt{ab}}{ab}$$

By replacing $\sqrt{ab} = 4$ and $ab = 16$

we get $\frac{-2 \cdot 4}{16} = \frac{-1}{2}$.

Problem 13.12

Find all values of h such that $\dfrac{3\sqrt{27}}{h} = \dfrac{h}{27\sqrt{3}}$.

Solution

When we cross multiplying we write

$$h^2 = 27\sqrt{3} \cdot 3\sqrt{27} \Rightarrow h^2 = 81 \cdot \sqrt{81}$$

$$\Rightarrow h^2 = 81 \cdot 9 \Rightarrow h = 9 \cdot 3 \Rightarrow h = \mp 27.$$

MathTopia Press

Problem 13.13

$$\sqrt{9+4\sqrt{5}} = ?$$

Solution

$$\sqrt{9+4\sqrt{5}} = \sqrt{9+2\cdot 2\sqrt{5}} = \sqrt{9+2\cdot\sqrt{4\cdot 5}}$$
$$= \sqrt{5} + \sqrt{4} = \sqrt{5} + 2.$$

Rationalizing Denominators and Numerators of Radical Expressions

1. If $n > m$, $b \neq 0$, and $K = \dfrac{a}{\sqrt[n]{b^m}}$ then

$$K = \frac{a}{\sqrt[n]{b^m}} = \frac{w}{\sqrt[n]{b^m}} \cdot \frac{\sqrt[n]{b^{n-m}}}{\sqrt[n]{b^{n-m}}} = \frac{a\cdot\sqrt[n]{b^{n-m}}}{b}$$

2. If $K = \dfrac{a}{\sqrt{b}-\sqrt{c}}$, then

$$K = \frac{a}{\sqrt{b}-\sqrt{c}} = \frac{a}{\sqrt{b}-\sqrt{c}} \cdot \frac{\sqrt{b}+\sqrt{c}}{\sqrt{b}+\sqrt{c}} = \frac{a(\sqrt{b}+\sqrt{c})}{b-c}$$

3. If $K = \dfrac{a}{\sqrt[3]{b}-\sqrt[3]{c}}$, then

$$K = \frac{a}{\sqrt[3]{b}-\sqrt[3]{c}} = \frac{a}{\sqrt[3]{b}-\sqrt[3]{c}} \times \frac{\sqrt[3]{b^2}+\sqrt[3]{bc}+\sqrt[3]{c^2}}{\sqrt[3]{b^2}+\sqrt[3]{bc}+\sqrt[3]{c^2}}$$
$$= \frac{a(\sqrt[3]{b^2}+\sqrt[3]{bc}+\sqrt[3]{c^2})}{b-c}$$

Example 13.9

$$\sqrt{4+2\sqrt{3}} = \sqrt{3} + \sqrt{1} = \sqrt{3} + 1$$
$$\sqrt{3+\sqrt{8}} - \sqrt{2} = \sqrt{3+2\sqrt{2}} - \sqrt{2} = |\sqrt{2} - \sqrt{1}| - \sqrt{2}$$
$$= \sqrt{2} - 1 - \sqrt{2} = -1$$

Remark 13.5

If $a > 0$, $b > 0$ and $a^2 > b$, then

$$\bullet\ \sqrt{a+\sqrt{b}} = \sqrt{\frac{a+\sqrt{a^2-b}}{2}} + \sqrt{\frac{a-\sqrt{a^2-b}}{2}}$$

$$\bullet\ \sqrt{a-\sqrt{b}} = \sqrt{\frac{a+\sqrt{a^2-b}}{2}} - \sqrt{\frac{a-\sqrt{a^2-b}}{2}}$$

MathTopia Press

Example 13.10

$$\sqrt{2+\sqrt{3}} = \sqrt{\frac{2+\sqrt{4-3}}{2}} + \sqrt{\frac{2-\sqrt{4-3}}{2}}$$

$$= \frac{\sqrt{3}}{\sqrt{2}} + \frac{1}{\sqrt{2}} = \frac{\sqrt{3}+1}{\sqrt{2}}$$

Example 13.11

$$\frac{4}{3-\sqrt{5}} - \frac{5}{\sqrt{5}} = \frac{4}{3-\sqrt{5}} \cdot \frac{3+\sqrt{5}}{3+\sqrt{5}} - \frac{5}{\sqrt{5}} \cdot \frac{\sqrt{5}}{\sqrt{5}}$$

$$= \frac{4(3+\sqrt{5})}{3^2-(\sqrt{5})^2} - \frac{5\sqrt{5}}{5}$$

$$= \frac{4(3+\sqrt{5})}{4} - \sqrt{5}$$

$$= 3+\sqrt{5} - \sqrt{5} = 3$$

Example 13.12

$$\frac{2}{3+2\sqrt{2}} - \frac{1}{3-\sqrt{8}} + \frac{12}{\sqrt{2}}$$

$$= \frac{2}{3+2\sqrt{2}} \cdot \frac{3-2\sqrt{2}}{3-2\sqrt{2}} - \frac{1}{3-\sqrt{8}} + \frac{3+\sqrt{8}}{3+\sqrt{8}} + \frac{12}{\sqrt{2}} \cdot \frac{\sqrt{2}}{\sqrt{2}}$$

$$= \frac{2(3-2\sqrt{2})}{\underbrace{3^2-(2\sqrt{2})^2}_{1}} - \frac{3+2\sqrt{2}}{\underbrace{3^2-(\sqrt{8})^2}_{1}} + \frac{12\sqrt{2}}{2}$$

$$= 6-4\sqrt{2}-3-2\sqrt{2}+6\sqrt{2} = 3$$

Example 13.13

$$\frac{1}{\sqrt[3]{2}\sqrt[4]{3^3}} = \frac{1}{\sqrt[3]{2}\sqrt[4]{3^3}} \cdot \frac{\sqrt[3]{2^2}\sqrt[4]{3}}{\sqrt[3]{2^2}\sqrt[4]{3}} = \frac{\sqrt[3]{4}\sqrt[4]{3}}{2\cdot 3} = \frac{\sqrt[3]{4}\sqrt[4]{3}}{6}$$

Problem 13.13

If $\dfrac{1}{\sqrt{2}+\sqrt{3}+\sqrt{5}} = \dfrac{a\sqrt{3}+b\sqrt{2}+c\sqrt{30}}{12}$,

then find $a+b+c$.

A) 1   B) 2   C) 3   D) 4   E) 5

Solution

$$\frac{1}{\sqrt{2}+\sqrt{3}+\sqrt{5}} = \frac{1}{(\sqrt{2}+\sqrt{3})+\sqrt{5}} \cdot \frac{(\sqrt{2}+\sqrt{3})-\sqrt{5}}{(\sqrt{2}+\sqrt{3})-\sqrt{5}},$$

$$= \frac{\sqrt{2}+\sqrt{3}-\sqrt{5}}{(\sqrt{2}+\sqrt{3})^2-(\sqrt{5})^2} = \frac{\sqrt{2}+\sqrt{3}-\sqrt{5}}{2+3+2\sqrt{6}-5}$$

$$= \frac{\sqrt{2}+\sqrt{3}-\sqrt{5}}{2\sqrt{6}} \cdot \frac{\sqrt{6}}{\sqrt{6}} = \frac{2\sqrt{3}+3\sqrt{2}-\sqrt{30}}{12}$$

$$\Rightarrow a+b+c = 4$$

Correct answer is D.

Example 13.14

$$\frac{1}{\sqrt[4]{2}-1} = \frac{1}{\sqrt[4]{2}-1} \cdot \frac{\sqrt[4]{2}+1}{\sqrt[4]{2}+1} = \frac{\sqrt[4]{2}+1}{(\sqrt[4]{2})^2-1^2} = \frac{\sqrt[4]{2}+1}{\sqrt{2}-1}$$

$$= \frac{\sqrt[4]{2}+1}{\sqrt{2}-1} \cdot \frac{\sqrt{2}+1}{\sqrt{2}+1} = (\sqrt[4]{2}+1)(\sqrt{2}+1)$$

Remark 13.6

Infinitely Nested Radicals,

- $\sqrt[n]{a\sqrt[n]{a\sqrt[n]{a\cdots}}} = \sqrt[n-1]{a}$

- $\sqrt[n]{a : \sqrt[n]{a : \sqrt[n]{a : \cdots}}} = \sqrt[n+1]{a}$

- $\sqrt{a+\sqrt{a+\sqrt{a+\cdots}}} = \dfrac{1+\sqrt{1+4a}}{2}$ $(a > 0)$

- $\sqrt{a-\sqrt{a-\sqrt{a-\cdots}}} = \dfrac{-1+\sqrt{1+4a}}{2}$ $(a \geq 0)$

Example 13.15

- $\underbrace{\sqrt{5+\sqrt{5+\sqrt{5+\cdots}}}}_{x} = x \Rightarrow \sqrt{5+x} = x$

$\Rightarrow x^2-x-5 = 0 \Rightarrow x = \dfrac{1+\sqrt{21}}{2}$

- $\sqrt[3]{x+1+\underbrace{\sqrt[3]{x+1+\sqrt[3]{x+1+\cdots}}}_{2}} = 2$

$\Rightarrow \sqrt[3]{x+1+2} = 2 \Rightarrow (\sqrt[3]{x+3})^3 = 2^3$

$\Rightarrow x+3 = 8 \Rightarrow x=5$

MathTopia Press

Problem 13.14

Simplify $\dfrac{\sqrt{7}}{\sqrt{7}+\sqrt{6}} + 7 + \sqrt{42}$.

Problem 13.15

$(\sqrt{60} + 3\sqrt{7})^2 (\sqrt{60} - 3\sqrt{7})^2$

Evaluate the above expression.

Problem 13.16

$\dfrac{1}{\sqrt{1}+\sqrt{2}} + \dfrac{1}{\sqrt{2}+\sqrt{3}} + \dfrac{1}{\sqrt{3}+\sqrt{4}} + \cdots \dfrac{1}{\sqrt{63}+\sqrt{64}} = ?$

Problem 13.17

Determine the exact value of $\sqrt[3]{\sqrt{4 + \sqrt{7}} + \sqrt{4 - \sqrt{7}}}$

1. Suppose that a and b are non-negative real numbers. For how many distinct integer valuesis $b = \sqrt{4-a}$?

   A) 1   B) 2   C) 3   D) 4   E) 5

2. If $\sqrt[4]{2^{x-2}} = \sqrt[3]{4^{1-x}}$ then find x.

   A) $\dfrac{11}{3}$ B) $\dfrac{11}{2}$ C) $\dfrac{12}{11}$ D) $\dfrac{13}{11}$ E) $\dfrac{14}{11}$

3. $\sqrt{4 + 2\sqrt{3}} + \sqrt{4 - 2\sqrt{3}}$?

   A) $\sqrt{3}$ B) 2   C) $2\sqrt{3}$ D) $3\sqrt{3}$ E) 6

4. If $\dfrac{x}{y} = 3 - 2\sqrt{2}$ then what is $\dfrac{\sqrt{x} + \sqrt{y}}{\sqrt{y}}$?

   A) $-\sqrt{2}$ B) -1 C) 0   D) 1   E) $\sqrt{2}$

5. $\sqrt{20 - \sqrt{n}} = 4$, what is the value of n?

   A) 9   B) 16   C) 25   D) 49   E) 64

6. For how many real values of x is $\sqrt{50 - \sqrt{x}}$ an integer?

   A) 4   B) 6   C) 8   D) 49   E) 50

7. If $x = \sqrt{6}$ and $y^2 = 12$, then find $\dfrac{12}{xy}$.

    A) $\sqrt{2}$ B) 2   C) $4\sqrt{2}$ D) $9\sqrt{2}$ E) None

10. For how many integer values of k is $\sqrt{200} - \sqrt{k}$ also an integer?

    A) 11   B) 13   C) 15   D) 17   E) 20

8. If $\sqrt{3\sqrt{3\sqrt{3}}} = 3^{\frac{3}{2}}$ find n.

    A) 4   B) 5   C) 6   D) 7   E) 8

11. If $a + \sqrt{a} = 3$, then what is $a + \dfrac{3}{\sqrt{a}}$?

    A) 1   B) 2   C) 3   D) 4   E) 5

9. $\dfrac{1}{\sqrt{2}+\sqrt{1}} + \dfrac{1}{\sqrt{3}+\sqrt{2}} + \dfrac{1}{\sqrt{4}+\sqrt{3}} + ... + \dfrac{1}{\sqrt{100}+\sqrt{99}} =$

    A) 100   B) 49   C) $\dfrac{49}{1+\sqrt{99}}$ D) $\dfrac{10}{\sqrt{99}}$ E) 9

12. Simplify $2\sqrt{3 + \sqrt{5 - \sqrt{13 + \sqrt{48}}}}$.

    A) $\sqrt{6} - \sqrt{2}$ B) $\sqrt{6} + \sqrt{2}$ C) $\sqrt{3} - \sqrt{2}$

    D) $2\sqrt{3} + \sqrt{2}$ E) None

MathTopia Press

1. Evaluate $(3\sqrt{2} - \sqrt{12})(\sqrt{18} + 2\sqrt{3})$.

   A) 36   B) 180   C) $\sqrt{6}$ D) 6   E) $6\sqrt{6}$

4. Find the value of $\sqrt{2 + \sqrt{2 + \sqrt{2}}}$

   A) $\sqrt{2}$ B) 2   C) $2\sqrt{2}$ D) $3\sqrt{2}$ E) None

2. Evaluate $\sqrt{\dfrac{11}{4} + \sqrt{1 + \dfrac{9}{16}}}$.

   A) $\sqrt{2}$ B) $2\sqrt{2}$ C) 2   D) 4   E) None

5. If $\sqrt{x\sqrt{x}} = 2\sqrt{2}$, then what is x?

   A) $\sqrt{2}$ B) $2\sqrt{2}$ C) 2   D) 4   E) 8

3. $(\sqrt{2} - 1)(\sqrt{3 + 2\sqrt{2}}) = ?$

   A) 1   B) $\sqrt{2}$ C) $\sqrt{2} - 1$ D) $\sqrt{2} + 2$ E) None

6. If $\sqrt{a + b} - \sqrt{a} = 8$, then what is $\sqrt{a + b} + \sqrt{a}$?

   A) 1   B) 8b   C) $\dfrac{8}{b}$ D) $\dfrac{b}{8}$ E) None

MathTopia Press

7. If $7 = x + \sqrt{x^2-3}$ and $b = x - \sqrt{x^2-3}$, then find b.

   A) 3   B) $\dfrac{7}{4}$ C) $\dfrac{3}{7}$ D) 4   E) None

10. If $x + \sqrt{x} = 3$, find the value of $x + \dfrac{3}{\sqrt{x}} + 1$.

    A) 1   B) 3   C) 5   D) 7   E) None

8. What is the value of $\dfrac{1}{2-\sqrt{3}} + \dfrac{1}{\sqrt{2}-\sqrt{3}} = ?$

   A) $1-\sqrt{3}$ B) $2-\sqrt{2}$ C) $2+\sqrt{3}$

   D) $\sqrt{3}-2$ E) None

11. The real number $\sqrt{19-8\sqrt{3}}$ can be expressed in the form of $a + b\sqrt{3}$ where a and b are integers and a is a positive. What is the value of $a + b$?

    A) 3   B) 4   C) 5   D) 6   E) 7

MathTopia Press

9. If $a = \dfrac{2-\sqrt{3}}{\sqrt{5}+2}$, then find $\dfrac{2-\sqrt{5}}{\sqrt{3}+2}$ in terms of a?

   A) $-a$ B) $-\dfrac{1}{a}$ C) $\dfrac{1}{a}$ D) $\dfrac{2}{a}$ E) a

12. For how many real values of x is $\sqrt{500-\sqrt{2x}}$ an integer?

    A) 23   B) 22   C) 21   D) 20   E) 12

Problem Set 1

1. $\sqrt{4-a}$ is only an integer when $4-a$ is a square, therefore:

$0 \geq 4 - a \geq 4$

Obviously, there are only B) 2 values of a that satisfy it.

2. Rewriting the equation:

$\sqrt[4]{2^{x-2}} - \sqrt[4]{2^{1-x}} = 2^{\frac{x-2}{4}} = 2^{\frac{2(1-x)}{3}} \Rightarrow \frac{x-2}{4} = \frac{2-2x}{3}$

$\Rightarrow 3x - 6 = 8 - 8x \Rightarrow 11x = 14 \Rightarrow x = \frac{14}{11}$

The answer is E

3. Recall the expression:

$(m+n) \pm 2\sqrt{mn} = \sqrt{m} \pm \sqrt{n}$

Therefore

$\sqrt{(3+1) \pm 2\sqrt{3 \times 1}} = \sqrt{3} \pm \sqrt{1}$;

$\sqrt{(3+1) - 2\sqrt{3 \times 1}} = \sqrt{3} - \sqrt{1}$

$\Rightarrow (\sqrt{3} + 1) + (\sqrt{3} - 1) = 2\sqrt{3}$

The answer is C

4. Recall the expression:

$\sqrt{(m+n) \pm 2\sqrt{mn}} = \sqrt{m} \pm \sqrt{n}$

Taking the square root of the given equation:

$\frac{\sqrt{x}}{\sqrt{y}} = \sqrt{3 - 2\sqrt{2}} = \sqrt{2} - \sqrt{1}$

Moreover:

$\frac{\sqrt{x} + \sqrt{y}}{\sqrt{y}} = \frac{\sqrt{x}}{\sqrt{y}} + 1 = \sqrt{2} - 1 + 1 = \sqrt{2}$

The answer is E

5. Squaring both sides:

$20 - \sqrt{n} = 16 \Rightarrow \sqrt{n} = 4 \Rightarrow n = 16$

The answer is B

6. $\sqrt{50 - \sqrt{x}}$ is an integer only when $50 - \sqrt{x}$ is a square,

Therefore:

$0 \geq 50\sqrt{x} \geq 50$

The largest square is $7^2 = 49$

so there are C)8 values

7. Taking the square root of y:

$y = \sqrt{12} \Rightarrow \frac{12}{xy} = \frac{\sqrt{x} + \sqrt{y}}{\sqrt{6} + \sqrt{12}} = \sqrt{\frac{12}{6}} = \sqrt{2}$

The answer is A

8. $\sqrt{3\sqrt{3\sqrt{3}}} = \sqrt{3\sqrt{3 \cdot 3^{\frac{3}{2}}}} = \sqrt{3 \times 3^{\frac{3}{4}}} = \sqrt{3^{\frac{7}{4}}} = 3^{\frac{7}{8}} = 3^{\frac{n}{8}}$

$\Rightarrow n = 7$

The answer is D

MathTopia Press

9. We multiply conjugates of each denominators

$$\frac{\sqrt{2}-1}{1} + \frac{\sqrt{3}-\sqrt{2}}{1} + \frac{\sqrt{4}-\sqrt{3}}{1} + \ldots + \frac{\sqrt{100}-\sqrt{99}}{1}$$

After cancelation we left

$\sqrt{100} - 1 = 10 - 1$

The answer is E

10. $\sqrt{200 - \sqrt{k}}$ is only an integer if $200 - \sqrt{k}$ is a square:

$0 \geq 200 - \sqrt{k} \geq 200$

The highest square is $14^2 = 196$, Therefore, there are C)15 values that make the expression an integer.

11. Taking $\sqrt{a}$ as a common factor:

$\sqrt{a}(\sqrt{a} + 1) = 3 \Rightarrow \frac{3}{\sqrt{a}} = \sqrt{a} + 1$

$\Rightarrow a + \frac{3}{\sqrt{a}} = a + \sqrt{a} + 1 = 3 + 1 = 4$

The answer is D

12. Knowing that $\sqrt{48} = 2\sqrt{12}$, we have:

$\sqrt{13 + 2\sqrt{12}} = \sqrt{12} + 1$

$\Rightarrow \sqrt{5 - 1 - \sqrt{12}} = \sqrt{3} - 1$

$\Rightarrow 2\sqrt{3} - 1 + \sqrt{3} = \sqrt{8 + 4\sqrt{3}} = \sqrt{8 + 2\sqrt{12}}$

$= \sqrt{6} + \sqrt{2}$

The answer is B

MathTopia Press

1. Manipulating the equation such that:

$(3\sqrt{2} - \sqrt{12})(\sqrt{18} + 2\sqrt{3})$

$= (\sqrt{18} - \sqrt{12})(\sqrt{18} + \sqrt{12}) = 18 - 12 = 6$

The answer is D

2.

$$\sqrt{\frac{11}{4} + \sqrt{1 + \frac{9}{16}}} = \sqrt{\frac{11}{4} + \sqrt{\frac{25}{16}}} = \sqrt{\frac{11}{4} + \frac{5}{4}}$$

$$\Rightarrow \sqrt{\frac{11}{4} + \frac{5}{4}} = \sqrt{\frac{16}{4}} = \frac{4}{2} = 2$$

The answer is D

3. Recall the expression:

$\sqrt{(m + n) \pm 2\sqrt{mn}} = \sqrt{m} \pm \sqrt{n}$

Therefore:

$(\sqrt{2} - 1)(\sqrt{(3 + 2) + 2\sqrt{2}}) = (\sqrt{2} - 1)(\sqrt{2} + 1)$

$= 2 - 1 = 1$

The answer is A

4. Let's x equals the whole expression then we can also write

$\sqrt{2 + x} = x$

$2 + x = x^2$

$x = -1$ or $x = 2$

This nested sum can not be negative.

Therefore, $x = 2$.

The answer is B

5. $\sqrt{x\sqrt{x}} = x^{\frac{3}{4}} = (x^{\frac{1}{2}})^{\frac{3}{2}} = 2^{\frac{3}{2}} \Rightarrow \sqrt{x} = 2 \Rightarrow x = 4$

    The answer is D

6. let $\sqrt{a+b} + \sqrt{a} = Z$, we have:

    $8Z = (\sqrt{a+b} - \sqrt{a})(\sqrt{a+b} + \sqrt{a})$

    $= a + b - a = b \Rightarrow Z = \dfrac{b}{8}$

    The answer is D

7. Multiplying b and 7:

    $7b = (x + \sqrt{x^2 + 3})(x - \sqrt{x^2 + 3}) = x^2 - x^2 + 3$

    $\Rightarrow b = \dfrac{3}{7}$

    The answer is C

8. Multiplying both fractions with their conjugates:

    $\dfrac{2 + \sqrt{3}}{4 - 3} = \dfrac{\sqrt{2} + \sqrt{3}}{2 - 3} = 2 + \sqrt{3} - \sqrt{2} - \sqrt{3}$

    $= 2 - \sqrt{2}$

    The answer is B

9. Multiplying the numerator and denominator of a by their respective conjugates:

    $a = \dfrac{2 - \sqrt{3}}{\sqrt{5} + 2} = \dfrac{(2 - \sqrt{3})(2 + \sqrt{3})(\sqrt{5} - 2)}{(\sqrt{5} + 2)(\sqrt{5} - 2)(2 + \sqrt{3})}$

    $= \dfrac{(4 - 3)\sqrt{5} - 2}{(5 - 4)2 + \sqrt{3}} \Rightarrow a = \dfrac{\sqrt{5} - 2}{2 + \sqrt{3}} = \dfrac{-\sqrt{5} + 2}{2 + \sqrt{3}} = -a$

    The answer is A

10. Taking $\sqrt{x}$ as a common factor:

    $\sqrt{x}(\sqrt{x} + 1) = 3 \Rightarrow \dfrac{3}{\sqrt{x}} = \sqrt{x} + 1$

    $\Rightarrow x + \dfrac{3}{\sqrt{x}} + 1 = x + px + 1 + 1 = 5$

    The Answer is C

11. Recall the expression:

    $\sqrt{(m + n) \pm 2\sqrt{mn}} = \sqrt{m} \pm \sqrt{n}$

    Therefore:

    $\sqrt{(19 + 8\sqrt{3}} = \sqrt{(19 + 2\sqrt{42}} = \sqrt{16} - \sqrt{3} = 4 - \sqrt{3}$

    $\Rightarrow a + b = 4 - 1 = 3$

    The answer is A

12. $\sqrt{500 - \sqrt{2x}}$ is an integer when $500 - \sqrt{2x}$ is a square.

    $0 \geq 500 - \sqrt{2x} \geq 500$

    The largest square possible is $22^2 = 484$,

    Therefore, dividing by two for one x and adding 1, there are only E)12 values correct.

MathTopia Press

MathTopia Press

CHAPTER 14

FACTORIZATIONS

Definition 14.1

If a,b, c represent any three real numbers then a(b+c) is always equal to ab+ac. This is called the distributive property for multiplication over addition. It is always true, no matter which values you give a,b and c. Since a(b+c) is always equal to ab+ac it follows that a and (b+c) are factors of ab+ac.

Example 14.1

What would be a quick method of finding the value of $1.03\times112-1.03\times12$ mentally, without using a calculator? What is the property which allows you to use that quick method? By the distributive property, $1.03\times112-1.03\times12$ is equal to $1.03\times(112-12)$, which equals 1.03×100 or 103.

Problem 14.1

If a,b,and c are numeral values. Which of the following is not always true?

a. $14\times(24+m) = 14\times24+14\times m$

b. $a+0.05\times a = 1.05\times a$

c. $18\times74 = 8\times74+10\times p$

Solution.

The first and the second expression are always true.

a. **By the distributive property**, $14\times24+14\times m$ equals $14\times(24+m)$.

b. **By the distributive property**, $a+0.05\times a$ equals $a\times(1+0.05)$, which equals 1.05a.

c. **By the distributive property**,

$18\times74 = 8\times74+10\times 74$, hence p = 74, is not always true

Problem 14.2

Which of the following is equal to

$382 \times 998 + 382 \times 2$?

   A. 382×1000 B. 382×998
   C. 390×998 D. $382\times998\times2$

Solution.

By the distributive property, $382\times998+382\times2$ is equal to $382\times(998+2)$, which equals 382×1000 or 382000.

The answer is A

MathTopia Press

Problem 14.3

If the sides of a rectangle are x and x+3, then what is the expression for the area of this rectangle?

A. x^2+3 B. $(x+3)^2$

C. x^2+3x D. $(x+3)x$

Solution

The length measure of the large rectangle is x+3 and the width measure is x. Both (C) x^2+3x and (D) $(x+3)x$ represent the area measure of the rectangle. The other two expressions do not.

Definition 14.2 — Factoring.

Factoring is an essential part of any mathematical toolbox. To factor, or to break an expression into factors, is to write the expression as a product of different terms.

Definition 14.3 — Common Factor.

We say that a is a "common factor" of ab and ac because a is common to both ab and ac. The other factor, (b+c), represents the sum of what is left over after the a is removed. To factor a polynomial means to express it as a product of two (or more) polynomials. The first step when factoring a polynomial is to determine whether its terms have any common factors.

Example 14.2

In the expression of $12x^2 + 20x$, the greatest common factor of $12x^2$ and 20x is 4x. By factoring out 4x the expression can be written as $4x(3x+5)$

Problem 14.4

a. What are the natural number factors of 24?

b. Factor 4m − 8mn completely.

c. Factor $16k^2 − 4k$ completely

d. Factor $21a^3b^2 − 14a^2b^3$ completely

Solution

a. The factors of 24 are 1, 2, 3, 4, 6, 12, and 24.

b. $4m(1-2n)$

c. $4k(4k-1)$

d. $7a^2b^2(3a-2b)$

Definition 14.4

Factoring by grouping is done by placing the terms in the expression into two or more groups, where each group can be factored by a known method. The results of these partial factorization can sometimes be combined to give a factorization of the original expression.

Example 14.3

FOIL factoring

$ax+ay+bx+by = a(x+y)+b(x+y) = (x+y)(a+b)$

Example 14.4

$10k+10m-2km-2m^2 = 10(k+m)-2m(k+m)$

$= (k+m)(10-2m)$

Problem 14.5

Factor xy+x+y+1.

Solution

$xy + x + y + 1 = x(y+1) + (y+1) = (x + 1)(y + 1)$

MathTopia Press

Problem 14.6

If $x-y = 5$ and $y-z = 4$, What is $yz-y^2-xz+xy$?

Solution

$yz - y^2 - xz + xy = y(z - y) - x(z - y)$

$= (z - y)(y - x) = (-4)(-5) = 20$

Problem 14.7

Find the values of a such that $2ab+2a-b-1 = 0$ is true for all values of b.

Solution

$2ab+2a-b-1 = 0) \; 2a(b+1)-(b+1)$

$= (2a-1)(b+1) = 0 \Rightarrow a = \dfrac{1}{2}$

Problem 14.8

If $a-b = 6$ and $b+c = 4$, then find the value of $a^2+ac-ab-bc$.

Solution

By grouping and after the rearrangement of the terms, we obtain

$a^2-ab+ac-bc = a(a-b)+c(a-b)$

$= (a-b)(a+c)$

Note that $a+c = a-b+b+c = 6+4 = 10$

Thus, the result is $6\times10 = 60$.

Problem 14.9

Given that, $x^2 = 2020$, find the value of $\dfrac{x^3-3x^2-2x+6}{x-3}$

Solution

$\dfrac{x^3-3x^2-2x+6}{x-3} = \dfrac{x^2(x-3)-2(x-3)}{x-3} = \dfrac{(x-3)(x^2-2)}{(x-3)}$

$= x^2-2 = 2020-2 = 2018$

MathTopia Press

A common type of algebraic factoring is for the difference of two squares. It is the application of the formula $a^2-b^2 = (a-b)(a+b)$ to any two terms, whether or not they are perfect squares.

Example 14.5

- $x^2-16 = (x-4)(x+4)$

- $9x^2-25 = (3x-5)(3x+5)$

- $2005^2-1995^2 = (10)(4000) = 40000$

Problem 14.10

Two number differ by 20 and their squares differ by 200. Find the product of the two numbers.

Solution

If $a-b = 20$ and $a^2-b^2 = (a-b)(a+b) = 200$, then $a+b = 10$. Thus, $a = 15, b = -5$, and $ab = -75$.

Problem 14.11

If $573^2-427^2 = 1460\times a$, find a.

Solution

$573^2-427^2 = (573-427)(573+427) = 146\times1000$

$= 1460\times100 \Rightarrow a = 100$

Problem 14.12

What is the value of a^2-b^2+8b if $a+b = 4$?

Solution

$a^2-b^2 = (a-b)(a+b)$

$a^2-b^2 = (a-b)\underset{4}{(\underline{a+b})}+8b$

$= 4(a-b)+8b$

$= 4a-4b+8b$

$=4a+4b = 4\underset{4}{(\underline{a+b})} = 16$

The answer is 16

Definition 14.6 – The Sum or Difference of Two Cubes

Another formula for factoring is for the sum or difference of two cubes. The sum can be factored by $x^3+y^3 = (x+y)(x^2-xy+y^2)$ and by replacing y to $-y$ above we get the difference by

$x^3-y^3 = (x-y)(x^2+xy+y^2)$.

Remark 14.1 — Additional Essential Identities

- $(x-y) = -(y-x)$
- $(x+y)^2 = x^2+2xy+y^2$
- $(x-y)^2 = x^2-2xy+y^2 = (y-x)^2$
- $(x+y)^3 = x^3+3x^2y+3xy^2+y^3$
- $(x-y)^3 = x^3-3x^2y+3xy^2-y^3 = -(y-x)^3$
- $x^3+y^3 = (x+y)^3-3xy(x+y)$
- $x^3-y^3 = (x-y)^3+3xy(x-y)$

Problem 14.13

Given $x-y = 8$ and $xy = -15$, then find the value of $(x+y)^2$.

Solution

$(x+y)^2 = x^2+y^2+2xy = x^2+y^2-2xy+4xy = (x-y)^2+4xy$
$= 64+4(-15) = 4$

Problem 14.14

If $xy = 2$ and $x+y = 4$ find x^3+y^3

Solution

$x^3+y^3 = (x+y)^3-3xy(x+y) = 4^3-3\times2\times(4) = 40$

Problem 14.15

If $x^3-y^3 = 80$ and $x-y = 5$ find xy.

Solution

$x^3-y^3 = (x-y)^3+3xy(x-y)$
$80 = 5^3+3xy(5)$
$80 = 125+15xy$
$-45 = 15xy$
$xy = 3$

Problem 14.16

Suppose that the number a satisfies the equation $a+\dfrac{1}{a} = 3$. What is the value $a^2+\dfrac{1}{a^2}$?

Solution

$a+\dfrac{1}{a} = 3 \Rightarrow \left(a+\dfrac{1}{a}\right)^2 = 9.$

$\left(a+\dfrac{1}{a}\right)^2 = a^2+2a\dfrac{1}{a}+\dfrac{1}{a^2} = a^2+\dfrac{1}{a^2}+2 = 9$

$\Rightarrow a^2+\dfrac{1}{a^2} = 9-2 = 7$

Problem 14.17

A rectangle has perimeter 12 and area 8.

What is the length of the diagonal?

Solution

Let a and b be the lengths of the rectangle where $a+b = 6$ and $ab = 8$.

The length of the diagonal is equal to $\sqrt{a^2+b^2}$.

Since $a^2+b^2 = (a+b)^2-2ab$,

then $a^2+b^2 = 6^2-16 = 20$.

Therefore the length of the diagonal is $2\sqrt{5}$.

MathTopia Press

Problem 14.18

If x = 13 and y = 18, what is the value of $x^3 - 3x^2y + 3xy^2 - y^3$?

Solution

Since $x^3 - 3x^2y + 3xy^2 - y^3 = (x-y)^3$

Therefore, the result is $(13-18)^3 = -125$.

Problem 14.19

If $x = \sqrt[3]{7} + 1$, find $x^3 - 3x^2 + 3x$.

Solution

$x - 1 = \sqrt[3]{7}$ and $(x-1)^3 = 7$.

The expression $x^3 - 3x^2 + 3x$ is equal to $(x-1)^3 + 1$.

Thus, the result is 8.

Problem 14.20

If x = 12, find $(x+3)^3 - 3(x+3)^2 + 3(x+3) + 7$.

Solution

The expression $(x+3)^3 - 3(x+3)^2 + 3(x+3) + 7$ can be written

$(x+3)^3 - 3(x+3)^2 + 3(x+3) - 1 + 8 = (x+3-1)^3 + 8$

$= (x-2)^3 + 8 = 10^3 + 8 = 1008$

Problem 14.21

If $x^3 + y^3 = 25$ and $xy(x+y) = 13$, what is $x+y$?

Solution

$(x+y)^3 = x^3 + 3x^2y + 3xy^2 + y^3 = x^3 + y^3 + 3xy(x+y)$

by grouping and 3xy as a common

factors $25 + 3 \times 13$ by substituting given values

$(x+y)^3 = 64 \Rightarrow (x+y) = 4$

MathTopia Press

- $x^3 + y^3 = (x+y)(x^2 - xy + y^2)$
- $x^3 - y^3 = (x-y)(x^2 + xy + y^2)$

Problem 14.22

Show that $2^{27} + 3^{27}$ is divisible by 35.

Solution

$2^{27} + 3^{27} = (2^9)^3 + (3^9)^3 = (2^9 + 3^9) \cdots$

$= (2^3 + 3^3)(\cdots)(\cdots) = 35(\cdots)(\cdots)$ is multiple of 35.

Problem 14.23

If $x = -\dfrac{4}{5}$ and $y = (x+1)(x^2+1)(x^4+1)$,

what is the value of $9y + 5x^8$?

Solution

We multiply each side by $(x-1)$ then the RHS becomes $x^8 - 1$ and the LHS becomes

$y(x-1) = y(\dfrac{-9}{5})$.

So, we obtained $\dfrac{-9y}{5} = x^8 - 1$.

Therefore the desired expression $9y + 5x^8$ equals 5.

Problem 14.24

What is the value of $\dfrac{x^4 + 9}{x^2}$ if $x^2 - 5x + 3 = 0$

Problem 14.25

Compute
$999997^2 - 999994 \times 999997 - 3000000$

GAME 24

Object of the game: Make the number 24 from the four numbers shown. You can add, subtract, multiply and divide. Use all four numbers on the card, but use each number only once. You do not have to use all four operations.

Can you solve the card below?

$4 \times 3 = 12$

$12 \times 2 = 24$

$24 \div 1 = 24$

2. a)

b)

c)
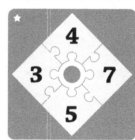

1. a)

b)

c)

3. a)

b)

c)

MathTopia Press

1. The expression $x^3y - xy^3$ can be factored as

   A) $(x - y)(x^2 + y^2)$ B) $xy(x - y)^2$ C) $(x - y)^2x$

   D) $(x - y)(x + y)xy$ E) None

2. Factor the following completely
   $7ax + 7ay - 4y - 4x$.

   A) $(7a - 4)(x - y)$

   B) $(7a - 4)(x + y)$

   C) $7a(x + y) - 4(x + y)$

   D) $(7a - 4)(x + y)(x - y)$

   E) None

3. $98 \times 0.31 + 2 \times 0.31 + 42 \times \dfrac{1}{5} + 8 \times \dfrac{1}{5} = ?$

   A) 31   B) 41   C) 72   D) 107   E) None

4. Let $\sqrt{m} + \sqrt{n} = m - n = 13$, what is $\sqrt{mn}$?

   A) 15   B) 30   C) 36   D) 42   E) 48

5. $a + c = 4.98$ and $b + c = 6.48$.

   Find the value of $b^2 + bc - ab - ac$

   A) 7.47   B) 8.16   C) 9.08   D) 9.72   E) 12.96

6. Which of the following is a factor of
   $a^2 + b^2 + 2ab - 1$?

   A) 2   B) $a + b$ C) $a - 1$ D) $a + b - 1$ E) None

MathTopia Press

7. If $(x - 1)(x + 1)(x^2 + 1)(x^4 + 1) = 255$.
   What is the positive value of x?

   A) 1   B) $\dfrac{3}{2}$ C) 2   D) $\dfrac{5}{2}$ E) 3

10. Which of the following n value makes the
    expression $2^{10} + 2^{13} + 2^n$ a complete square?

    A) 10   B) 12   C) 14   D) 16   E) None

8. Suppose $a - b = 3$ and $ab = 5$,
   what is the value of $a^3 - b^3 = $?

   A) 48   B) 54   C) 60   D) 64   E) 72

11. Given that $a^2 + 4a + 1 = 0$, what is the value of
    $\left(a + \dfrac{1}{a}\right)^2$?

    A) 12   B) 16   C) 18   D) 36   E) 49

MathTopia Press

9. Suppose $x - y = y + z = 3$, what is the value of
   $\dfrac{x^2 - z^2}{y}$?

   A) 3   B) 6   C) 12   D) 18   E) 24

12. Suppose that $a \neq 2b$ and $(2a - 4b) = 8a^3 - 64b^3$.
    Find the exact value of $a^2 + 2ab + 4b^2$?

    A) $\dfrac{1}{4}$ B) 1   C) $\dfrac{3}{2}$ D) $\dfrac{9}{4}$ E) $\dfrac{16}{9}$

1. What is the value of $(x + y)^2 - 4xy$, if $x = 2001$ and $y = 1999$?

   A) 2   B) 4   C) 8   D) 16   E) 24

2. What is the value of $\dfrac{5^{69} - 5^{68}}{5^{68} + 5^{67}}$?

   A) $\dfrac{1}{6}$ B) $\dfrac{5}{6}$ C) $\dfrac{5}{3}$ D) $\dfrac{10}{3}$ E) $\dfrac{1}{2}$

3. Find the value when $(10^{2018} + 10^{2016})$ divide by $(10^{2018} - 10^{2016})$.

   A) $\dfrac{2018}{2016}$ B) $\dfrac{101}{99}$ C) $\dfrac{11}{9}$ D) $\dfrac{10}{9}$ E) 2018

4. Suppose $a + b = 3$ and $b + c = 4$, what is the value of $a^2 + ab - ac - bc$?

   A) 4   B) 3   C) –4   D) –3   E) 12

5. Evaluate $\dfrac{3^{20} - 3^{10}}{(3^5 - 1)(3^5 + 1)}$.

   A) 1   B) 3^{10} C) 3^{15} D) 3^{20} E) 3^{30}

6. Which of the following is equal to $\left(x + \dfrac{4}{x}\right)^2 - \left(x - \dfrac{4}{x}\right)^2$?

   A) 8   B) 16   C) $\dfrac{8}{x}$ D) $\dfrac{16}{x}$ E) $\dfrac{4}{x}$

MathTopia Press

7. Let $a^3 + b^3 = \frac{1}{4}$ and $a + b = \frac{1}{2}$, what is the value of $a \cdot b$?

   A) $-\frac{1}{12}$ B) $-\frac{1}{3}$ C) $\frac{1}{12}$ D) $\frac{1}{14}$ E) $\frac{1}{24}$

8. If $x = a + 30$ and $y = 20 - a$ then, find $x^2 + y^2 + 2xy$.

   A) 2000   B) 2200   C) 2500   D) 3000   E) 3600

9. Find the simplest form of $\sqrt{\frac{9}{4} - \frac{6}{5} + \frac{4}{25}}$.

   A) 0.4   B) 1.1   C) 1.2   D) 3.2   E) 4

10. Simplify $\dfrac{2007^3 - 1}{2007^2 + 2008}$

    A) 2005   B) 2006   C) 2007   D) 2008   E) 2010

11. If a is an non-zero number such that $a^2 + \dfrac{1}{a^2} = 7$, then find $a^2 - \dfrac{1}{a^2}$.

    A) $2\sqrt{7}$ B) $3\sqrt{5}$ C) $3\sqrt{7}$ D) 3   E) 5

12. Which of the following is not a factor of $13^4 - 1$?

    A) 3   B) 4   C) 7   D) 11   E) 12

MathTopia Press

1. Real numbers x and y satisfy the equation
   $x^2 + y^2 = 8x - 4y - 20$.

   What is $x + y$?

   A) 2   B) 4   C) 6   D) 8   E) 9

4. If $x^2y + xy^2 = 15$ and $x^3 + y^3 = 19$, then what is $(x - y)^2$?

   A) 9   B) 4   C) 3   D) 16   E) 1

2. What is the minimum value of x that makes $4^{30} + 4^{999} + 4^x$ a complete square?

   A) 1952   B) 1953   C) 1967
             D) 1975   E) None

5. Which of the following is a factor of $x^2 - y^2 + 10x + 8y + 9$?

   A) $x - y - 9$ B) $x + y - 9$ C) $x + y + 1$
             D) $x + y - 1$ E) $x - y - 1$

MathTopia Press

3. Suppose x and y are two distinct real numbers that satisfy $x^2 - 2018x = y^2 - 2018y$.
   What is $x + y$?

   A) 18   B) 20   C) 486   D) 2018   E) None

6. Find the value of $\sqrt{18 \cdot 19 \cdot 20 \cdot 21 + 1}$

   A) 379   B) 381   C) 401   D) 441   E) None

7. If a is positive real number such that $a + \sqrt{a} = \frac{1}{3}$, find $a + \frac{\sqrt{a}}{2a}$?

    A) $\frac{1}{2}$ B) 1   C) $\frac{3}{2}$ D) 2   E) 3

10. Let x and y be positive real numbers if

    $\frac{x}{y} + \frac{y}{x} + \frac{x^2}{y^2} + \frac{y^2}{x^2} = 28$ then find $\frac{(x+y)^2}{xy}$.

    A) 3   B) 4   C) 7   D) 8   E) None

8. Suppose x, y, and z are real numbers such that
    $x^2 + y^2 + 2z^2 = 16x + 2yz - 8z - 80$.
    What is $x + y + z$?

    A) 0   B) 1   C) 2   D) 3   E) 4

11. Find the value of $(7 + 4\sqrt{3})^{3/2} + (7 - 4\sqrt{3})^{3/2}$

    A) 28   B) 36   C) 42   D) 54   E) 64

MathTopia Press

12. Suppose x and y are real numbers such that
    $y^4 + 9x^2 - 4y^2 - 30x + 29 = 0$.
    What is $y^2 + 3x$?

    A) 7   B) 11   C) 15   D) 33   E) 48

9. If $2a^2 - 14a - 1 = 0$, what is the numerical value of $a^2 + \frac{1}{4a^2}$?

    A) 45   B) 46   C) 49   D) 50   E) 51

Problem Set 1

1. Taking xy as a common factor from the given expression:

    $$x^3y - xy^3 = xy(x^2 - y^2)$$

    Now, we can use the expression:

    $$x^2 - y^2 = (x + y)(x - y)$$

    We end up with:

    $$xy(x - y)(x + y)$$

    The answer is D

2. For this question, the trick is by taking two common factors for the two similar terms, such that:

    $$7ax + 7ay = 7a(x + y) \; ; \; -4y - 4x = -4(y + x)$$

    Therefore:

    $$7ax + 7ay - 4y - 4x = 7a(x + y) - 4(y + x)$$

    Immediately, one can see that we can take x+y as a common factor:

    $$7a(x + y) - 4(y + x) = (y + x)(7a - 4)$$

    The answer is B

3. Similar to the previous question, we can take two common factors such that:

    $$98 \times 0.31 + 2 \times 0.31 = 0.31(98 + 2);$$

    $$42 \times \frac{1}{5} + 8 \times \frac{1}{5} = \frac{1}{5}(42 + 8)$$

    Therefore:

    $$98 \times 0.31 + 2 \times 0.31 + 42 \times \frac{1}{5} + 8 \times \frac{1}{5}$$

    $$= 0.31(100) + \frac{1}{5}(42 + 8) = 41$$

    The answer is B

4. Using the expression:

    $$a^2 - b^2 = (a + b)(a - b)$$

    we get:

    $$\sqrt{m} + \sqrt{n} = (\sqrt{m} + \sqrt{n})(\sqrt{m} - \sqrt{n})$$

    $$\Rightarrow (\sqrt{m} - \sqrt{n}) = 1$$

    Now, we can add $(\sqrt{m} - \sqrt{n})$ to $(\sqrt{m} + \sqrt{n})$ to find m, such that:

    $$(\sqrt{m} + \sqrt{n}) + (\sqrt{m} - \sqrt{n}) = 2\sqrt{m} = 14$$

    $$\Rightarrow m = 49 \Rightarrow n = 36$$

    Therefore: $\sqrt{mn} = \sqrt{49 \times 36} = 7 \times 6 = 42$

    The answer is D

5. Let's start by taking two common factors such that:

    $$b^2 + bc = b(b + c); \; -ab - ac = -a(b + c)$$

    The expression will look like:

    $$b^2 + bc - ab - ac = b(b + c) - a(b + c)$$

    Taking (b + c) as a common factor:

    $$b(b + c) - a(b + c) = (b + c)(b - a)$$

    We know the value of (b + c). Furthermore, to get (b − a), we can simply subtract the two given equations such that:

    $$(b + c) - (a + c) = b - a = 6.48 - 4.98 = 1.5$$

    So the answer is:

    $$(b + c)(b - a) = 1.5 \times 6.48 = 9.72$$

    The answer is D

6. The given expression is simply:

    $$a^2 + b^2 + 2ab - 1 = (a + b)^2 - 1$$

    Therefore, none of the options is factor of it.

    The answer is E

MathTopia Press

7. Using the following expression:

$(a - b)(a + b) = a^2 - b^2$

We can simplify the problem such that:

$(x - 1)(x + 1) = x^2 - 1$

$\Rightarrow (x - 1)(x + 1)(x^2 + 1)(x^4 + 1)$

$= (x^2 - 1)(x^2 + 1)(x^4 + 1)$

Repeating the same simplification:

$(x^4 - 1)(x^4 + 1) = x^8 - 1 = 255$

$\Rightarrow x^8 = 256 \Rightarrow x = 2$

The answer is C

8. Let's remember the following expression:

$a^3 - b^3 = (a - b)(a^2 + ab + b^2)$

Notice that we know the values of (a-b) and ab. Furthermore, we can square the a-b equation such that:

$(a - b)^2 = a^2 - 2ab + b^2 = 9 \Rightarrow a^2 + b^2 = 19$

Therefore:

$a^3 - b^3 = (3)(19 + 5) = 72$

The answer is E

9. Manipulating the given equation:

$x - y = y + z = 3 \Rightarrow x - z = 2y = 3 \Rightarrow y = \dfrac{3}{2}$

Knowing that:

$x - y = 3; \, y + z = 3$

Adding them:

$x + z - y + y = x + z = 6$

Moreover, using the expression:

$x^2 - z^2 = (x + z)(x - z)$

we end up with:

$\dfrac{x^2 - z^2}{y} = \dfrac{(x + z)(x - z)}{y} = \dfrac{3 \times 6}{\frac{3}{2}} = 12$

The answer is C

10. Looking at the requested expression, we can notice that one of the terms has an odd power.

Therefore, none of the choices makes the expression a complete square.

The answer is E

11. Rearranging the requested expression:

$(a + \dfrac{1}{a})^2 = (\dfrac{a^2 + 1}{a})^2$

Immediately, one can notice that we can get the numerator from the given expression, such that:

$a^2 + 4a + 1 = 0 \Rightarrow a^2 + 1 = -4a$

Therefore:

$(\dfrac{a^2 + 1}{a})^2 = (\dfrac{-4a}{a})^2 = -4^2 = 16$

The answer is B

12. for this question, the following expression can help us:

$a^3 - b^3 = (a - b)(a^2 + ab + b^3)$

Applying it:

$8a^3 - 64b^3 = (2a - 4b)(4a^2 + 8ab + 16b^2)$

$= (2a - 4b) \Rightarrow (4a^2 + 8ab + 16b^2) = 1$

$\Rightarrow (a^2 + 2ab + 4b^2) = \dfrac{1}{4}$

The answer is A

MathTopia Press

Problem Set 2

1. Using the expression:

$(x + y)^2 = x^2 + 2xy + y^2$

We get:

$x^2 + 2xy + y^2 - 4xy = x^2 - 2xy + y^2 = (x - y)^2$

$= 2^2 = 4$

The answer is B

2. Looking at the question, we can notice that there is a common factor for both the numerator and denominator, which is 5^{67}:

$$\frac{5^{69} - 5^{68}}{5^{68} + 5^{67}} = \frac{5^{67}(5^2 - 5)}{5^{67}(5 + 1)} = \frac{5^2 - 5}{5 + 1} = \frac{10}{3}$$

The answer is D

3. Similar to the previous question, we can take the same common factor from the numerator and denominator such that:

$$\frac{10^{2018} + 10^{2016}}{10^{2018} - 10^{2016}} = \frac{10^{2016}(10^2 + 1)}{10^{2016}(10^2 - 1)} = \frac{10^2 + 1}{10^2 - 1} = \frac{101}{99}$$

The answer is B

4. Let's start by taking two common factors for the terms that have the same variable, such that:

$a^2 + ab - ac - bc = a(a + b) - c(a + b)$

$= (a + b)(a - c)$

The value of $(a + b)$ is known. Moreover, to get the value of $(a - c)$, we can simply subtract the two given equations from each other, such that:

$(a + b) - (b + c) = a - c = -1$

Therefore:

$(a + b)(a - c) = 3 \times -1 = -3$

The answer is D

5. Remember the expression:

$a^2 - b^2 = (a + b)(a - b)$

Looking at the denominator, one can notice that we can use the above expression, such that:

$$\frac{3^{20} - 3^{10}}{(3^5 - 1)(3^5 + 1)} = \frac{3^{20} - 3^{10}}{(3^{10} - 1)}$$

Now, taking 3^{10} as a common factor in the numerator:

$$\frac{3^{20} - 3^{10}}{(3^{10} - 1)} = \frac{3^{10}(3^{10} - 1)}{(3^{10} - 1)}$$

The answer is B

6. Remember the expression:

$a^2 - b^2 = (a + b)(a - b)$

Using the above expression, denoting $(x + \frac{4}{x})$ as a and the other as b:

$(x + \frac{4}{x})^2 - (x - \frac{4}{x})^2 = (x + \frac{4}{x} + x - \frac{4}{x})$

$(x + \frac{4}{x} - x + \frac{4}{x}) = (2x)(\frac{8}{x}) = 16$

The answer is B

7. Knowing that:

$a^3 + b^3 = (a + b)(a^2 - ab + b^2) = \frac{1}{4}$

We know the value of $(a + b)$. Furthermore, to get the value of $(a^2 + b^2)$, we can square the equation of $(a + b)$, such that:

$(a + b)^2 = a^2 + 2ab + b^2 = \frac{1}{4} \Rightarrow a^2 + b^2 = \frac{1}{4} - 2ab$

Plugging back:

$(a + b)(a^2 - ab + b^2) = (\frac{1}{2})(\frac{1}{4} - 2ab - ab) = \frac{1}{4}$

$\Rightarrow \frac{-3}{2}ab + \frac{1}{8} = \frac{1}{4} \Rightarrow ab = \frac{1}{8} \times \frac{-2}{3} = \frac{-1}{12}$

The answer is A

MathTopia Press

8. Using the expression:

$$x^2 + y^2 + 2xy = (x + y)^2$$

We get:

$$(x + y)^2 = (a + 30 + 20 - a)^2 = 50^2 = 2500$$

The answer is C

9. Equating the denominators such that:

$$\sqrt{\frac{9}{4} - \frac{6}{5} + \frac{4}{25}} = \sqrt{\frac{9}{4} + \left(\frac{-30 + 4}{25}\right)} = \sqrt{\frac{9}{4} - \frac{26}{25}}$$

Again:

$$\sqrt{\frac{9}{4} - \frac{26}{25}} = \sqrt{\frac{225 - 104}{100}} = \sqrt{\frac{121}{100}} = \frac{11}{10} = 1.1$$

The answer is B

10. Recall the expression:

$$a^3 - b^3 = (a - b)(a^2 + ab + b^2)$$

Applying it to the numerator:

$$2007^3 - 1 = (2007 - 1)(2007^2 + 2007 + 1)$$

Therefore:

$$\frac{2007^3 - 1}{2007^2 + 2008} = \frac{(2007 - 1)(2007^2 + 2008)}{2007^2 + 2008}$$

$$= 2007 - 1 = 2006$$

The answer is B

11. The trick for this question is knowing the following expression(s):

$$(a + \frac{1}{a})^2 = a^2 + \frac{1}{a^2} + 2 \Rightarrow (a + \frac{1}{a})^2 = 7 + 2 = 9$$

$$\Rightarrow a + \frac{1}{a} = 3$$

Moreover, the other important expression is:

$$(a - \frac{1}{a})^2 = a^2 + \frac{1}{a^2} - 2 \Rightarrow (a + \frac{1}{a})^2 = 7 + 2 = 9$$

$$\Rightarrow a - \frac{1}{a} = \sqrt{5}$$

Finally, using the difference of two squares identity on the requested expression, we get:

$$a^2 - \frac{1}{a^2} = (a + \frac{1}{a})(a - \frac{1}{a}) = 3\sqrt{5}$$

The answer is B

12. Using the expression:

$$a^2 - b^2 = (a + b)(a - b)$$

We get:

$$13^4 - 1 = (13^2 + 1)(13^2 - 1)$$

$$= (170)(13 + 1)(13 - 1) = 17 \times 10 \times 14 \times 12$$

Therefore, the only choice that is not a factor is 11.

The Answer is D

Problem Set 3

1. The solution of this question requires implementing a technique called completing a square, where one should add and subtract a term to an expression and then compare it to:

$$x^2 + y^2 + 2xy = (x + y)^2$$

Rearranging:

$$x^2 - 8x + y^2 + 4y + 20$$

$$= x^2 - 8x + 4^2 - 4^2 + y^2 + 4y + 2^2 - 2^2 + 20$$

$$x^2 - 8x + 4^2 - 4^2 + y^2 + 4y + 2^2 - 2^2 + 20$$

$$= (x - 4)^2 - 16 + (y + 2)^2 - 4 + 20$$

$$= (x - 4)^2 + (y + 2)^2 = 0$$

Therefore:

$$x = 4; y = -2 \Rightarrow x + y = 2$$

The answer is A

2. Assuming a complete square is of the form:

$$a^2 + 2ab + b^2 = (a + b)^2$$

Then, denoting 4^{999} as a^2, and 4^{30} as b^2, gives us:

$$2ab = 2 \times 4^{999/2} \times 4^{30/2} = 4^x \Rightarrow 2^{2x} = 2 \times 2^{999} \times 2^{30}$$

$$2x = 2 + 999 + 30 \Rightarrow x = 515$$

The answer is E

MathTopia Press

3. The trick for this question is simply rearranging the terms, such that:

$x^2 - 2018x = y^2 - 2018y$

$\Rightarrow x^2 - y^2 = 2018x - 2018y$

Then, using the difference of two squares identity, we get:

$a^2 - b^2 = (a + b)(a - b)$

$\Rightarrow x^2 - y^2 = (x + y)(x - y) = 2018(x - y)$

$\Rightarrow (x + y) = 2018$

The answer is D

4. Remember the following cubic identity:

$(x + y)^3 = x^3 + 3x^2y + 3xy^2 + y^3$

Plugging in the given numbers:

$(x + y)^3 = 3 \times 15 + 19 = 64 \Rightarrow x + y = 4$

Moreover, we know that:

$x^2y + xy^2 = xy(x + y) = 15 \Rightarrow xy = \dfrac{15}{4}$

Also, we can get $x^2 + y^2$ from:

$(x + y)^2 = x^2 + y^2 + 2xy$

$\Rightarrow x^2 + y^2 = 16 - \dfrac{15}{2} = \dfrac{17}{2}$

Finally:

$(x - y)^2 = x^2 - 2xy + y^2 = \dfrac{17}{2} - \dfrac{15}{2} = 1$

The answer is E

5. We can factorize the given expression with the following identity:

$(x + y + a)(x - y + b)$

$= x^2 - xy + bx + xy - y^2 + by + ax - ay + ab$

$= x^2 - y^2 + x(a + b) + y(-a + b) + ab$

Comparing the coefficients, we can see that:

$a + b = 10$ and $-a + b = 8 \Rightarrow b = 9; a = 1$

$\Rightarrow (x + y + 1)(x - y + 9)$ are the factors.

The answer is C

6. To solve this question, we can rearrange the terms and then choose an assumption to change the expression into something factorisable, such that:

$\sqrt{18 \times 19 \times 20 \times 21 + 1} = \sqrt{(18 \times 21) \times (19 \times) + 1}$

$= \sqrt{378 \times 380 + 1}$

Now, assume that $378 = a$:

$\sqrt{378 \times 380 + 1} = \sqrt{a \times (a + 2) + 1}$

$= \sqrt{a^2 + 2a + 1} = \sqrt{(a + 1)^2} = a + 1 = 379$

The answer is A

7. Taking $\sqrt{a}$ as a common factor:

$\sqrt{a}(\sqrt{a} + 1) = 3 \Rightarrow \dfrac{3}{\sqrt{a}} = \sqrt{a} + 1$

$\Rightarrow a + \dfrac{3}{\sqrt{a}} = a + \sqrt{a} + 1 = 3 + 1 = 4$

The answer is D

8. To solve this question, we can use a technique called completing a square. Let us rearrange the given equation such that:

$x^2 - 16x + y^2 - 2yz + 2z^2 + 8z + 80 = 0$

Now, we can add and subtract terms to complete a square three times, such that:

$x^2 - 16x + 8^2 - 8^2 = (x - 8)^2 - 8^2$

$y^2 - 2yz + z^2 - z^2 = (y - z)^2 - z^2$

So the equation will be:

$x^2 - 16x + y^2 - 2yz + 2z^2 + 8z + 80$

$= (x - 8)^2 - 8^2 + (y - z)^2 - z^2 + 2z^2 + 8z + 80$

$= 0$

Finally:

$z^2 + 8z + 4^2 - 4^2 = (z + 4)^2 - 4^2$

$\Rightarrow (x - 8)^2 - 8^2 + (y - z)^2 - z^2 + 2z^2 + 8z + 80$

$= (x - 8)^2 + (y - z)^2 + (z + 4)^2 = 0$

$\Rightarrow x = 8; y = z = -4 \Rightarrow x + y + z = 0$

The answer is A

MathTopia Press

9. Let's begin by equating the denominators in the requested expression, such that:

$$a^2 + \frac{1}{4a^2} = \frac{4a^4 + 1}{4a^2}$$

Knowing that:

$$2a^2 = 14a + 1 \Rightarrow 4a^4 = 196a^2 + 28a + 1$$

substituting back:

$$\frac{4a^4 + 1}{4a^2} = \frac{196a^2 + 28a + 2}{4a^2} = \frac{196a^2 + 4a^2}{4a^2}$$

$$= \frac{200}{4} = 50$$

The answer is D

11. $\sqrt{7 + 4\sqrt{3}} = \sqrt{7 + 2\sqrt{12}} = \sqrt{4} + \sqrt{3}$

$\sqrt{7 - 4\sqrt{3}} = \sqrt{7 - 2\sqrt{12}} = \sqrt{4} - \sqrt{3}$

$\Rightarrow (2 + \sqrt{3})^3 + (2 - \sqrt{3})^3$

$= (2 + \sqrt{3} + 2 - \sqrt{3})^3 - 3 \times (2 - \sqrt{3})(2 + \sqrt{3})$
$(2 - \sqrt{3} + 2 + \sqrt{3})$

$= 4^3 - 3(4 - 3)(4) = 64 - 12 = 52$

The answer is D) 52

10. To solve this question, we can simplify the given equation such that: assume $\frac{x}{y} = a$, then:

$$\frac{x}{y} + \frac{y}{x} + \frac{x^2}{y^2} + \frac{y^2}{x^2} = a + \frac{1}{a} + a^2 + \frac{1}{a^2} = 28$$

knowing that:

$$a^2 + \frac{1}{a^2} = (a + \frac{1}{a})^2 - 2$$

Then, we can solve for $a + \frac{1}{a}$ by plugging back, such that:

let $a + \frac{1}{a} = Z \Rightarrow a + \frac{1}{a} + a^2 + \frac{1}{a^2}$

$= Z + Z^2 - 2 - 28 = 0 \Rightarrow Z = -6$ and $Z = 5$

Now, let's apply the assumption we took to the requested expression:

$$\frac{(x + y)^2}{xy} + \frac{x^2}{xy} + \frac{y^2}{xy} + \frac{2xy}{xy} = \frac{x}{y} + \frac{y}{x} + 2$$

$$= a + \frac{1}{a} + 2$$

Since $Z = 9$, then:

$$Z = a + \frac{1}{a} = 5 \Rightarrow a + \frac{1}{a} + 2 = 5 + 2 = 7$$

The answer is C

12 Again, let's use completing a square technique, Rearranging the terms:

$$y^4 - 4y^2 + 9x^2 - 30x + 29 = 0$$

Now, let's add and subtract terms:

$$y^4 - 4y^2 + 2^2 - 2^2 = (y^2 - 2)^2 - 4$$

$$9x^2 - 30x + 5^2 - 5^2 = (3x - 5)^2 - 25$$

Plugging back:

$$y^4 - 4y^2 + 9x^2 - 30x + 29$$

$$= (y^2 - 2)^2 - 4 + (3x - 5)^2 - 25 + 29$$

$$= (y^2 - 2)^2 + (3x - 5)^2 = 0$$

$$\Rightarrow y^2 = 2; 3x = 5 \Rightarrow y^2 + 3x = 7$$

The answer is A

MathTopia Press

FINITE SUMS

1. CONSECUTIVE NUMBERS

Definition 15.1 — Consecutive Integers.

Consecutive integers are integers that follow each other in order. They have a difference of 1 between every two numbers. If n is an integer, then n, n+1, and n+2 would be consecutive integers.

Odd consecutive integers are odd integers that follow each other. They have a difference of 2 between every two numbers. If n is an odd integer, then n, n+2, n+4, and n+6 will be odd consecutive integers.

Even consecutive integers are even integers that follow each other. They have a difference of 2 between every two numbers. If n is an even integer, then n, n+2, n+4 and n+6 will be even consecutive integers.

MathTopia Press

Problem 15.1

If the sum of 7 consecutive integers is 224, what is the smallest number?

A) 25   B) 27   C) 29   D) 30   E) 31

Solution

If $(n-3)+(n-2)+(n-1)+n+(n+1)+(n+2)+(n+3)$ $= 224$, then $7n = 224$, $n = 32$
so the minimum of 7 consecutive numbers is
$n-3 = 32-3 = 29$.
The answer is C.

Problem 15.2

If the sum of 11 even consecutive integers is 330, what is the largest number?

A) 34   B) 36   C) 38   D) 40   E) 42

Solution

If $(x-10)+(x-8)+ \ldots +x+ \ldots +(x+8)+(x+10)$ $= 330$, then $11x = 330$, $x = 30$
so the maximum of 11 even consecutive numbers is $x+10 = 30+10 = 40$.
The answer is D.

Problem 15.3

If the sum of 4 odd consecutive integers is x, what is the smallest number in terms of x?

A) $\frac{x-4}{4}$ B) $\frac{x-8}{4}$ C) $\frac{x-10}{4}$ D) $\frac{x-12}{4}$ E) $\frac{x-16}{4}$

Solution

If $(n-3)+(n-1)+(n+1)+(n+3) = x$, then $4n = x$,

$n = \frac{x}{4}$ that is $n-3 = \frac{x}{4} - 3 = \frac{x-12}{4}$.

The answer is D.

Problem 15.4

Suppose a, b, c are three even consecutive integers and $a < b < c$, what is the value of $(a-b)^3(a-c)(c-b)^2 = ?$

A) 128 B) 120 C) 100 D) 80 E) 64

Solution

We can choose any three even consecutive integers such as a = 2, b = 4, c = 6.

$(a-b)^3(a-c)(c-b)^2 = (2-4)^3(2-6)(6-4)^2$

$= (-2)^3(-4)(2)^2 = (-8)(-4)(4) = 128$

The answer is A.

Problem 15.5

If the product of two odd consecutive whole numbers is 195, what is the sum of the numbers?

A) 24 B) 26 C) 28 D) 30 E) 32

Solution

If two odd consecutive whole numbers are $n-1$ and $n+1$, then $(n-1)(n+1) = 195$

$\Rightarrow n^2-1 = 195 \Rightarrow n^2 = 196$ and n = 14 that is $(n-1)+(n+1) = 2n = 28$.

The answer is C.

Problem 15.6

If the product of three consecutive integers is 56 times the largest number, what is the sum of the numbers?

A) 20 B) 21 C) 22 D) 24 E) 26

Solution

Let n, n+1, n+2 be three consecutive integers, then,

$n(n+1)\cancel{(n+2)} = 56\cancel{(n+2)} \Rightarrow n(n+1) = 56 \Rightarrow n = 7$

$n+(n+1)+(n+2) = 3n+3 = 3 \cdot 7 + 3 = 24$

The answer is D.

2. GAUSS SUMS

Definition 15.2 — Arithmetic Sequences

Arithmetic sequence is a sequence of numbers such that the difference between the consecutive terms is constant. For instance, the sequence 5, 7, 9, 11, 13, 15, . . . is an arithmetic progression with common difference of 2.

Suppose a sequence of numbers is arithmetic and we want to find the sum of the consecutive n terms. There are two simple formula which can be proven easily, Let NT, LT, CD, S, and FT represents number of terms, last term, common difference, sum and first term respectively.

$$NT = \frac{LT - FT}{CD} + 1 \qquad S = \frac{FT + LT}{2}(NT)$$

Problem 15.7

What is the number of terms in the arithmetic sequence $25+28+31+ \ldots +73$?

A) 16 B) 17 C) 18 D) 19 E) 20

Solution

If FT = 25, LT = 73 and CD = 3, then

$NT = \frac{73-25}{3} + 1 = 17$.

The answer is B.

MathTopia Press

Problem 15.8

$21+25+29+ \cdots +81 =?$

A) 800   B) 808   C) 812   D) 816   E) 820

Solution

If $NT = \dfrac{81-21}{4} + 1 = 16$, then

$Sum = \left(\dfrac{81+21}{2}\right) \cdot 16 = 51 \cdot 16 = 816.$

The answer is D.

Problem 15.9

What is the sum of all two-digit numbers that when divided by 6 leaves a remainder of 3?

A) 800   B) 825   C) 840   D) 855   E) 870

Solution

The smallest and the largest two-digit number which satisfy the given condition is 15 and 99 respectively.

To find this sum $15+21+27+ \ldots +93+99$

If $NT = \dfrac{99-15}{6} + 1 = 15$, then

the $Sum = \left(\dfrac{99+15}{2}\right) \cdot 15 = 57 \cdot 15 = 855$

The answer is D.

Remark 15.1 — GAUSS SUMS

1. $1+2+3+\cdots+n = \dfrac{n(n+1)}{2}$

2. $2+4+6+\cdots+2n = n(n+1)$

3. $1+3+5+\cdots+2n-1 = n^2$

Problem 15.10

$3+6+9+\cdots+120 =?$

A) 2400   B) 2410   C) 2440   D) 2450   E) 2460

MathTopia Press

Solution

$3+6+9+\cdots+120 = 3(1+2+3+\cdots+40)$

$= 3 \cdot \left(\dfrac{40+41}{2}\right) = 2460$

The answer is E.

Problem 15.11

If the first and the second factor of each terms of $T = 1 \cdot 2+2 \cdot 3+3 \cdot 4+\cdots+100 \cdot 101$ are increased by 1 , then the new sum is S.
What is $S-T$?

A) 10000 B) 10100 C) 10200 D) 10300 E) 10400

Solution

When we add 1 to each factors we get

$S = 2 \cdot 3+3 \cdot 4+4 \cdot 5\cdots+101 \cdot 102$, then

$S-T = 2 \cdot 3+3 \cdot 4+4 \cdot 5\cdots +101 \cdot 102-(1 \cdot 2+2 \cdot 3+$
$\qquad 3 \cdot 4+\cdots + 100 \cdot 101)$

$S-T = 2\cancel{\cdot 3}+3\cancel{\cdot 4}+4\cancel{\cdot 5}\cdots + (\cancel{100 \cdot 101} + 101 \cdot 102 - 1$
$\qquad \cdot 2-2\cancel{\cdot 3}-3\cancel{\cdot 4}-\cdots -\cancel{99 \cdot 100} - \cancel{100 \cdot 101})$

$S-T = 101 \cdot 102-1 \cdot 2 = 10302 - 2 = 10300$

The answer is D.

Problem 15.12

If the first factor of each terms of $T = 1 \cdot 3+3 \cdot 5+5 \cdot 7+\cdots + 19 \cdot 21$ are increased by 3, then the new sum is S. What is $S - T$?

A) 300   B) 320   C) 340   D) 350   E) 360

Solution

When we add 3 to first factors of each term we get
$S = 4 \cdot 3+6 \cdot 5+8 \cdot 7+\cdots +22 \cdot 21$, then

$S-T = 4 \cdot 3 + 6 \cdot 5 + 8 \cdot 7 + \cdots + 22 \cdot 21-(1 \cdot 3 + 3 \cdot 5$
$\qquad +5 \cdot 7+\cdots + 19 \cdot 21)$

$S-T = 3 \cdot 3+3 \cdot 5+3 \cdot 7+\cdots + 3 \cdot 21 = 3(3 + 5 + 7$
$\qquad +\cdots 21)$

$S-T = 3\left(\dfrac{21+3}{2}+3\right)\left(\dfrac{21+3}{2}\right) = 3 \cdot 10 \cdot 12 = 360$

The answer is E.

Problem 15.13

If $x = 1+2+3+\cdots+n$, $y = 5+6+7+\cdots+n$ and $x+y = 100$, what is the value of x?

A) 55   B) 60   C) 62   D) 64   E) 66

Solution

If $x = 1+2+3+4+5+6+\cdots+n$ and $y = 5+6+\cdots+n$, then

$x-y = 1+2+3+4+5+6+\cdots+n-(5+6+\cdots+n)$

$x-y = 1+2+3+4+\cancel{5}+\cancel{6}+\cdots+\cancel{n}-\cancel{5}-\cancel{6}-\cdots-\cancel{n}$

$\quad\quad = 1+2+3+4 = 10$

If $x-y = 10$ and $x+y = 100$, then $x = 55$

The answer is A.

Problem 15.14

The sum of all consecutive integers from 1 to n is x and the sum of all consecutive integers from $n+1$ to $2n$ is y. If $y-x = 144$, what is $x =$?

A) 52   B) 60   C) 65   D) 70   E) 78

Solution

If $y = (n+1)+(n+2)\cdots+(2n)$ and $x = 1+2+\cdots n$, then $y-x = \underbrace{n+n+\cdots n}_{n} = n^2$

If $n^2 = 144$, then $n = 12$ that is

$x = 1+2+\cdots n = 1+2+\cdots 12 = \dfrac{12\cdot 13}{2} = 78$.

The answer is E.

3. ARITHMETIC & GEOMETRIC SEQUENCES

Suppose a and d represent any positive whole numbers. Then consider the arithmetic sequence t_n where:

$t_1 = a$	First term
$t_2 = a+d$	Second term
$t_3 = a+2d$	Third term
$t_4 = a+3d$	Fourth term
$t_5 = a+4d$	Fifth term
$t_6 = a+5d$	Sixth term

An arithmetic sequence t_n is such that $t_{n+1} - t_n$ is constant. The difference between the $(n+1)$th term and the nth term is called the common difference and is often denoted by d, The first term, t_y, is often denoted by a.

MathTopia Press

Remark 15.2

You should see that with an arithmetic sequence (linear sequence), with first term a and common difference d, the nth term t_n is given by

$t_n = a+(n-1)d$

Example 15.1

Consider the arithmetic sequence tn whose first five terms are 2, 5, 8, 11, and 14. The first term t_1 is 2, the common difference is 3, and since $t_n = a+(n-1)d$, we get $t_n = 2+(n-1)3.$, so $t_n = 2+3n-3. \ t_n = 3n-1$.

Problem 15.15

Find the 100th term of the arithmetic sequence 4, 7, 10, 13, ...

Solution

$t_{100} = 4+99\times3 = 301$

Problem 15.16

If the first three terms of an arithmetic sequence are 5, 8, and 11, and one of the later terms of the arithmetic sequence is 281 ($a_n = 281$), what is n?

Solution

The common difference, $d = 8-5 = 11-8 = 3$ any nth term is $t_n = 5+(n-1)3 = 281$ by solving it we get $n = 93$.

The Sum of The First n Terms

We start with the statement for S_n, the sum of the first n term.

$$S_n = a+(a+d)+(a+2d)+\cdots+(a+(n-1)d)$$

Remember that the "Gauss Sums", the sum of the first n natural numbers in the following way

$$S_n = 1+2+3+4+\cdots+(n-1)+\ldots n$$

...1 By "starting at the other end" we can also say that S_n is also given by:

$$S_n = n+(n-1)+(n-2)+(n-3)+\cdots+(2)+1$$

...2 Adding [1] and [2] gave $2S_n = n(n+1)$, and therefore $S_n = n(n+1)/2$. More generally, S_n is given by: $S_n = a+(a+d)+(a+2d)+\cdots+(a+(n-1)d)$.

...3 S_n is also given by $S_n = (a+(n-1)d)+(a+(n-2)d)+\cdots+(a+2d)+(a+d)+a$.

...4 Adding [3] and [4] gives: $2S_n = n\times[2a+(n-1)d]$, because there are n lots of $[2a+(n-1)d]$.

Hence $S_n = \dfrac{n\times[2a+(n-1)d]}{2}$

Example 15.2

The first term, a equals 2, the common difference d is 3, and we can get S_{30} as follows:

$$S_n = \frac{n\times[2a+(n-1)d]}{2}$$

$$S_{30} = \frac{30\times[2\times2+(30-1)\times3]}{2} = 1365$$

Definition 15.3 — Geometric or Exponential Sequences.

A geometric sequence or exponential sequence – each successive term is found by multiplying the present term by a fixed constant, which is called the *common ratio*.

Thus, if t_1 is the first term of a sequence and the second term is equal to $a\times r$, and the following pattern can be found;

$t_1 = a$		First term
$t_2 = a\times r$		Second term
$t_3 = a\times r^2$		Third term
$t_4 = a\times r^3$		Fourth term
$t_5 = a\times r^4$		Fifth term
$t_6 = a\times r^5$		Sixth term

In general, the nth term is equal to $t_n = ar^{n-1}$

Problem 15.17

Find the 6th term of a geometric sequence whose first term is 1 and common ratio is 2.

Solution

$t_6 = t_1\times r^5 = 1\times2^5 = 32$

Problem 15.18

Given that the 2nd term of a geometric sequence is 4 and the 8th term of the geometric sequence is $\dfrac{41}{16}$, find the first term and the common ratio.

Solution

$t_2 = 4 = t_1\times r$ and $t_8 = \dfrac{1}{16} = t_1\times r^7$.

By diving t_8 to t_2 we can find $r = \dfrac{1}{2}$ and $t_1 = 8$

Problem 15.19

Find the 15th term of the geometric progression $\dfrac{1}{\sqrt{2}}, -2, 4\sqrt{2}, \ldots$

Solution

The common ratio is $\dfrac{-2}{\frac{1}{\sqrt{2}}} -2\sqrt{2}.$

The 15th term is $\dfrac{1}{\sqrt{2}}(-2\sqrt{2})^{14} = \dfrac{2^{21}}{\sqrt{2}} = 2^{21}\cdot\sqrt{2}$

Problem 15.20

The fourth term of a geometric progression is 24 and its seventh term is 192. Find its second term.

Solution

We are given that $ar^3 = 24$ and $ar^6 = 192$, for some a and r. Clearly, $ar \neq 0$, and so we find

$$\frac{ar^6}{ar^3} = r^3 = \frac{192}{24} = 8 \qquad r = 2.$$

Now, $a(2)^3 = 24$, giving $a = 3$.

The second term is $ar = 6$.

Definition 15.4 — The sum of The First n Term Geometric Sequence.

The sum of the first n terms of a geometric series is given by $Sn = \dfrac{a_1(1-r^n)}{1-r}$ where n tells the number of terms, a_1 is the first term of the sequence, and r is a common ratio.

Let us sum now the geometric series
$S = a+ar+ar^2+\cdots+ar^{n-1}$. If $r = 1$ then $S = na$, so we may assume that $r \neq 1$.

We have $rS = ar+ar^2+\cdots+ar^n$. Hence

$S-rS = a+ar+ar^2+\cdots+ar^{n-1}-ar-ar^2-\cdots-ar^n$
$= a-ar^n$

From this we deduce that $S = \dfrac{a-ar^n}{1-r}$.

Example 15.3

Find the sum of the first 8 terms of the geometric series if $a_1=1$ and $r = 2$. Find the sum of the first 8 terms -6, -3, -1.5, -.75, . . .

$a = -6$ and $r = \dfrac{-3}{6} = \dfrac{1}{2}$

$$S_8 = \frac{-6\left(1-\frac{1}{2}\right)}{1-\frac{1}{2}} = -12 = \frac{255}{256} = \frac{-765}{64}$$

Problem 15.21

Find the geometric sum
$$S = \frac{1}{3} + \frac{1}{3^2} + \frac{1}{3^3} + \cdots + \frac{1}{3^{100}}.$$

Solution

The first term is $\dfrac{1}{3}$, the common ratio is $\dfrac{1}{3}$, and the number of total terms is 100. By using the sum formula

$$S_{100} = \frac{\frac{1}{3}\left(1-\left(\frac{1}{3}\right)^{100}\right)}{1-\frac{1}{3}} = \frac{1}{2}\left(1-\left(\frac{1}{3}\right)^{100}\right)$$

Problem 15.22

Find the sum $2+2^2+2^3+2^4+\cdots+2^{64}$.

Solution

Let $S = 2+2^2+2^3+2^4+\cdots+2^{64}$.

The common ratio is 2. We multiply S by 2 and notice that every term, with the exception of the last, appearing on this new sum also appears on the first sum. We subtract S from 2S:

$S \quad = 2 \quad + 2^2 + 2^3 + 2^4 + \cdots + 2^{64}$
$2S \quad = \qquad\quad 2^2 + 2^3 + 2^4 + \cdots + 2^{64} + 2^{65}$

$2S-S = -2+2^{65}$
Thus $S = 2^{65}-2$.

Problem 15.23

$1+2\cdot2+3\cdot2^2 + 4\cdot2^3 + \cdots + 100\cdot2^{99}$.

Solution

Let S be the desired sum. Then

$2S = 1\cdot2+2\cdot2^2 + 3\cdot2^3 + \cdots + 100\cdot2^{100}$.

$S = 2S - S = -(1+2+2^2+2^3+\cdots+2^{99})+100\cdot2^{100}$.

Using the formula for the sum of a geometric sequence, we have

$1+2+2^2+2^3+\cdots+2^{99} = 2^{100}-1$.

Hence, our answer is

$100\cdot2^{100}-(2^{100}-1) = 99\cdot2^{100}+1$.

Problem 15.24

If d represents the difference between the sum of the first 2n natural numbers and the sum of the first n even numbers, then d equals

Sum of 2n $\Rightarrow \dfrac{2n(2n+1)}{2} = \dfrac{4n^2+2n}{2}$

Sum of n $\Rightarrow n(n+1) = \dfrac{2n^2+2n}{2}$

$d = \dfrac{4n^2+2n}{2} - \left(\dfrac{2n^2+2n}{2}\right)$

$d = \dfrac{2n^2}{2}$

$d = n^2$

4. TELESCOPIC SUMS

Definition 15.5 — Telescopic cancellation.

Say we are trying to find the sum of a series $a_1 + a_2 + ... + a_n$. If we can express each term a_k as the difference of two terms $b_k - b_{k-1}$, then the sum becomes $b_1 - b_0 + b_2 - b_1 + ... + b_n - b_{n-1} = b_n - b_0$. This massive cancellation is called telescopic cancellation. This also applies when we are trying to find the product of a series $a_1 \times a_2 \times ... \times a_n$ and we can express each term a_k as some quotient b_k / b_{k-1} since the product becomes $b_1 / b_0 * b_2 / b_1 * ... * b_n / b_{n-1} = b_n / b_0$.

Problem 15.25

Find the product

$K = \left(1-\dfrac{1}{2^2}\right)\cdot\left(1-\dfrac{1}{3^2}\right)\cdot\left(1-\dfrac{1}{4^2}\right) \cdots \left(1-\dfrac{1}{2018^2}\right)$

Solution

By using the identity $a^2 - b^2 = (a-b)(a+b)$

$K = \left(1-\dfrac{1}{2}\right)\left(1-\dfrac{1}{3}\right) \cdots \left(1-\dfrac{1}{2018}\right)\left(1+\dfrac{1}{2}\right)\left(1+\dfrac{1}{3}\right)$
$\cdots \left(1+\dfrac{1}{2018}\right)$

$= \dfrac{1}{2}\cdot\dfrac{2}{3}\cdot\dfrac{3}{4}\cdot\dfrac{4}{5} \cdots \dfrac{2017}{2018} \cdot \dfrac{3}{2}\cdot\dfrac{4}{3}\cdot\dfrac{5}{4} \cdots \dfrac{2019}{2018}$

$= \dfrac{2019}{2\cdot2018}$

MathTopia Press

Problem 15.26

Find the sum

$\dfrac{1}{1\cdot2} + \dfrac{1}{2\cdot3} + \dfrac{1}{3\cdot4} + \cdots + \dfrac{1}{99\cdot100}.$

Solution

Observe that

$$\dfrac{1}{k(k+1)} = \dfrac{1}{k} - \dfrac{1}{k+1}.$$

Thus

$$\dfrac{1}{1\cdot2} = \dfrac{1}{1} - \dfrac{1}{2}$$

$$\dfrac{1}{2\cdot3} = \dfrac{1}{2} - \dfrac{1}{3}$$

$$\dfrac{1}{3\cdot4} = \dfrac{1}{3} - \dfrac{1}{4}$$

$$\vdots \qquad \vdots \qquad \vdots$$

$$\dfrac{1}{99\cdot100} = \dfrac{1}{99} - \dfrac{1}{100}$$

Adding both columns,

$\dfrac{1}{1\cdot2} + \dfrac{1}{2\cdot3} + \dfrac{1}{3\cdot4} + \cdots + \dfrac{1}{99\cdot100} = 1 - \dfrac{1}{100} = \dfrac{99}{100}.$

Problem 15.27

Find the value of

$$\left(1-\dfrac{1}{2^2}\right)\left(1-\dfrac{1}{3^2}\right)\left(1-\dfrac{1}{4^2}\right)\cdots$$

Solution

Note that

$$1 - \dfrac{1}{n^2} = \dfrac{n^2-1}{n^2} = \dfrac{(n-1)(n+1)}{n^2}$$

Thus,

$$\dfrac{1\cdot3}{2^2}\cdot\dfrac{2\cdot4}{3^2}\cdot\dfrac{3\cdot5}{4^2}\cdot\dfrac{4\cdot6}{5^2}\cdots = \dfrac{1}{4}\cdot2 = \dfrac{1}{2}.$$

Problem 15.28

Evaluate the sum

$\dfrac{1}{1\cdot3} + \dfrac{1}{3\cdot5} + \cdots + \dfrac{1}{(2n-1)(2n+1)}.$

Problem 15.29

$2^2 + 2^4 + 2^6 + \cdots + 2^{20} = ?$

A) $\dfrac{2^{24}-4}{3}$ B) $\dfrac{2^{20}+4}{3}$ C) $\dfrac{2^{20}-4}{3}$ D) $\dfrac{2^{22}+4}{3}$ E) $\dfrac{2^{22}-4}{3}$

GAME 24

Object of the game: Make the number 24 from the four numbers shown. You can add, subtract, multiply and divide. Use all four numbers on the card, but use each number only once. You do not have to use all four operations.

Can you solve the card below?

$4 \times 3 = 12$

$12 \times 2 = 24$

$24 \div 1 = 24$

2. a)

b)

c)

MathTopia Press

1. a)

b)

c)

3. a)
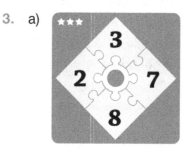

b)

c)

1. Which of the following consecutive integers can be written as the sum of six odd integers?

   A) 18   B) 62   C) 72   D) 86   E) 126

2. Suppose n is a whole number and the sum

   $S = 1 + 3 + 5 + \cdots + (2n + 1)$.

   If each term increases by 3 then how much the total would increase?

   A) n^3 B) $3n + 3$ C) $n + 3$

   D) $3n$ E) $3n - 3$

3. Simplify $\dfrac{3 + 6 + 9 + \cdots + 57}{2 + 4 + 6 + 8 + \cdots + 38}$

   A) $\dfrac{3}{4}$ B) $\dfrac{3}{2}$ C) $\dfrac{17}{3}$ D) $\dfrac{57}{58}$ E) $\dfrac{38}{57}$

4. The sum of four consecutive odd integers is x. What is the smallest of the four numbers in terms of x?

   A) $\dfrac{x - 16}{4}$ B) $\dfrac{x - 12}{4}$ C) $\dfrac{x - 8}{4}$

   D) $\dfrac{x - 4}{4}$ E) $\dfrac{x - 1}{4}$

5. Suppose n is a whole number

   $x = 1 + 3 + 5 + \cdots + (2n + 1)$ and

   $y = 2 + 4 + 6 + \cdots + (2n)$.

   If $x - y = 40$, then find n.

   A) 31   B) 33   C) 35   D) 37   E) 39

6. x, y, and z are consecutive numbers (x < y < z).

   If $\left(1 - \dfrac{1}{x}\right)\left(1 - \dfrac{1}{y}\right)\left(1 - \dfrac{1}{z}\right) = \dfrac{10}{3}$.

   What is x?

   A) $-\dfrac{15}{7}$ B) $\dfrac{17}{7}$ C) $-\dfrac{23}{7}$ D) $-\dfrac{20}{9}$ E) $-\dfrac{19}{9}$

MathTopia Press

7. If $a = 2 + 4 + 6 + \cdots + 50$ and
$b = 3 + 5 + 7 + \cdots + 51$,
what is b in terms of a.

A) $a + 25$ B) $a - 25$ C) $2a + 10$

D) $a + 5$ E) $a + 20$

8. Find sum: $1 \cdot 2 + 2 \cdot 3 + 3 \cdot 4 + ... + 100 \cdot 101$.

A) 345050   B) 346050   C) 3414040

D) 3424000   E) 3434000

9. The product of three consecutive numbers is
$2^5 \cdot 3 \cdot 7 \cdot 5$.
What is the sum of these three numbers?

A) 45   B) 50   C) 60   D) 65   E) None

10. If $1 + x + x^2 + x^3 + x^4 = 0$
What is $1 + x + x^2 + x^3 + ... + x^{2019} = ?$

A) 0   B) 1   C) 2019   D) 2020   E) None

11. A sequence with the removed perfect squares numbers such that 2, 3, 5, 6, 7, 8, 10, 11, 12, ... , then, find 2008th term of this sequence.

A) 2038   B) 2053   C) 2042   D) 2063   E) None

12. Find the sum of the series:
$$\frac{1}{2} + \left(\frac{1}{3} + \frac{2}{3}\right) + \left(\frac{1}{4} + \frac{2}{4} + \frac{3}{4}\right) + \left(\frac{1}{5} + \frac{2}{5} + \frac{3}{5}\right.$$
$$\left. + \frac{4}{5}\right) + ... + \left(\frac{1}{100} + \frac{2}{100} + \frac{3}{100}\right) + \frac{99}{100}\right)$$

A) 2525   B) 2505   C) 2475   D) 2250   E) 1250

MathTopia Press

1. The first term of an arithmetic sequence is -2 and the third term is 5. Which of the following is the 10th term of this sequence?

   A) $\dfrac{55}{2}$ B) $\dfrac{57}{2}$ C) $\dfrac{59}{2}$ D) $\dfrac{67}{2}$ E) None

2. If x, y, and $-1/2$ create respectively an arithmetic progression and 4, x, y create respectively a geometric progression, find the sum of x and y.

   A) $\dfrac{6}{5}$ B) $\dfrac{5}{3}$ C) $\dfrac{5}{4}$ D) 5   E) 3

3. Consider the sequence 1, -2, 3, -4, 5, -6, ... What is the average of the first 50 term of the sequence?

   A) -50 B) -10 C) 10   D) 50   E) $\dfrac{-1}{2}$

4. If the sum of 13 even integers is zero, what is the largest of these thirteen numbers?

   A) 8   B) 10   C) 12   D) 13   E) 14

5. $A = 1 \cdot 4 + 4 \cdot 7 + 7 \cdot 10 + ... + 17 \cdot 20$.

   If each term's first and second product increases by 3, what is the total change?

   A) 442   B) 456   C) 460   D) 554   E) 560

6. The first four term of an arithmetic sequence are a, x, b, and 2x. What is $\dfrac{a}{b}$?

   A) $\dfrac{1}{2}$ B) $\dfrac{2}{3}$ C) $\dfrac{1}{3}$ D) $\dfrac{3}{2}$ E) 2

MathTopia Press

7. Find the sum of the following terms
   5, 9, 13, ... , 97.

   A) 2448   B) 2346   C) 2442   D) 2500   E) None

8. What is the sum of the first 100 terms of the arithmetics sequence 2, 7, 12, 17, ...

   A) 25452   B) 25351   C) 25500

       D) 25000   E) 24950

9. An arithmetic sequence has first term a and common difference d. If the sum of the first four terms is half of the sum of the next 4 four terms. What is the ratio $\frac{a}{b}$?

   A) 1   B) 2   C) $\frac{5}{2}$ D) 3   E) $\frac{7}{2}$

10. a, 9, 3a − b, and 3a + b are the first four terms of an arithmetic sequence. Find 100th term of this sequence.

    A) 401   B) 499   C) 501   D) 555   E) 565

11. Consider an arithmetic sequence with $a_3 = 20$ and $a_{13} = 70$. For what value of n is $a_n = 505$?

    A) 101   B) 100   C) 99   D) 98   E) 95

12. Let $a_1, a_2, a_3, ... a_k$ a finite arithmetic sequence with $a_2 + a_3 + a_4 = 30$ and $a_4 + a_5 + a_6 = 48$. If $a_k = 31$, find k.

    A) 8   B) 9   C) 10   D) 11   E) 12

MathTopia Press

1. The first three terms of a geometric progression are $\sqrt{2}$, $\sqrt[3]{2}$, and $\sqrt[6]{2}$.

   What is the fourth term?

   A) $\sqrt[8]{2}$ B) $\sqrt[9]{2}$ C) $\sqrt[12]{2}$ D) 1   E) 2

2. Positive integers a, b, 775 , with a < b < 775, form a geometric sequence with an integer ratio.

   What is a?

   A) 21   B) 25   C) 29   D) 31   E) 36

3. A geometric sequence has its first term $a_1 = \dfrac{32}{9}$ and a common ratio of /. $r = \dfrac{-3}{2}$.

   What is a_6?

   A) –16   B) –21   C) –27   D) –81   E) –162

4. The sum of the first 16 terms of a geometric sequence is 650, and the sum of the first 8 terms of that geometric sequence is 10.

   What is the common ratio?

   A) 2   B) 4   C) 6   D) 8   E) None

5. Express the following sum as a simple fraction in lowest terms.

   $$\frac{1}{1\times 2} + \frac{1}{2\times 3} + \frac{1}{3\times 4} + \frac{1}{4\times 5} + \frac{1}{5\times 6}$$

   A) $\dfrac{13}{24}$ B) $\dfrac{2}{3}$ C) $\dfrac{5}{6}$ D) $\dfrac{7}{12}$ E) None

6. Find the sum

   $$\frac{1}{1\cdot 2} + \frac{1}{2\cdot 3} + \frac{1}{3\cdot 4} + \frac{1}{4\cdot 5} + \dots + \frac{1}{9\cdot 10}$$

   A) $\dfrac{13}{24}$ B) $\dfrac{2}{3}$ C) $\dfrac{5}{6}$ D) $\dfrac{7}{12}$ E) None

MathTopia Press

7. Find the sum

$$\frac{1}{\sqrt{1}+\sqrt{2}}+\frac{1}{\sqrt{2}+\sqrt{3}}+\frac{1}{\sqrt{3}+\sqrt{4}}+...+\frac{1}{\sqrt{99}+\sqrt{100}}$$

A) $\sqrt{101}$ B) 10   C) $\sqrt{99}$

      D) $\sqrt{101}-1$ E) None

8. Find the product of fractions

$$\left(1-\frac{1}{2^2}\right)\cdot\left(1-\frac{1}{3^2}\right)\cdot\left(1-\frac{1}{4^2}\right)=\left(1-\frac{1}{10^2}\right)$$

in lowest term?

A) $\frac{110}{99}$ B) $\frac{99}{100}$ C) $\frac{2}{21}$ D) $\frac{10}{7}$ E) $\frac{1}{7}$

9. Find the sum of the following

$$1\cdot 3+3\cdot 7+5\cdot 11+7\cdot 15+...+17\cdot 35$$

A) 2181   B) 2245   C) 2455   D) 2500   E) None

10. Find the sum $\frac{1}{1\cdot 3}+\frac{1}{3\cdot 5}+\frac{1}{5\cdot 7}+...+\frac{1}{19\cdot 21}$

A) $\frac{19}{9}$ B) $\frac{19}{21}$ C) $\frac{2}{21}$ D) $\frac{10}{7}$ E) $\frac{1}{7}$

11. Find the following product

$$\left(1+\frac{1}{2}\right)\cdot\left(2+\frac{2}{3}\right)\cdot\left(3+\frac{3}{4}\right)...\left(10+\frac{10}{11}\right)$$

A) $\frac{10!}{9}$ B) 10!   C) $3\times 10!$ D) 4×10 E) 6×10

12. Which of the following is equal to

$$S = 1(1!) + 2(2!) + 3(3!) + ... + 10(10!)?$$

A) $11!-1$ B) $11!+1$ C) $12!-1$

      D) $12!+9$ E) $10\cdot 10!-1$

MathTopia Press

Problem Set 1

1. Let the numbers be $2a - 5$, $2a - 3$, $2a - 1$, $2a + 1$, $2a + 3$, and $2a + 5$.

   Their sum is $12a$, and the only options which is divisible by 12 is 72.

   The answer is C

2. The numbers are consecutive odd numbers starting with 1. In this sequence, k-th term is $2k - 1$.

   Hence, $2n + 1$ is the $(n + 1)$-th term. If we increase each term by 3, the whole sum will increase $3(n + 1) = 3n + 3$.

   The answer is B

3. Common factor of the numbers in the numerator is 3, and in the denominator is 2. Therefore,

   $$\frac{3 + 6 + 9 + \cdots + 57}{2 + 4 + 6 + 8 + \cdots + 38}$$

   $$\frac{3(1 + 2 + 3 + \cdots 19)}{2(1 + 2 + 3 + \cdots + 19)} = \frac{3}{2}$$

   The answer is B

4. Let these numbers be $2a - 3$, $2a - 1$, $2a + 1$, and $2a + 3$. Their sum is $8a = x$. Hence,

   $$a = \frac{x}{8} \Rightarrow 2a - 3 = \frac{x}{4} - 3 = \frac{x - 12}{4}$$

   The answer is B

5. Let's calculate directly,

   $$x = 1 + 3 + 5 + \cdots + (2n - 1) + (2n + 1)$$

   $$= n^2 + (2n + 1) = (n + 1)^2$$

   $$y = 2 + 4 + 6 + \cdots + 2n = 2(1 + 2 + \cdots + n)$$

   $$= n(n + 1)$$

   Hence, $x - y = (n + 1)^2 - n(n + 1) = n + 1 = 40$ and $n = 39$.

   The answer is E

6. It is given that $y = x + 1$ and $z = x + 2$.

   By putting these to the equation,

   $$(1 - \frac{1}{x})(1 - \frac{1}{x + 1})(1 - \frac{1}{x + 2})$$

   $$= \frac{x - 1}{x} \cdot \frac{x}{x + 1} \cdot \frac{x + 1}{x + 2} \Rightarrow \frac{x - 1}{x + 2} = \frac{10}{3}$$

   $$\Rightarrow 3x - 3 = 10x + 20 \Rightarrow x = -\frac{23}{7}$$

   The answer is C

7. Let's calculate $b - a$,

   $$b - a = (3 - 2) + (5 - 4) + \cdots + (51 - 50) = 25$$

   Therefore, $b = a + 25$.

   The answer is A

8. Each term of the sum is in form of

   $n(n + 1) = n^2 + n$.

   Therefore, the sum is

   $$= (1^2 + 1) + (2^2 + 2) + \cdots + (100^2 + 100)$$

   $$= (1^2 + 2^2 + \cdots + 100^2) + (1 + 2 + \cdots + 100)$$

   $$= \frac{100 \cdot 101 \cdot 201}{6} = \frac{100 \cdot 101}{2}$$

   $$= \frac{101 \cdot 101 \cdot 204}{6} = 100 \cdot 101 \cdot 34 = 343400$$

   The answer is E

9. Let these numbers be $a - 1$, a, and $a + 1$.

   Their product is $a^3 - a = 2^5 \cdot 3 \cdot 5 \cdot 7 = 3360$.

   Therefore,

   $$(a - 1)^3 < a^3 - a = 3360 < a^3$$

   Since $14^3 = 2744$ and $15^3 = 3375$, it is found that $a = 15$. Their sum is

   $$(a - 1) + a + (a + 1) = 3a = 45.$$

   The answer is A

MathTopia Press

10. If we multiply the equation with x^{5k} for

k = 0, 1, . . . , 403, they are

$1 + x + x^2 + x^3 + x^4 = 0$

$x^5 + x^6 + x^7 + x^8 + x^9 = 0$

$$\vdots$$

$x^{2015} + x^{2016} + x^{2017} + x^{2018} + x^{2019} = 0$

Their sum is

$1 + x + x^2 + \cdots + x^{2019} = 0$

The answer is A

11. Assume that this number is N. Then the place of

N is $N - \lfloor \sqrt{N} \rfloor$.

Assume that $\lfloor \sqrt{N} \rfloor = m$, then $(m + 1)^2 > N > m^2$.

$(m + 1)^2 - m > N - m > m^2 - m$

$\Rightarrow m^2 + m + 1 > 2008 > m^2 - m$

Because $(m + 1)^2 > m^2 + m + 1$ and

$m^2 - m > (m - 1)^2$,

$(m + 1)^2 > 2008 > (m - 1)^2$

Since $45^2 > 2008 > 44^2$, $(m - 1) = 44$ or

$(m + 1) = 45$. If m = 44,

$2008 > 44^2 + 44 + 1$ is a contradiction.

Then, m = 45. N = 2008 + 45 = 2053.

The answer is B

12. Each term is in form of

$$\frac{1}{n} + \frac{2}{n} + \cdots + \frac{n-1}{n} = \frac{\frac{(n-1)n}{2}}{n} = \frac{n-1}{2}$$

Therefore, the sum is

$$\frac{1}{2} + \frac{2}{2} + \frac{3}{2} + \cdots + \frac{90}{2} = \frac{\frac{99 \cdot 100}{2}}{2} = \frac{99 \cdot 100}{2}$$

$= 2475$

The answer is C

1. Assume that common difference of the sequence

is d. Then, first 10 terms are

$-2, -2 + d, -2 + 2d, \ldots, -2 + 9d$

Third term is $-2 + 2d = 5$, therefore, $d = \frac{7}{2}$.

10th term is $-2 + 9d = -2 + \frac{63}{2} = \frac{59}{2}$.

The answer is C

2. Since the first sequence is arithmetic,

$2y = x - \frac{1}{2}$

Also, the second sequence is geometric, hence,

$4y = x^2$

Therefore,

$$x^2 = 4y = \left(2y + \frac{1}{2}\right)^2 \Rightarrow 4y^2 - 2y + \frac{1}{2}$$

$$= \left(2y - \frac{1}{2}\right)^2 = 0$$

So, $y = \frac{1}{2}$ and x = 1, and their sum is $\frac{5}{4}$.

The answer is C

3. Let's calculate directly,

$$\text{Average} = \frac{(1 - 2) + (3 - 4) + \cdots + (49 - 50)}{50}$$

$$= \frac{-25}{50} = -\frac{1}{2}$$

The answer is E

4. Let those numbers be

$2a - 12, 2a - 10, \ldots, 2a - 2, 2a, 2a + 2, \ldots,$

$2a + 12$

Their sum is 26a = 0, and thus, a = 0.

The largest number is 2a + 12 = 12.

The answer is C

5. Assume new sum is B,

   $A = 1 \cdot 4 + 4 \cdot 7 + \cdots + 17 \cdot 20$

   $B = 4 \cdot 7 + 7 \cdot 10 + \cdots + 17 \cdot 20 + 20 \cdot 23$

   It can be seen that

   $B - A = 20 \cdot 23 - 1 \cdot 4 = 456.$

   The answer is B

6. Assume that the common difference is d.

   Then $x = a + d$, $b = a + 2d$, $2x = a + 3d$.

   The difference between the second and fourth term is $2x - x = 2d$. So, $d = \dfrac{x}{2}$.

   By that, $a = \dfrac{x}{2}$ and $b = \dfrac{3x}{2}$. Their ratio is $\dfrac{1}{3}$

   The answer is C

7. n-th term of the sequence is $4n + 1$. So,

   $4n + 1 = 97 \Rightarrow n = 24$

   Hence, there are 24 terms. The sum is

   $$\sum_{n=1}^{24}(4n+1) = 4\sum_{n=1}^{24}n + \sum_{n=1}^{24}1 = \frac{4 \cdot 24 \cdot 25}{2} + 24 = 1224$$

   The answer is A

8. n-th term of the sequence is $5n - 3$. Hence,

   $$\sum_{n=1}^{100}(5n-3) = 5\sum_{n=1}^{100}n - \sum_{n=1}^{100}3 = \frac{5 \cdot 100 \cdot 101}{2} - 300$$

   $$= 24950$$

   The answer is E

9. First 8 terms are

   $a, a + d, a + 2d, \ldots, a + 6d, a + 7d$

   The sum of the first four terms is $4a + 6d$ and other four is $4a + 22d$. Therefore,

   $2(4a + 6d) = 4a + 22d \Rightarrow 4a = 10d$

   $\Rightarrow \dfrac{a}{d} = \dfrac{5}{2}$

   The answer is C

10. Assume that the common difference is r.

    Then, $a + r = 9$, $a + 2r = 3a - b$, and

    $a + 3r = 3a + b$. If we write $a = 9 - r$,

    $2r = 2a - b = 18 - 2r - b \Rightarrow b = 18 - 4r$

    $3r = 2a + b = 18 - 2r + 18 - 4r = 36 - 6r$

    $\Rightarrow r = 4$

    By that $a = 5$ and $b = 2$. The sequence is

    $5, 9, 13, 17, \ldots$

    n-th term of the sequence is $4n + 1$.

    Hence, 100th term is 401.

    The answer is A

11. Let the common difference be d.

    Then $a_3 = a_1 + 2d$ and $a_{13} = a_1 + 12d$. Therefore,

    $10d = a_{13} - a_3 = 50$ and $d = 5$, and $a_1 = 10$.

    $a_n = (n - 1)d + a_1 = 10 + 5(n - 1) = 505$

    $\Rightarrow n = 100$

    The answer is B

MathTopia Press

12. Let the common difference be d.

Then $a_n = (n - 1)d + a_1$.

So,

$a_2 + a_3 + a_4 = 3a_1 + 6d = 30$

$a_4 + a_5 + a_6 = 3a_1 + 12d = 48$

By solving these two equation, we can find that $(a_1, d) = (4, 3)$.

$a_k = (k - 1)d + a_1 = 3k + 1 = 31 \Rightarrow k = 10$

The answer is C

Problem Set 3

1. Assume that the common ratio is r, then

$2^{\frac{1}{3}} = r \cdot 2^{\frac{1}{2}}$. Hence,

$r = 2^{-\frac{1}{6}}$ The fourth term is $r \cdot 2^{\frac{1}{6}} = 1$.

The answer is D

2. Because it is a geometric sequence,

$775a = 5^2 \cdot 31 \cdot a = b^2$.

Therefore, there exists a positive integer k, such that $a = 31k^2$, and $5 \cdot 31k = 155k$.

$775 > 155k > 31k^2 \Rightarrow 5 > k$

Also,

$\frac{b}{a} = \frac{155k}{31k^2} = \frac{5}{k} \in \mathbb{Z} \Rightarrow k = 1$

Hence, $a = 31$.

The answer is D

3. Let's calculate directly,

$a_6 = a_1 \cdot r^5 = \frac{32}{9} \cdot \left(-\frac{3}{2}\right)^5 = -\frac{2^5}{3^2} \cdot \frac{3^5}{2^5} = -27$

The answer is C

4. Assume that the first term is a and the common ratio is r. Then,

$a + ar + ar^2 + \cdots + ar^{15} = 650$

$a + ar + ar^2 + \cdots + ar^7 = 10$

Since $1 + r + r^2 + \cdots + r^k = \frac{r^{k+1} - 1}{r - 1}$,

$650 = a(1 + r + r^2 + \cdots + r^{15}) = \frac{a(r^{16} - 1)}{r - 1}$

$10 = a(1 + r + r^2 + \cdots + r^7) = \frac{a(r^8 - 1)}{r - 1}$

By dividing them, $\frac{(r^{16} - 1)}{r^8 - 1} = r^8 + 1 = 65$ and

$r^8 = 64 = 2^6$. Therefore, $r = 2^{\frac{3}{4}}$.

The answer is E

5. Each term of the sum is in form of

$\frac{1}{n(n + 1)} = \frac{1}{n} - \frac{1}{n + 1}$. Hence,

$\frac{1}{1 \times 2} + \frac{1}{2 \times 3} + \cdots + \frac{1}{5 \times 6}$

$= \left(1 - \frac{1}{2}\right) + \left(\frac{1}{2} - \frac{1}{3}\right) + \cdots + \left(\frac{1}{5} - \frac{1}{6}\right)$

$= 1 - \frac{1}{6} = \frac{5}{6}$

The answer is C

6. Each term of the sum is in form of

$\frac{1}{n(n + 1)} = \frac{1}{n} - \frac{1}{n + 1}$. Hence,

$\frac{1}{1 \cdot 2} + \frac{1}{2 \cdot 3} + \cdots + \frac{1}{9 \cdot 10}$

$= \left(1 - \frac{1}{2}\right) + \left(\frac{1}{2} - \frac{1}{3}\right) + \cdots + \left(\frac{1}{9} - \frac{1}{10}\right)$

$= 1 - \frac{1}{10} = \frac{9}{10}$

The answer is E

MathTopia Press

7. Each term of the sum is in form of
$$\frac{1}{\sqrt{n} + \sqrt{n+1}} = \sqrt{n+1} - \sqrt{n}.$$
$$\frac{1}{\sqrt{1} + \sqrt{2}} + \frac{1}{\sqrt{2} + \sqrt{3}} + \cdots + \frac{1}{\sqrt{99} + \sqrt{100}}$$
$$= (\sqrt{2} - \sqrt{1}) + (\sqrt{3} - \sqrt{2}) + \cdots + (\sqrt{100} - \sqrt{99})$$
$$\sqrt{100} - \sqrt{1} = 9$$
The answer is E

8. Each term is in form of
$$1 - \frac{1}{n^2} = \frac{n^2 - 1}{n^2} = \frac{(n-1)(n-1)}{n^2}.$$
Therefore, the product is
$$\frac{(1 \cdot 3)(2 \cdot 4) \cdots (9 \cdot 11)}{2^2 \cdot 3^2 \cdots 10^2} = \frac{9! \cdot \frac{11!}{2}}{(10!)^2} = \frac{\frac{11}{2}}{10} = \frac{11}{20}$$
The answer is E

9. Each term of the sum is in form of
$(2n - 1)(4n - 1)$. Therefore,
$$\sum_{n=1}^{9} (2n - 1)(4n - 1) = \sum_{n=1}^{9} (8n^2 - 6n + 1)$$
$$= 8 \sum_{n=1}^{9} n^2 - 6 \sum_{n=1}^{9} n + \sum_{n=1}^{9} 1$$
$$= \frac{8 \cdot 9 \cdot 10 \cdot 19}{6} - \frac{6 \cdot 9 \cdot 10}{2} + 9 = 2019$$
The answer is E

10. Each term of the sum is in form of
$$\frac{1}{n(n+2)} = \frac{1}{2}\left(\frac{1}{n} - \frac{1}{n+2}\right)$$
Hence,
$$\frac{1}{1 \cdot 3} + \frac{1}{3 \cdot 5} + \cdots + \frac{1}{19 \cdot 21}$$
$$= \frac{1}{2}\left(\left(1 - \frac{1}{3}\right) + \left(\frac{1}{3} - \frac{1}{5}\right) + \cdots + \left(\frac{1}{19} - \frac{1}{21}\right)\right)$$
$$= \frac{1}{2}\left(1 - \frac{1}{21}\right) = \frac{10}{21}$$
The answer is A

11. Each term in the product is in form of
$$n + \frac{n}{n+1} = \frac{n^2 + 2n}{n+1} = \frac{n(n+2)}{n+1}.$$
Hence, the product is
$$\frac{1 \cdot 3}{2} \cdot \frac{2 \cdot 4}{3} \cdots \frac{10 \cdot 12}{11} = \frac{10! \cdot \frac{12!}{2}}{11!} = 10! \cdot 6$$
The answer is E

12. Each term of the sum is in form of
$n(n!) = (n + 1 - 1)n! = (n+1)! - n!.$
Therefore, the sum is
$$(2! - 1!) + (3! - 2!) + \cdots + (11! - 10!) = 11! - 1$$
The answer is A

MathTopia Press

MathTopia Press

CHAPTER 16

FUNCTIONS and OPERATIONS

1. FUNCTIONS

> **Definition 16.1 — FUNCTIONS.**
>
> A function is an association between two sets (called the domain and co domain) so that each element in the domain (INPUT) is associated with one and only one element in the co domain (OUTPUT) by a rule. The set of all images in the co domain is called the range of the function.

$f : R \rightarrow R, f(x) = 3x+1$

- f is called the **name** of the function.
- R, the set of real numbers, is the **domain** of f .
- R is also the **range** of f , in this case also the co domain
- The rule of f is f (x) = 3x+1.

The Function Machine Metaphor: This metaphor portrays a function as a machine that generates input-output ordered pairs, such that each input has one and only one output. The DOMAIN of a function is the set of inputs. The RANGE of a function is the set of all outputs. This must be equal to, or a subset of, the Co-domain. The RULE of a function is the rule by which an input generates an output. The RULE of a

function is the rule by which an input generates an output.

If f is the name of a function then a statement like f(x) = x²+1 defines the rule for the function. This particular rule means that for every input element x in the domain, the machine goes to work, squares the input and then adds 1, to get the output. We write, for example, f(3) = 3²+1 = 10. We say that f(x) is the IMAGE of x for the function f .

> **Example 16.1**
>
> Suppose we want to find r(4) for $r(x) = \dfrac{2x}{x^2-16}$.
>
> Substitution gives $r(4) = \dfrac{2(4)}{(4)^2-16} = \dfrac{6}{0}$
>
> which is undefined. The number 4 is not an allowable input to the function r; in other words, 4 is not in the domain of r. The reason r(4) is undefined is because substitution results in a division by 0.

> **Example 16.2**
>
> If f(x) = 3x+7, what is f(5)? f(5) = 3 · (5)+7 = 22

Problem 16.1

Find the domain of the following functions.

1. $g(x) = \sqrt{3-2x}$

2. $h(x) = \sqrt[3]{6-3x}$

3. $f(x) = \dfrac{4}{1-\dfrac{2x}{x-3}}$

Solution

Function g is not defined if the radicand is negative. To avoid this, we set $3-2x \geq 0$.

From this, we get $2x \leq 3$ or $x \leq \dfrac{3}{2}$.

The domain is $\left(-\infty, \dfrac{3}{2}\right]$.

The formula for h(x) involves an odd indexed root (the cube root). Since odd roots of real numbers (even negative real numbers) are real numbers, there is no restriction on the inputs to h. Hence, the domain is $(-\infty, \infty)$.

In the expression for f, there are two denominators. We need to make sure neither of them is 0. To that end, we set each denominator equal to 0 and solve. For the 'small' denominator, we get $x-3 = 0$ or $x = 3$. For the 'large' denominator

$$1 - \frac{2x}{x-3} = 0$$

$$1 = \frac{2x}{x-3}$$

$$(1)(x-3) = \left(\frac{2x}{x-3}\right)(x-3) \quad \text{clear denominators}$$

$$x-3 = 2x$$

$$-3 = x$$

So we get two real numbers which make denominators 0, namely $x = -3$ and $x = 3$. Our domain is all real numbers except -3 and 3.

Problem 16.2

Let f be a function for which $f(3x+1) = x^2+x+3$, what is f(4)?

Solution

We need to find the correct x. Solving $3x+1 = 4$ gives $x = 1$. If we let $x = 1$ in the function definition, we find $f(3 \cdot 1+1) = 1^2+1+3$, from which we obtain $f(4) = 5$

Problem 16.3

Let f be a function for which $f(3x-2) = 3x^2+5$, what is f(1)?

Solution

Again, we need to find the correct x. Solving $3x-2 = 1$ gives $x = 1$. If we let $x = 1$ in the function definition, we find $f(3 \cdot 1-2) = 3 \cdot 1^2+5$, from which we obtain $f(1) = 8$

Problem 16.4

Let f be a function for which $f(x) = \dfrac{x+2}{x-2}$, find the value of a such that $f(a) = 2$.

Solution

If we express $f(a) = \dfrac{a+2}{a-2}$, then solving $\dfrac{a+2}{a-2} = 2$ gives $a = 6$.

Problem 16.5

Let $f(2x+1) = 3 f(x)+2$ Given that $f(1) = 0$, find f(11).

Solution

We can start by replacing $x = 1$, then $f(3) = 3 f(1)+2 = 2$. For $x = 3$, $f(1) = 3 f(3)+2 = 8$. Finally, for $x = 5$ gives $f(11) = 3 f(5)+2 = 26$

Problem 16.6

The function g is defined by $g(x+1) = g(x)+g(x-1)$ where $g(6) = 11$ and $g(4) = 5$ are given. What is the value of g(1)?

Solution

By replacing x = 5 we get g(6) = g(5)+g(4)

$$\Rightarrow 11 = g(5)+5 \Rightarrow g(5) = 6$$

By replacing x = 4 we get g(5) = g(4)+g(3)

$$\Rightarrow 6 = 5+g(3) \Rightarrow g(3) = 1$$

By replacing x = 3 we get g(4) = g(3)+g(2)

$$\Rightarrow 5 = 1+g(2) \Rightarrow g(2) = 4$$

By replacing x = we get g(3) = g(2)+g(1)

$$\Rightarrow 1 = 4+g(1) \Rightarrow g(1) = -3$$

Problem 16.7

Let f be a function satisfying f (2x+4) = x^2-2. Find

1. f(8)
2. f(1)
3. f(x)

Solution

We need to make all inputs equal to 2x+4 .

1. We need 2x+4 = 8 $\Rightarrow$ x = 2.

   Hence f(8) = f(2(2)+4) = 2^2-2 = 2.

2. We need 2x+4 = 1 $\Rightarrow$ x = $-\frac{3}{2}$.

   Hence f(1) = $f\left(2\left(-\frac{3}{2}\right)+4\right) = \left(-\frac{3}{2}\right)^2 -2 = \frac{1}{4}$.

3. We rewrite the function with a different variable and rename the dummy variable:

   say f(2a+4) = a^2-2.

   We need 2a+4 = x $\Rightarrow$ a = $\frac{x-4}{2}$.

   Hence f(x) = $f\left(2\left(\frac{x-4}{2}\right)+4\right) = \left(\frac{x-4}{2}\right)^2 - 2$

   $$= \frac{x^2}{4} - 2x+2.$$

Problem 16.8

Let f be a function satisfying

f(6) = 2 and f(x+6) = f(6) f(x). Find f(−6).

Solution

Since we want to find f(−6), we first put x = −6 in the relation, obtaining

f(0) = f(6) f(−6)

Thus we must also know f(0). Letting x = 0 in the relation,

f(6) = f(6) f(0) $\Rightarrow$ f(6) = f(6) f(6) f(−6)

$$\Rightarrow 2 = 4f(-6) \Rightarrow f(-6) = \frac{1}{2}.$$

Problem 16.9

The function f is defined for all positive integers such

f(a)+ f(b) = f(ab)

for all positive integer a and b.

If f(4) = 14, f(3) = 10, then find f(6).

Solution 1

Note that f(3)+ f(4) = f(12) = 24 we can then write f(12) as f(2) + f(2) + f(3).

From here we can find f(2) = 7.

Rewriting f(12) = f(2)+f(6) gives us f(6) = 17

Solution 2

We start by breaking down the first given information

f(4) = f(2)+ f(2) = 14 = 2f(2) $\Rightarrow$ f(2) = 7

Since we want f(6) = f(2·3)

f(6) = f (2·3) = f(2)+ f(3) = 7+10 = 17

Problem 16.10

Let h be given by h(1−x) = 2x. Find h(3x).

Solution

Rewrite the function with a new variable, say h(1−s) = 2s. Now, if 1−s = 3x then s = 1−3x. Hence

h(3x) = h(1−s) = 2s = 2(1−3x) = 2−6x.

MathTopia Press

Problem 16.11

A function f satisfies $y^3f(x) = x^3f(y)$ and f(3) 0.

What is the value of $\dfrac{f(20) - f(2)}{f(3)}$?

Solution

By putting $x = 20$ and $y = 3$ in the equation $y^3f(x) = x^3f(y)$, we have $27f(20) = 8000f(3)$.
Hence

$$f(20) = \frac{8000}{27}f(3).$$

By putting $x = 2$ and $y = 3$ in the same equation, we have $27f(2) = 8f(3)$. Hence

$$f(2) = \frac{8}{27}f(3).$$

Therefore,

$$f(20) - f(2) = \frac{8000}{27}f(3) - \frac{8}{27}f(3)$$

$$\frac{f(20) - f(2)}{f(3)} = \frac{800 - 8}{27} = 296.$$

Problem 16.12

Given that $f(x) = ax + b$ where a and bare real constants, and that $f(f(f(x))) = 8x + 21$, what is the value of, $a + b$?

Solution

$f(f(x)) = f(ax+b) = a(ax+b)+b = a^2x+ab+b$
We can also write $f(f(f(x))) = f(a^2x+ab+b)$
$= a(a^2x+ab+b)+b = a^3x+a^2b+ab+b = 8x+21$.
So, $a^3 = 8$ and $a^2b+ab+b=21$
$\Rightarrow a=2$ and $4b+2b+b = 21$
$7b = 21$
$b = 3$
Therefore, $a+b = 2+3 = 5$.

Problem 16.13

Define a function f on the set of integers by

$$f(n) = \begin{cases} n - 1 & \text{if n is even} \\ n^2 - 1 & \text{if n is odd} \end{cases}$$

List all values of n for which $f(f(n)) = 8$.

Solution

Case 1: If n is even
$f(f(n)) = f(\underbrace{n-1}_{\text{odd}}) = (n-1)^2 - 1$
$\Rightarrow (n-1)^2 - 1 = 8 \Rightarrow n = -2, 4$
Case 2: If n is odd
$f(f(n)) = f(\underbrace{n^2-1}_{\text{even}}) = n^2 - 1 - 1$
$\Rightarrow n^2 - 2 = 8 \Rightarrow n \pm \sqrt{10}$

Problem 16.14

Suppose $f(x) = x^4 - x^3 + ax + b$, $f(1) = 4$, and $f(2) = 6$. What is the ordered pair (a, b)?

Solution

$f(1) = 1^4 - 1^3 + a(1) + b = 4 \Rightarrow a + b = 4 \dots 1$
$f(2) = 2^4 - 2^3 + a(2) + b = 6 \Rightarrow 2a + b = -2 \dots 2$
By solving equations 1 and 2 we get
$(a, b) = (-6, 10)$.

Problem 16.15

If $f(x) = \dfrac{2^{19} + 2^{20}}{x^2 + 2^{20}x + 2^{20}}$

find the value of $f(1) + f(2) + f(4) + f(8) + \cdots + f(2^{20})$

Solution

Notice that

$$f(2^{20}/x) = \frac{2^{19} \cdot 2^{20}/x + 2^{20}}{(2^{20})^2/x^2 + (2^{20})^2/x + 20^2}$$

$$= \frac{2^{19}x + 2^2}{x^2 + 2^{20}x + 20^{20}}, \text{ so } f(x) + f(2^{20}/x) = 1.$$

Thus the desired sum is

$(f(1) + f(2^{20})) + (f(2) + f(2^{19})) + \cdots (f(2^9) + f(2^{11})) +$

$\dfrac{1}{2}(f(2^{10}) + f(2^{10})) = \dfrac{21}{2}$.

MathTopia Press

2. OPERATIONS

Definition 16.2 — BINARY OPERATIONS

Operations are functions of two variables and work just like functions. Operations are written with a different notations.

For example, instead of a two variable function such as $f(x, y) = x + y - 4$, we could define an operation ∇ to mean $x \nabla y = x + y - 4$. These types of more than one input functions require careful computation and algebraic manipulation skills.

For example, the normal rules of addition, subtraction, multiplication, and division are binary operations. These might be expressed in binary operation form as

$\clubsuit(a, b) = a + b$, $\diamondsuit(a, b) = a - b$, $\heartsuit(a, b) = a \cdot b$, and $\spadesuit(a, b) = \dfrac{a}{b}$.

Problem 16.16

Let $a \Phi b = \dfrac{a}{2} + b - ab$. Compute $(4\Phi 2)\Phi 2$.

Solution

Computation yields $4\Phi 2 = (4/2) + 2 - 8 = -4$ then $4\Phi 2 = (-4/2) + 2 + 8 = 8$

Problem 16.17

Define $x * y = x^2 - y$. What is $a * (a * a)$?

Solution

$a * a = a^2 - a$ and $a * (a^2 - a) = a^2 - (a^2 - a) = a$

Problem 16.18

Let Ψ be defined as $a \Psi b = a^3 + 3a^2b + 3ab^2 + b^3 - 7$. What is $(2\Psi 3)$?

Solution

$a \Psi b = a^3 + 3a^2b + 3ab^2 + b^3 - 7 = (a + b)^3 - 7$ by replacing 2 for a and 3 for b we get $(2 + 3)^3 - 7 = 118$

Problem 16.19

For all real numbers x and y, define $x * y = x^2 - y^2$. What if $1001 * 999$?

Solution

Since $x * y = x^2 - y^2 = (x - y)(x + y)$ by replacing the given values we get $(1001 - 999)(1001 + 999) = 2 \cdot 2000 = 4000$

Problem 16.20

For all real numbers a and b, the mathematical operations are defined as $a * b = (a \triangle b) - ab$ and $a \triangle b = 2(a * b) - 5$. Find $2 * 3$.

Solution

$2 * 3 = (2\triangle 3) - 6$ and $2\triangle 3 = 2(2 * 3) - 5$

Let $2 * 3$ be x and $2\triangle 3$ be y then by solving the system of the following equation $x = y - 6$ — (1) $y = 2x - 5$ — (2) we obtain $x = 2 * 3 = 11$

Problem 16.21

For all real numbers a and b, the mathematical operations are defined as

$aob = (a\triangle b) - ab$

$a\triangle b = 2(aob) - 5$

Find $1 \text{ o } 2$.

Problem 16.22

The function f(x + 1) = f(x) + 2x, where f(10) = 92.

What is the value of f(1)?

Problem 16.24

The graph to the right represents the function f(x).
What is the sum of all integers a in interval [−3, 1]
such that f(a) + f(a+4) > 0?

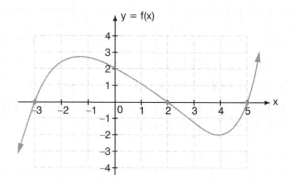

Problem 16.23

For the positive integer n, the function f(5) = 20
where f(x) = 2x + n.
What is the value of f(3)?

Problem 16.25

f(x) is a linear function and
f(x−1) + f(x+1) = 4x + 2
What is f(4)?

MathTopia Press

1. $f(x) = 2x^2 - 3x$,

   find the value of $f(3) + f(-4)$.

   A) 30   B) 34   C) 38   D) 43

   E) None of the preceding

2. If $f(x) = 5 - x - x^2$,

   and $f(-a) + f(a) = 22$, what is the positive value of a?

   A) 1   B) 2   C) 3   D) 4   E) 5

3. The symbol $\Diamond$ is defined by $x \Diamond y = x^y - y^x$.

   What is the value of $(2 \Diamond 3) \Diamond 4$?

   A) -3   B) $-\dfrac{3}{4}$ C) 0   D) $\dfrac{3}{4}$ E) 3

4. Define the operation "o" by $x \circ y = 4x - 3y + xy$, for all real numbers x and y.

   For how many real numbers y does $12 = 3 \circ y$?

   A) 0   B) 1   C) 3   D) 4   E) more than 4

5. The operation $a \spadesuit b$ is defined by

   $a \spadesuit b = ab - 2(a + b)$

   for all integers a and b.

   What is the value of $(2 \spadesuit (3 \spadesuit (4 \spadesuit (5 \spadesuit 6))))$?

   A) -4   B) -2   C) 0   D) 2   E) 3

6. Suppose that $a \ast b$ means $3a - b$.

   What is the value of x if $2 \ast (5 \ast x) = 1$?

   A) $\dfrac{1}{10}$ B) 2   C) $\dfrac{10}{3}$ D) 10   E) 14

MathTopia Press

7. If $f(x) = ax + b$ and $f^{-1}(x) = bx + a$ with a and b real, what is the value of $a + b$?

   A) –2   B) –1   C) 0   D) 1   E) 2

8. Suppose f is a function such that for every real number x,

   $f(x) + f(1 - x) = 10$ and $f(1 + x) = 4 + f(x)$.

   What is the value of $f(1)$?

   A) 4   B) 5   C) 7   D) 10   E) 14

9. The function $f(x + 1) = f(x) + 2x$, where $f(10) = 92$.

   What is the value of $f(1)$?

   A) 1   B) 2   C) 3   D) 4   E) 5

10. (1986 AJHSME -19)

    What is the 100th number in the aritmetic sequence: 1, 5, 9, 13, 17, 21, 25, ... ?

    A) 397   B) 399   C) 401   E) 403   E) 405

11. (Math Day at the Beach -2012-Individual -13)

    Let f be a function such that $f(x + y)$ $f(x)$ $f(y)$ for all real numbers x and y.

    If $f(1) = \dfrac{1}{16}$, then the value of $f(-1)$ is

    A) 16   B) $\dfrac{1}{16}$ C) $-\dfrac{1}{16}$ D) –16   E) 1

12. The graph below represents the function of f(x). What is the area of the shape bounded by f(2x) and x-axis?

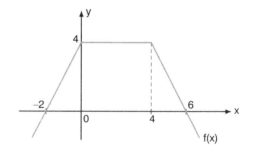

    A) 10   B) 12   C) 16   D) 24   E) 32

MathTopia Press

1. The function $f(x + 1) = f(x) + 2x$,
   where $f(10) = 92$.
   What is the value of $f(1)$?

   A) 1   B) 2   C) 3   D) 4   E) 5

4. If f is a liner function and for all real x
   $f(x + 3) = f(x) + 3$ and $f(7) = 0$
   What is $f(2017)$?

   A) 2010   B) 2014   C) 2017   D) 2018   E) 2020

2. The function $f(x + 1) = f(x + 2) + 2x$,
   where $f(4) = 5$.
   Find the value of $f(7)$.

   A) −19   B) −15   C) 0   D) 1   E) 2

5. Let $f(x) = \begin{cases} x + 5 & \text{if} & x \le -4 \\ \sqrt{9 - x^2} & \text{if} & -4 < x \le -4 \\ -x + 5 & \text{if} & x > 4 \end{cases}$

   Compute the value of $f(0) + f(-5) + f(6)$.

   A) 1   B) 2   C) 3   D) 6   E) None

3. If $f\left(\dfrac{7}{x}\right) = x + 3 \cdot f\left(\dfrac{x}{7}\right)$ then what is the value of
   $f(1)$?

   A) $-\dfrac{1}{2}$ B) $-\dfrac{3}{2}$ C) $-\dfrac{5}{2}$ D) $-\dfrac{7}{2}$ E) $\dfrac{1}{2}$

6. Which of the following is in the domain of the
   function $f(x) = \dfrac{\sqrt{5 - x}}{x^2 - 36}$?

   A) −6   B) −4   C) 6   D) 7   E) 8

MathTopia Press

7. An on-line used-book store charges shipping costs according to the following formula

$$P(n) = \begin{cases} 3.5n + 4 & \text{if } \quad 1 \le n \le 14 \\ 0 & \text{if } \quad n > 14 \end{cases}$$

where n is the number of books purchased and P(n) is the shipping cost in dollars.

What is the cost to ship 6 books?

A) 15   B) 22.5   C) 24   D) 25   E) 27

8. If $f(4x) = 4 \cdot f(x) + 3$ and $f(2) = 3$, then what is $f(10)$?

A) 15   B) 16   C) 19   D) 21   E) 25

9. Consider the function $f(x) = \frac{x}{3} \cdot f(x+1)$, where $f(5) = \frac{3}{2}$.

What is the value of $f(3)$?

A) 4   B) 3   C) 2   D) 1   E) 0

10. The exponential function f(x) is defined by $f(x) = 3^{x+1}$. Find the function $f(2x + 1)$ in terms of the function f(x).

A) $f^2(x)$ B) $3f^2(x)$ C) $f^2(x) + 3$ D) $3f^2(x) + 1$ E) $f(x)$

11. If $f(x + \frac{1}{x}) = x^2 + \frac{1}{x^2}$,

then which of the following is equal to f (x)?

A) $f(x) = x^2 + 1$ B) $f(x) = x^2 - 1$ C) $f(x) = x^2 - 2$ D) $f(x) = x^2 - 4$ E) $f(x) = 4x + 1$

12. A function f is such that

$f(x) - f(x - 1) = 4x - q$

If $(fx) = 2x^2 + px + q$,

what is $p + q$?

A) –4   B) –3   C) 0   D) 4   E) 5

MathTopia Press

1. The function f is defined as follows.

   • x + 1, If x is integer

   • 2x, If x is not integer

   Which of the following is equal to f(5) + f(f(1/4))?

   A) 8   B) 7   C) $\frac{13}{2}$ D) $\frac{11}{2}$ E) $\frac{15}{2}$

2. For all real numbers a and b, the mathematical operation $*$ and $\odot$ are defined as $a * b = 2a + b$ and $a \odot b = a + b^2$. Find $1 * (2 \odot 3)$.

   A) 13   B) 11   C) 9   D) 7   E) 6

3. Let $a @ b = \frac{a}{2} + b$.

   What is $2 @ 4 - 6 @ 2$?

   A) –2   B) –1   C) 0   D) 2   E) 4

4. Let $m * n = m^n - n * m$. What is $3 * (2 * 1)$?

   A) 1   B) 2   C) 3   D) –1   E) None

5. Let Ψ be define as

   $a\Psi b = a^3 + 3a^2b + 3ab^2 + b^3 + 7$.

   What is $(3\Psi - 5)$?

   A) –1   B) 0   C) 3   D) 8   E) 15

6. For all real numbers x and y, define $x * y = x^2 - y^2$.

   What if $101 * 99$?

   A) 101   B) 200   C) 202   D) 9999   E) None

MathTopia Press

7. Let $a \otimes b = \sqrt{a^2 + b^2}$.

   Find the sum of all values of n such that $2n \otimes n = 5$?

   A) 0   B) 4   C) 5   D) 6   E) 8

8. If $f(x) = ax^3 + x + 4$ and $f(-5) = 6$ then what is $f(5)$?

   A) 1   B) 2   C) 4   D) 6   E) 8

9. For all real numbers a and b, the mathematical operations are defined as $a * b = (a \triangle b) - ab$ and $a \triangle b = 2(a * b) - 5$.

   Find $1 * 2$.

   A) 3   B) 5   C) 7   D) 8   E) 9

10. If "$*$" operation is defined as $\dfrac{4}{x * y} = \dfrac{1}{x} - \dfrac{1}{y}$.

    What is the value of $3 * 5$?

    A) 15   B) 30   C) $\dfrac{15}{2}$ D) $\dfrac{45}{2}$ E) None

11. For all real numbers the operation "$\triangle$" is defined as $2^{a \triangle b} = \dfrac{4^{a-b}}{2}$. Find $4 \triangle 2$.

    A) 0   B) 1   C) 2   D) 3   E) 4

12. For all positive real numbers operation "$\otimes$" is given as $x \otimes y = \dfrac{x + y}{x \otimes y}$

    A) −6   B) −3   C) 0   D) 3   E) 6

MathTopia Press

Problem Set 1

1. Let's calculate directly, $f(3) + f(-4)$

$= (2 \cdot 3^2 - 3 \cdot 3) + \left(2 \cdot (-4)^2 - 3 \cdot (-4)\right)$

$= 9 + 44 = 53$

The answer is E

2. Firstly, calculate $f(a)$ and $f(-a)$, then sum them,

$f(a) + f(-a) = (5 - a - a^2) + (5 + a - a^2)$

$= 10 - 2a^2 = 2 \Rightarrow a^2 = 4 \Rightarrow a = \pm 2$

The positive value is $a = 2$.

The answer is B

3. Firstly, calculate $2 \diamond 3$,

$2 \diamond 3 = 2^3 - 3^2 = -1$

$\Rightarrow (2 \diamond 3) \diamond 4 = (-1) \diamond 4 = (-1)^4 - 4^{-1} = \dfrac{3}{4}$

The answer is D

4. If we calculate $3 \circ y$,

$3 \circ y = 12 - 3y + 3y = 12$

for all $y \in \mathbb{R}$.

The answer is E

5. Let's start from inner parentheses,

$5 \spadesuit 6 = 5 \cdot 6 - 2(5 + 6) = 8$

$4 \spadesuit (5 \spadesuit 6) = 4 \spadesuit 8 = 4 \cdot 8 - 2(4 + 8) = 8$

$3 \spadesuit (4 \spadesuit (5 \spadesuit 6)) = 3 \spadesuit 8 = 3 \cdot 8 - 2(3 + 8) = 2$

$2 \spadesuit (3 \spadesuit (4 \spadesuit (5 \spadesuit 6))) = 2 \spadesuit 2 = 2 \cdot 2 - 2(2 + 2)$

$= -4$

The answer is A

6. Because $a * b = 3a - b$,

$2 * (5 * x) = 2 * (15 - x) = 6 - (15 - x)$

$= x - 9 = 1 \Rightarrow x = 10$

The answer is D

7. Since $f\left(f{-1}(x)\right) = x$,

$x = f\left(f^{-1}(x)\right) = f(bx + a) = a(bx + a) + b$

$= abx + a^2 + b$

Hence, $ab = 1$ and $a^2 + b = 0$,

$ab = a(-a^2) = -a^3 = 1 \Rightarrow a = -1 \Rightarrow b = -1$

Therefore, $a + b = -2$.

The answer is A

8. For $x = 0$ in the first and the second equations,

$f(0) + f(1) = 10$

$f(1) - f(0) = 4$

By these equations, $f(1) = 7$.

The answer is C

9. If we write the equations for $x = 1, 2, \ldots, 9$

$$f(10) - f(9) = 18$$

$$f(9) - f(8) = 16$$

$$\vdots$$

$$f(2) - f(1) = 2$$

By summing them,

$f(10) - f(1) = 2 + 4 + \cdots + 18 = 90$.

Because $f(10) = 92$, $f(1) = 2$.

The answer is B

MathTopia Press

10. The common difference of the sequence is
    $d = 4$, and the first term is $a_1 = 1$. Therefore,
    $a_n = a_1 + d(n - 1) = 4n - 3 \Rightarrow a_{100} = 397$
    The answer is A

11. For $x = 1$ and $y = 0$,
    $f(1) = f(1) \cdot f(0) \Rightarrow f(0) = 1$
    For $x = 1$ and $y = -1$,
    $f(0) = f(1) \cdot f(-1) \Rightarrow 1 = \dfrac{f(-1)}{16} \Rightarrow f(-1) = 16$
    The answer is A

12. If $f(x) = 0$, then $x = -2$ or $x = 6$.
    For $g(x) = f(2x)$, $g(x) = 0 \Rightarrow x = -1$ or $x = 3$
    Also, f is constant on $[0, 4]$, then g is constant on
    $[0, 2]$. The area is
    $$\frac{(\text{Long Base} + \text{Short Base}) \cdot \text{Altitude}}{2}$$
    $$= \frac{(2 + 4) \cdot 4}{2} = 12$$
    The answer is B

Problem Set 2

1. If we write the equations for $x = 1, 2, 3, 4, 5$
    $$f(6) - f(5) = 10$$
    $$f(5) - f(4) = 8$$
    $$\vdots$$
    $$f(2) - f(1) = 2$$
    By summing them,
    $f(5) - f(1) = 2 + 4 + \cdots + 10 = 30$.
    Because $f(10) = 32$, $f(1) = 2$.
    The answer is B

2. For $x = 3, 4, 5$,
    $f(4) - f(5) = 6$
    $f(5) - f(6) = 8$
    $f(6) - f(7) = 10$
    Their sum is $f(4) - f(7) = 24$.
    Because $f(4) = 5$, $f(7) = -19$.
    The answer is A

3. For $x = 7$,
    $f(1) = 7 + 3f(1) \Rightarrow f(1) = -\dfrac{7}{2}$
    The answer is D

4. For $f(x) = ax + b$,
    $f(x + 3) = f(x) + 3 \Rightarrow ax + 3a + b$
    $= ax + b + 3 \Rightarrow a = 1$
    $f(7) = 0 \Rightarrow 7a + b = 7 + b = 0 \Rightarrow b = -7$
    Hence, $f(x) = x - 7$, and $f(2017) = 2010$.
    The answer is A

5. Let's calculate directly,
    $f(0) + f(-5) + f(6)$
    $= \sqrt{16 - 0^2} + (-5 + 5) + (-6 + 5)$
    $= 4 + 0 - 1 = 3$
    The answer is C

6. -6 is not in the domain because $(-6)^2 - 36 = 0$.
    $x = 6, 7, 8$ are not in the domain because
    $5 - x < 0$ for these values.
    Only -4 is in the domain.
    The answer is B

MathTopia Press

7. Let's calculate,

    $P(6) = 3.5 \cdot 6 + 4 = 21 + 4 = 25$

    The answer is D

8. Assume that $f(x) = ax + b$,

    $f(4x) = 4f(x) + 3 \Rightarrow 4ax + b = 4ax + 4b + 3$

    $\Rightarrow b = -1$

    $f(2) = 3 \Rightarrow 2a - 1 = 3 \Rightarrow a = 2$

    Hence, $f(x) = 2x - 1$, and $f(10) = 19$.

    The answer is C

9. For $x = 3$, $f(4) = f(3)$. For $x = 4$,

    $\dfrac{4}{3}f(5) = f(4) = f(3) \Rightarrow f(3) = \dfrac{4}{3} \cdot \dfrac{3}{2} = 2$

    The answer is C

10. Let's calculate directly,

    $f(2x + 1) = 3^{2x+2} = (3^{x+1})^2 = f^2(x)$

    The answer is A

11. For $x = 1$, $f(2) = 2$. Only $f(x) = x^2 - 2$ satisfies.

    $f\left(x + \dfrac{1}{x}\right) = \left(x + \dfrac{1}{x}\right)^2 - 2 = x^2 + \dfrac{1}{x^2}$ is true.

    The answer is C

12. If we write $f(x) = 2x^2 + px + q$,

    $f(x) - f(x - 1)$

    $= 2x^2 + px + q - 2(x - 1)^2 - p(x - 1) - q$

    $= 4x + p - 2 = 4x - q \Rightarrow p + q = 2$

    The answer is D

Problem Set 3

1. Firstly, $f(5) = 6$. Let's calculate $f\left(\dfrac{1}{4}\right)$,

    $f\left(\dfrac{1}{4}\right) = \dfrac{1}{2} \Rightarrow f\left(f\left(\dfrac{1}{4}\right)\right) = f\left(\dfrac{1}{2}\right) = 1$

    Hence, $f(5) + f\left(f\left(\dfrac{1}{4}\right)\right) = 6 + 1 = 7$.

    The answer is B

2. Let's calculate directly,

    $2 \odot 3 = 2 + 3^2 = 11 \Rightarrow 1 * (2 \odot 3) = 1 * 11$

    $= 2 + 11 = 13$

    The answer is A

3. Let's calculate directly,

    $2@4 - 6@2 = (1 + 4) - (3 + 2) = 0$

    The answer is C

4. Let's calculate directly,

    $2 * 1 = 2^1 - 2 \cdot 1 = 0 \Rightarrow 3 * (2 * 1) = 3 * 0$

    $= 3^0 - 3 \cdot 0 = 1$

    The answer is A

MathTopia Press

5. It can be seen that
    $a^3 + 3a^2b + 3ab^2 + b^3 + 7 = (a + b)^3 + 7$
    Therefore,
    $3\psi(-5) = (3 - 5)^3 + 7 = -8 + 7 = -1$
    The answer is A

6. Let's calculate directly,
    $101 * 99 = 101^2 - 99^2 = (101 + 99)(101 - 99)$
    $= 400$
    The answer is E

7. $2n \otimes n = \sqrt{4n^2 + n^2} = 5$ implies $n^2 = 5$.
    Therefore, $n = \pm\sqrt{5}$.
    Sum of values of n is 0.
    The answer is A

8. Let's calculate $f(-5)$,
    $f(-5) = -125a - 5 + 4 = 6 \Rightarrow 125a = -7$
    By that,
    $f(5) = 125a + 5 + 4 = -7 + 9 = 2$
    The answer is B

9. For $1 * 2 = x$ and $1\triangle2 = y$,
    $x = y - 1 \cdot 2 = y - 2$ and $y = 2x - 5$
    $\Rightarrow x = y - 2 = 2x - 5 \Rightarrow x = 1 * 2 = 7$
    The answer is C

10. Because $x * y = \dfrac{4}{\dfrac{1}{x} - \dfrac{1}{y}}$,
    $3 * 5 = \dfrac{4}{\dfrac{1}{3} - \dfrac{1}{5}} = \dfrac{4}{\dfrac{2}{15}} = 30$
    The answer is B

11. Let's calculate directly,
    $2^{4\triangle2} = \dfrac{4^{4-2}}{2} = 8 = 2^3 \Rightarrow 4\triangle2 = 3$
    The answer is D

12. $1 * 2 = (1\triangle2) - 2$ and $1\triangle2 = 2(1 * 2) - 5$
    Let $1 * 2$ be x and $1\triangle2$ be y then by solving of
    the system of equation
    $x = y - 2$
    $y = 2x - 5$
    We get $x = 1 * 2 = 7$
    The answer is C

POLYNOMIALS

Definition 17.1 — Polynomial

A polynomial is any expression that consist of variables and coefficients where all variables are only non-negative integer powers. In general, a polynomial with degree of n is

$$P(x) = a_n x^n + a_{n-1} x^{n-1} + \ldots + a_1 x_1 + a_0$$

for some collection of constants $a_0, a_1, \ldots, a_n$, with the leading coefficient $a_n \neq 0$. We will assume that these constants are all real numbers.

Monomial: one-term expressions such as x, 7, $8x^2$, etc.

Binomial: two-term expressions such as $x^2 + 7$, $x + 7$, $3 + x^2$, etc.

Example 17.1

The expression $\sqrt{x^3}$ and $\dfrac{x^3 + 2x^2 + 1}{x + 1}$ are not polynomials.

The degree of a polynomial is the highest exponent of any term with nonzero coefficient.

Example 17.2

The polynomial $34x^4 + x^3$ has degree 4.
And $2x - 1$ has degree 1.

Definition 17.2

A root of a polynomial P(x) is any number a such that P(a) = 0.

Example 17.3

The polynomial $x^2 + 4x - 12$ factors to $(x + 6)(x - 2)$, and has two roots for $x + 6 = 0$ and $x - 2 = 0$, then $x = -6$ and $x = 2$.

Definition 17.3

A zero r of a polynomial P(x) is a number with P(r) = 0. A zero of a polynomial is also called a root of the equation P(x) = 0.

A number r is a zero of a polynomial of P(x) if and only if P(x) has a factor of the form x − r. The number of such factors gives the multiplicity of the zero.

Remark 17.1

Suppose r_1 and r_2 are zeroes of a quadratic polynomial of the form $P(x) = x^2 + bx + c$. Then

$$x^2 + bx + c = (x - r_1)(x - r_2) = x^2 - (r_1 + r_2)x + r_1 r_2,$$

so $c = r_1 r_2$ and $b = -(r_1 + r_2)$.

MathTopia Press

Remark 17.2

If $P(x)$ has degree n and is divided by linear factor $x - c$, then

$$P(x) = (x - c)Q(x) + P(c)$$

for some polynomial $Q(x)$ of degree $n - 1$. In general, if $x = c$ is a root, then $x - c$ is a factor of $P(x)$ and $P(c) = 0$.

Remark 17.3

If the zeroes of $P(x)$ are $r_1, r_2, \ldots, r_n$, then

$a_n x^n + a_{n-1} x^{n-1} + \ldots + a_1 x + a_0$
$= (x - r_1)(x - r_2) \ldots (x - r_n)$.

Problem 17.1

Let $P(x)$ be a linear polynomial with

$$P(-6) - P(2) = 12.$$

What is $P(12) - P(2)$?

Solution

$P(x) = ax + b$ is a linear polynomial.

$P(-6) - P(2) = a(-6) + b - (2a + b)$

$= -6a + \cancel{b} - 2a - \cancel{b} = -8$

$\therefore -8a = 12 \implies a = -\dfrac{3}{2}$

$P(12) - P(2) = 12a + \cancel{b} - 2a - \cancel{b} = 10a = 10(-\dfrac{3}{2})$

$= -15$

Definition 17.4

The discriminant of a quadratic $ax^2 + bx + c$ is defined to be $\Delta = b^2 - 4ac$

Remark 17.4

- If $\Delta > 0$, then the quadratic has two distinct real roots.
- If $\Delta = 0$, then the quadratic has one distinct real root (a double root).
- If $\Delta < 0$, then the quadratic has no real root.

Problem 17.2

Let $y = x^2 + bx + c$ be a quadratic function that has only one root. If b is positive, find $\dfrac{\sqrt{c}}{b}$.

Solution

Since the equation has only one root, then $b^2 - 4ac = 0$. Since $a = 1$ then we have

$b^2 = 4c \implies b = 2\sqrt{c}$

Therefore $\dfrac{\sqrt{c}}{b} = \dfrac{1}{2}$.

Problem 17.3

The roots of the polynomial $x^2 - x - 1$ are a and b. Find $a^2 + b^2$.

Solution

$a^2 + b^2 = (a + b)^2 - 2ab$

Using the root sum and product formula, we find that $a + b = 1$ and $a \cdot b = -1$

Combining these, we get

$a^2 + b^2 = (a + b)^2 - 2ab = (1)^2 - 2(-1) = 3$.

Remark 17.5

- $P(0)$ is the constant term of $P(x)$.
- $P(1)$ is the sum of the coefficients of $P(x)$: $P(1) = a_0 + a_1 + \ldots + a_n$.
- $P(-1)$ is the alternating sum of the coefficients of $P(x)$: $P(-1) = a_0 - a_1 + a_2 + \ldots + (-1)^n a_n$.

Problem 17.4

Suppose that a and b are constants and $(x + 3)(x + a) = x^2 + bx + 12$. What is b?

Solution

First, replace x with 0.

$(0 + 3)(0 + a) = 0^2 + b \cdot 0 + 12$

$3a = 12 \implies a = 4$

Second, replace x with 1.

$(1 + 3)(1 + 4) = 1 + b + 12 \implies 4 \cdot 5 = b + 13$

Therefore, $b = 7$.

MathTopia Press

Remark 17.6

The degree of the product of two polynomials is the sum of their degrees. In symbols, if p, q are polynomials, deg pq = deg p + deg q.

Example 17.4

The polynomial $P(x) = (1 + 2x + 3x^3)^4(1 - x^2)^5$ has leading coefficient $3^4(-1)^5 = -81$ and degree $3 \cdot 4 + 2 \cdot 5 = 22$.

Polynomial Divison

Long Division.

If $P(x)$ and $D(x)$ are polynomials with $D(x) \neq 0$, then there exists unique polynomials $Q(x)$ and $R(x)$, where $R(x)$ is either 0 or of degree less than the degree of $D(x)$, such that

$$P(x) = D(x) \cdot Q(x) + R(x).$$

The polynomials $P(x)$ and $D(x)$ are called the dividend and divisor, respectively, $Q(x)$ is the quotient, and $R(x)$ is the remainder.

Example 17.5

- When $P(x) = 3x^2 + 5x - 7$ is divided by $x + 2$, find the quotient and remainder by long division.

```
                 3x − 1
       x + 2)  3x² + 5x − 7
              −3x² − 6x
              ──────────
                    −x − 7
                     x + 2
                    ──────
                       −5
```

Therefore, $Q(x) = 3x - 1$ and $R(x) = -5$.

- When $P(x) = 3x^4 - 5x^3 + x^2 + 2$ is divided by $x^2 + 3$, find the quotient and remainder by long division.

```
                      3x²  −5x  −8
     x² + 3)   3x⁴  −5x³  +x²         +2
              −3x⁴        −9x²
              ───────────────────
                    −5x³−8x²
                     5x³         +15x
                    ──────────────────
                         −8x² + 15x  +2
                          8x²            + 24
                         ──────────────────
                               15x + 26
```

Therefore, $Q(x) = 3x^2 - 5x - 8$ and

$$R(x) = 15x + 26.$$

Synthetic Division

Example 17.6

Use synthetic division to find the quotient and remainder of the polynomial $2x^4 - 3x^3 - x^2 + 5x + 6$ when it is divided by $x + 1$.

```
         │  2   −3   −1    5    6
     −1  │      −2    5   −4   −1
         └─────────────────────────
            2   −5    4    1    5
```

Thus, $Q(x) = 2x^3 - 5x^2 + 4x + 1$ and $R(x) = 5$.

Problem 17.5

Find, by synthetic division the quotient and remainder of

$2x^3 - 5x^2 + 4x + 1$ when it is divided by $x - 2$.

Solution

```
     2  │  2   −5    4    1
        │       4   −2    4
        └──────────────────
           2   −1    2    5
```

$Q(x) = 2x^2 - x + 2$ and $R(x) = 5$

MathTopia Press

Problem 17.6

Let $P(x) = x^3 - 7x + 6$. Show that $P(1) = 0$, and use this fact to factor $P(x)$ completely.

Solution

If $P(1) = 0$, then $x - 1$ is a factor of $P(x)$ which leaves a remainder of 0.

By doing the synthetic division

$$
\begin{array}{r|rrrr}
1 & 1 & 0 & -7 & 6 \\
  &   & 1 & 1 & -6 \\
\hline
  & 1 & 1 & -6 & \boxed{0} \\
\end{array}
$$

We get $x^2 + x - 6$

$x^2 + x - 6 = (x + 3)(x - 2)$.

Therefore, $x^3 - 7x + 6 = (x - 1)(x + 3)(x - 2)$.

Remark 17.7 — Rational Root Theorem

Let $P(x) = a_n x^n + a_{n-1}x^{n-1} + \ldots + a_1 x + a_0$

be a polynomial with integer coefficients. If a rational number $\dfrac{p}{q}$, where p and q are relatively prime, is a root of $P(x)$, then

$$p \mid a_0 \quad \text{and} \quad q \mid a_n.$$

Problem 17.7

Factor $P(x) = x^3 - 6x + 4$

Solution

By using the Rational Root Theorem we can see that $x = 2$ is one root of the polynomial. We then use the synthetic division

$$
\begin{array}{r|rrrr}
2 & 1 & 0 & -6 & +4 \\
  &   & 2 & 4 & -4 \\
\hline
  & 1 & 2 & -1 & 0 \\
\end{array}
$$

$Q(x) = x^2 + 2x - 2$ (Prime)

Therefore, $x^3 - 6x + 4 = (x - 2)(x^2 + 2x - 2)$

Remark 17.8 — Vieta's Formula

Let r_1, r_2, r_3 be roots of the cubic equation $ax^3 + bx^2 + cx + d = 0$. Then we have

$$r_1 + r_2 + r_3 = -\frac{b}{a}, \quad r_1 r_2 + r_1 r_3 + r_2 r_3 = \frac{c}{a},$$

$$r_1 r_2 r_3 = -\frac{d}{a}.$$

Problem 17.8

The polynomial $x^3 + 3x^2 + 8x - 2$ has three roots, a, b, and c. What is the value of the sum of the reciprocals of the roots?

Solution

We want to find $\dfrac{1}{a} + \dfrac{1}{b} + \dfrac{1}{c} + = \dfrac{bc + ac + ab}{abc}$

By vieta's formula $bc + ac + ab = \dfrac{8}{1} = 8$

$abc = -\dfrac{(-2)}{1} = 2$

The answer is 4.

Problem 17.9

The cubic polynomial $x^3 + 9x^2 + 24x + 16$ has exactly two distict real roots, both of which are integers. What is the sum of these two roots?

Solution

Note that this cubic polynomial must factor into the form $(x - a)^2(x - b)$, where a and b are the integer roots.

By vieta's formula $a + a + b = -9 \Rightarrow 2a + b = -9$

$a \cdot a \cdot b = -16 \Rightarrow a^2 \cdot b = -16$

$a \cdot a + a \cdot b + ab = 24 \Rightarrow a^2 + 2ab = 24$

By solving above equations,

we get $a = -4$ and $b = -1$

$a + b = -4 - 1 = -5$

MathTopia Press

Problem 17.10

If x satisfies $x^4 + 2x^3 - 22x^2 + 2x + 1 = 0$

What is the product of the possible values of

$x + \dfrac{1}{x}$?

Solution

When we devide the equation by x^2 we get

$\left(x + \dfrac{1}{x}\right)^2 + 2\left(x + \dfrac{1}{x}\right) - 24 = 0$

$\left(x + \dfrac{1}{x}\right)^2 = x^2 + \dfrac{1}{x^2} + 2$

Therefore, the product of two the values of

$x + \dfrac{1}{x}$ is -24

Problem 17.11

A quadratic polynomial f satisfies

$f(x) \geq 0$ for all x, $f(1) = 0$ and $f(3) = 3$.

What is f(5)?

Problem 17.12

Given that

$P(x+1) = x^3 - ax^2 + 14x - b$

$P(x-1) = x^3 + x^2 - 2x - 3$

What is $a \cdot b$?

Problem 17.13

Let x_1 and x_2 be two roots of the equation

$x - 7 - \dfrac{41}{x} = 0$.

What is $\dfrac{x_1^2 - 7x_1 + 23}{4x_2^2 - 28x_2 - 100}$?

MathTopia Press

KEN KEN.

KenKen was born in a Japanese classroom in 2004 and now boasts a proven track record of academic benefits–from increasing math skills and logical thinking to developing concentration, perseverance, and determination.

RULES FOR KENKEN

Fill the grid with digits so as not to repeat a digit in any row or column, and so the digits within each heavily outlined box or boxes (called a cage) will produce the target number shown in that cage by using the operation (addition, subtraction, multiplication, or division) shown by the symbol after the numeral.

For single box cages, simply enter the number that is shown in the corner. So, for example, the notation 6+ means that the numerals in the cage should add up to 6, and the notation 48× means that by multiplying the numbers in the cage you will get 48. A 4×4 grid will use the digits 1-4. A 5×5 grid will use 1-5. A 6×6 grid will use 1-6, and so on.

MathTopia Press

Box Algebra

1. Let a and b are the roots of the equation $x^2 - 5x + 8 = 0$. Find $(a + 1)(b + 1)$.

   A) −8   B) −5   C) 8   D) 13   E) 14

2. If the two roots of the equation $x^2 - 6x - 2 = 0$ are m and n, what is $m^2 + n^2$?

   A) 32   B) 36   C) 40   D) 42   E) 44

3. Factor $21x^2 + 2x - 8$ into the form $(ax + b)(cx + d)$, where a, b, c, and d are all integers. What is $a + b + c + d$?

   A)   B)   C)   D)   E)

4. What is the remainder when $x^{41} + 41$ is divided by $x + 1$

   A) 0   B) 1   C) 39   D) 40   E) 41

5. If the expension of $(x + 3y)(ax + 9y)$ gives $3x^2 + bxy + 18y^2$, where a and b are constants, what is $a + b$?

   A) 9   B) 12   C) 15   D) 18   E) 21

6. What is the sum of the reciprocal of the roots of the equation $\frac{2020}{2021}x - \frac{1}{x} + 1 = 0$

   A) −2021   B) −2020   C) −1
           D) 2020   E) 2021

MathTopia Press

7. Find the value of a so the polynomaial
   $P(x) = x^3 - 3ax^2 + 2$ be disivible by $x + 1$.

   A) $\dfrac{1}{3}$ B) $\dfrac{1}{6}$ C) $\dfrac{4}{6}$ D) 2   E) 3

8. What is the quotient when $12x^3 - 11x^2 + 9x + 18$ divided by $4x + 3$?

   A) $3x^2 - 5x - 6$ B) $3x^2 + 5x - 6$

   C) $3x^2 + 5x + 6$ D) $3x^2 - 5x + 6$

          E) $3x^2 - 6x + 6$

9. If the polynomial $x^3 + 6x^2 + cx - 1$ divide by $x - 1$ the the remainder is 66.

   What is the value of c?

   A) 48   B) 60   C) 64   D) 66   E) 74

10. Given that $f(x) = x^4 + 3x^3 + 8x^2 - kx + 11$ is divisible by $x + 3$, find te value of k.

    A) $\dfrac{5}{6}$ B) $\dfrac{6}{7}$ C) $-\dfrac{17}{5}$ D) $-\dfrac{83}{3}$ E) $\dfrac{43}{4}$

11. $P(x)$ and $Q(x)$ are two polynomials with

    $$\frac{P(x-2)}{Q(x+1)} = x + 2.$$

    When $Q(x)$ is divided by $x-4$, the remainder is 4. What is the value of $P(1)$?

    A) 8   B) 12   C) 18   D) 20   E) 28

12. The complex numbers r_1, r_2, and r_3 are the roots of the polynomial $x^3 + 20x - 1$.

    What is the value of $r_1^2 + r_2^2 + r_3^2$?

    A) −40   B) −20   C) 0   D) 20   E) 40

MathTopia Press

1. If a, b, and c are positive numbers such that

   $(x - a)(x - b)(x^2 + x + c)$

   $= x^4 - 5x^3 + 7x^2 - 43x + 40.$

   Find $a + b + c$.

   A)   B)   C)   D)   E)

2. Let a and b be the two roots of the quadratic equation $x^2 - mx + n = 0$, and $a + b$ and ab be the two roots of the quadratic equation $x^2 - 4x + 1 = 0$.

   What is the value of $m^2 + n^2$?

   A) 9   B) 14   C) 16   D) 25   E) 26

3. Let a, b, and c are the root of the cubic equation $2x^3 - 2x^2 + 4x - 9 = 0$.

   If $\dfrac{1}{a} + \dfrac{1}{b} + \dfrac{1}{c} = \dfrac{m}{n}$,

   where m and n are relatively prime, what is the value of $m + n$?

   A) 9   B) 10   C) 11   D) 12   E) 13

4. What is the sum of all real roots of the polynomial $x^3 + 2x^2 + 2x - 20$

   A) –2   B) –4   C) 0   D) 2   E) 20

5. Given that $f(x) = x4 - ax^2 - bx + 2$ is divisible by $(x + 1)(x + 2)$, find the values of a and b.

   Find the value of $a + b = ?$

   A) 5   B) 6   C) 9   D) 10   E) 11

6. Let a, b, and c be the roots of

   $p(x) = -x^3 - 4x^2 + 8x - 2.$

   What is $a^2 + b^2 + c^2$?

   A) 12   B) 16   C) 24   D) 32   E) 36

MathTopia Press

7. Suppose one of the roots of the quadratic equation is $x^2 + 2ax + b = 0$ is $\sqrt{4 + \sqrt{12}}$.

   If a and b are rational numbers, what is the value of ab?

   A) –2   B) –1   C) $\frac{1}{2}$ D) 2   E) 3

8. Let $P(x)$ be polynomial which when divided by $x-9$ has the remainder 19, and when divided by $x-19$ has the remainder 9.

   What is the remainder when $P(x)$ is divided by $(x-9)(x-19)$?

   A) $-x + 10$ B) $x + 10$ C) 0

   D) $-x + 28$ E) $x + 28$

9. The polynomial $p(x) = x^3 - 5x^2 + cx - 12$ has three roots, two of which sum to 4. What is a?

   A) –12   B) –8   C) 0   D)   E)

10. If a, b, and c are the roots of $x^3 - x - 1 = 0$,

    what is $\dfrac{1-a}{1+a} + \dfrac{1-b}{1+b} + \dfrac{1-c}{1+c}$?

    A) –1   B) 1   C) 2   D) 4   E) 8

11. The fourth degree polynomial equation

    $x^4 - 5x^3 + 4x^2 + 3x - 2$ has four real roots, x_1, x_2, x_3, and x_4.

    What is the value of the sum $\dfrac{1}{x_1} + \dfrac{1}{x_2} + \dfrac{1}{x_3} + \dfrac{1}{x_4}$?

    Express your answer as a common fraction.

    A) $\dfrac{-2}{3}$ B) $\dfrac{-3}{4}$ C) $\dfrac{4}{3}$ D) $\dfrac{3}{3}$ E) $\dfrac{5}{2}$

12. Suppose $a \le b \le c$ and given that

    $a + b + c = -4$, $ab + ac + bc = 1$,

    and $abc = 6$, what is $a - b + c$?

    A) –4   B) 0   C) 4   D) 5   E) 6

MathTopia Press

Problem Set 1

1. Since $(a + 1)(b + 1)$
$= ab + a + b + 1$ and $a + b = 5$, $ab = 8$
by Vieta's formulas,
$(a + 1)(b + 1) = ab + a + b + 1$
$= 8 + 5 + 1 = 14$
The answer is E

2. Because $m^2 + n^2 = (m + n)^2 - 2mn$,
$m^2 + n^2 = 62 - 2 \cdot (-2) = 40$
by Vieta's formulas.
The answer is C

3. Let's calculate the roots,
$\Delta = 2^2 - 4 \cdot 21 \cdot (-8) = 676 = 26^2$
$\Rightarrow x_{1,2} = \dfrac{-2 \pm \sqrt{26^2}}{42} \Rightarrow x_1 = \dfrac{4}{7}$ and $x_2 = \dfrac{2}{3}$
Also $-\dfrac{a}{b}$ and $-\dfrac{d}{c}$ are roots.
So, we can take that $(a, b, c, d) = (3, 2, 7, -4)$.
For these values $a + b + c + d = 8$.
The answer is D

4. The remainder when $P(x)$ polynomial is divided by $x - a$ is $P(a)$. So, the remainder we are looking for is $(-1)^{41} + 41 = 40$.
The answer is D

5. Let's expand the given expression,
$(x + 3y)(ax + 9y) = ax^2 + (9 + 3a)xy + 27y^2$
$= 3x^2 + bxy + 27y^2$
Hence, $a = 3$ and $b = 9 + 3a = 18$.
Their sum is 21.
The answer is E

6. Let's reorganize the equation,
$\dfrac{2020}{2021}x - \dfrac{1}{x} + 1 = 0$
$\Rightarrow 2020x^2 + 2021x - 2021 = 0$
If a and b are roots, reciprocal of the roots is
$\dfrac{1}{a} + \dfrac{1}{b} = \dfrac{a + b}{ab} = \dfrac{-\dfrac{2021}{2020}}{-\dfrac{2021}{2020}} = 1$
by Vieta's formulas.
The answer is C

7. If $x + 1$ is divide $P(x)$ without remainder,
$P(-1) = 0$. Therefore,
$P(-1) = -1 - 3a + 2 = 1 - 3a = 0$,
and thus, $a = \dfrac{1}{3}$.
The answer is A

8. For $P(x) = 12x^3 - 11x^2 + 9x + 18$,
we can eliminate $12x^3$ by
$P(x) - 3x^2(4x + 3) = -20x^2 + 9x + 18$.
Similarly, to eliminate $-20x^2$,
$P(x) - 3 x 2(4x + 3) + 5 x (4x + 3)$
$= -20 x 2 + 9x + 18 + 5x (4x + 3)$
$= 24x + 18 = 6(4x + 3)$
$\Rightarrow P(x) = 3x^2(4x + 3) - 5x(4x + 3) + 6(4x + 3)$
$= (4x + 3)(3x^2 - 5x + 6)$
The answer is D

9. For $P(x) = x^3 + 6x^2 + cx - 1$,
It is given that $P(1) = 66$. Therefore,
$P(1) = 1 + 6 + c - 1 = c + 6 = 66 \Rightarrow c = 60$
The answer is B

MathTopia Press

10. Since f(x) is divisible by x + 3, $f(-3) = 0$.

$f(-3) = (-3)^4 + 3(-3)^3 + 8(-3)^2 + 3k + 11$

$= 83 + 3k = 0 \Rightarrow k = -\dfrac{83}{3}$

The answer is D

11. Because the remainder when Q(x) is divided by x − 4 is 4, $Q(4) = 4$. For x = 3,

$\dfrac{P(3-2)}{Q(3+1)} = \dfrac{P(1)}{3} = 5 \Rightarrow P(1) = 5Q(4) = 20$

The answer is D

12. By Vieta's formulas,

$r_1^2 + r_2^2 + r_3^2 = (r_1 + r_2 + r_3)^2 - 2(r_1r_2 + r_1r_3 + r_2r_3)$

$= 0^2 - 2 \cdot 20 = -40$

The answer is A

Problem Set 2

1. a and b are both roots of

$x^4 - 5x^3 + 7x^2 - 43x + 40$.

Assume that other two roots are x_1 and x_2.

By Vieta's theorem, $x_1 + x_2 = -1$ and $x_1x_2 = c$.

Also, $a + b + x_1 + x_2 = 5$ implies $a + b = 6$

$ab + ax_1 + ax_2 + bx_1 + bx_2 + x_1x_2$

$= ab + x_1x_2 + (a+b)(x_1 + x_2) = 7$

$\Rightarrow ab + c = 13$

$abx_1 + abx_2 + ax_1x_2 + bx_1x_2$

$= ab(x_1 + x_2) + x_1x_2(a + b) = 43$

$\Rightarrow -ab + 6c = 43$

By summing last two equations,

$7c = 56$ and $c = 8$.

Therefore $a + b + c = 6 + 8 = 14$.

The answer is E

2. By Vieta's formulas

$m^2 + n^2 = (m + n)^2 - 2mn$

$= (a + b + ab)^2 - 2(a+b)ab = 4^2 - 2 \cdot 1 = 14$

The answer is B

3. Because $\dfrac{1}{a} + \dfrac{1}{b} + \dfrac{1}{c} = \dfrac{ab + ac + bc}{abc}$,

by Vieta's formulas

$\dfrac{ab + ac + bc}{abc} = \dfrac{\frac{4}{2}}{\frac{9}{2}} = \dfrac{4}{9}$

The answer is E

4. Let's check if this polynomial has an integer root. If r is a root, then 20 is divisible by r. If we check for 20's divisor, we can find that r = 2 satisfies. By dividing it with x − 2,

$x^3 + 2x^2 + 2x - 20 = (x - 2)(x^2 + 4x + 10)$

However, $x^2 + 4x + 10 = (x+2)^2 + 6$ has no roots.

Hence, x = 2 is the only solution.

The answer is D

5. Since f is divisible by

$(x + 1)(x + 2)$, $f(-1) = f(-2) = 0$.

$f(-1) = 3 - a + b = 0 \Rightarrow a - b = 3$

$f(-2) = 18 - 4a + 2b = 0 \Rightarrow 2a - b = 9$

By those equations, a = 6 and b = 3.

The answer is E

6. Let's calculate directly,

$a^2 + b^2 + c^2 = (a + b + c)^2 - 2(ab + ac + bc)$

$= (-4)^2 - 2(-8) = 32$

The answer is D

7. Observe that

$$4 + \sqrt{12} = 4 + 2\sqrt{3} = (\sqrt{3} + 1)^2$$

$$\Rightarrow \sqrt{4 + \sqrt{12}} = \sqrt{3} + 1$$

Assume that the other root is c.

By Vieta's formulas, $c + \sqrt{3} + 1 = -2a \in \mathbb{Q}$

Therefore, $c = d - \sqrt{3}$ for some rational number d.

$b = (d - \sqrt{3})(1 + \sqrt{3}) = d\sqrt{3} + d - 3 - \sqrt{3} \in \mathbb{Q}$

Hence, d = 1.

By that, $a = \dfrac{(\sqrt{3} + 1) + (-\sqrt{3} + 1)}{abc} = -1$, and

$b = (\sqrt{3} + 1)(-\sqrt{3} + 1) = -2$.

Their product is ab = 2.

The answer is D

8. It is given that P(9) = 19 and P(19) = 9. Assume that the remainder is ax + b, then there exists a polynomial Q such that

$P(x) = (x - 9)(x - 19)Q(x) + (ax + b)$

For x = 9 and x = 19,

9a + b = 19 and 19a + b = 9

$\Rightarrow$ (a, b) = (-1, 28)

So, the remainder is -x + 28.

The answer is D

9. By Vieta's formulas, sum of all roots is 5. Because sum of two of them is 4, other root is 1.

Hence, p(1) = a - 16 = 0, and a = 16.

The answer is E

10. If we reorganize the expression,

$$\frac{1 - a}{1 + a} + \frac{1 - b}{1 + b} + \frac{1 - c}{1 + c}$$

$$= 2\left(\frac{1}{1 + a} + \frac{1}{1 + b} + \frac{1}{1 + c}\right) - 3$$

By Vieta's formula,

$$\frac{1}{1 + a} + \frac{1}{1 + b} + \frac{1}{1 + c}$$

$$= \frac{3 + 2(a + b + c) + (ab + ac + bc)}{1 + (a + b + c) + (ab + ac + bc) + abc}$$

$$= \frac{3 + 2 \cdot 0 + (-1)}{1 + 0 + (-1) + 1} = 2$$

Therefore, the expression is equal to

$2 \cdot 2 - 3 = 1$.

The answer is B

11. The wanted expression is equal to

$$\frac{x_1 x_2 x_3 + x_1 x_2 x_4 + x_1 x_3 x_4 + x_2 x_3 x_4}{x_1 x_2 x_3 x_4} = \frac{-3}{-2} = \frac{3}{2}$$

by Vieta's formulas.

The answer is D

12. Let's define a polynomial

$P(x) = (x - a)(x - b)(x - c)$.

$P(x) = x^3 - (a + b + c)x^2 + (ab + ac + bc)x - abc$

$= x^3 + 4x^2 + x - 6$

Therefore,

$P(x) = x^3 + 4x^2 + x - 6 = (x - 1)(x + 2)(x + 3)$

As a result, 1, -2, -3 are roots.

Because a, b, c are also roots,

(a, b, c) = (-3, -2, 1).

The wanted expression is

$a - b + c = -3 + 2 + 1 = 0$.

The answer is B

MathTopia Press

MathTopia Press

SOLVING EQUATIONS

LINEAR EQUATIONS

In mathematics, a linear equation is an equation that may be put in the form where the variables are on one sides and the constants are on the other which are often real numbers. The constants may be considered as parameters of the equation, and may be arbitrary expressions, provided they do not contain any of the variables. It will be very useful to apply these methods below to solve linear equations.

Remove Denominators: When each term of the given equation is multiplied by the lowest common multiple of denominators, all the denominators of the terms can be removed after multiplying both sides by the same number. After removing the denominators, we get an algebraic expression, and we will solve the equation.

Remove Brackets: We can remove brackets by using the distributive law and the rules for removing brackets. Be careful with the minus sign before the brackets.

Move Terms: Move all the terms with the unknown variable to one side of the equation and the other terms to the other side of the equation according to the Principle for moving terms: when moving a term from one side to the other side of an equation, its sign must be changed. All unmoved terms keep their signs unchanged.

Combine Like Terms: After moving the terms, the like terms should be combined, so that the given equation is in the form $ax = b$ where a, b are constants but sometimes are unknown. An unknown constant in an equation is called a parameter

Normalize the Coefficient of x: When $a \neq 0$, we have unique solution $x = \dfrac{b}{a}$. If $a = 0$ but $b \neq 0$, the equation has no solution. If $a = b = 0$, any real value is a solution for x. In particular, when a contains parameters, a cannot be moved to the right as denominator unless it is not zero, and thus it is needed to discuss the value of a on a case by case basis.

MathTopia Press

Example 18.1

Let's follow the steps above to solve the given linear equation.

$$\left(\frac{1}{3} - \left\{\frac{1}{7}\left[\frac{x-1}{7} - 1\right] + 1\right\}\right) + 3 = 1 \iff$$

$$\frac{1}{3} - \left\{\frac{1}{7}\left[\frac{x-1}{7} - 1\right] + 1\right\} = -2$$

$$-\frac{1}{7}\left[\frac{x-1}{7} - 1\right] - 1 = -\frac{7}{3} \iff \frac{1-x}{49} + \frac{1}{7} = -\frac{4}{3}$$

$$\frac{1-x}{49} = -\frac{31}{21} \iff 21 - 21x = 49 \cdot (-31) \iff$$

$$x = \frac{1540}{21} = \frac{220}{3}$$

Problem 18.1

Given that $\dfrac{3}{2+\dfrac{1}{1+\dfrac{1+x}{1+\dfrac{1}{2}}}} = 1$, find x.

A) −2   B) −1   C) 0   D) 1   E) 2

Solution

$$\dfrac{3}{2+\dfrac{1}{1+\dfrac{1+x}{1+\dfrac{1}{2}}}} = 1 \iff 2+\dfrac{1}{1+\dfrac{1+x}{1+\dfrac{1}{2}}} = 3$$

$$\iff \dfrac{1}{1+\dfrac{1+x}{1+\dfrac{1}{2}}} = 1 \iff 1+\dfrac{1+x}{1+\dfrac{1}{2}} = 1$$

$$\iff \dfrac{1+x}{1+\dfrac{1}{2}} = 0 \iff 1+x = 0 \iff x = -1.$$

Problem 18.2

a,b be integers and $\sqrt{3}(a-b) = 2a - b + 3$, find a.

A) −3   B) −2   C) −1   D) 2   E) 3

Solution

Let's apply the rules we learned.

$$\sqrt{3}(a-b) = 2a - b + 3$$

If a,b are integers, then a = b (Irrational numbers can't be ratio of the integers)

$$a = \dfrac{b-3}{2}$$

For a = b = −3, given equality holds.

LINEAR EQUATIONS WITH ABSOLUTE VALUES

Let's examine the properties of equations with absolute values.

1. Let $a \in \mathbb{R}$ and $a \geq 0$. If $|x| = a$, then $x = a$ or $x = -a$

2. If $|x| = |y|$, then $x = y$ or $x = -y$.

3. For the absolute value equation $|x + a| + |x + b| = c$, find the roots for each absolute value separately such as x = a and x = −b. Assuming −b < −a there are three cases according to the roots found such as $-b \geq x$, $-b < x \leq -a$, $x > -a$. For each case we solve the absolute value equation and then check if the solutions satisfy the given absolute value equation.

Problem 18.3

Solve the equation $|2x + |x - 5|| = 10$

Solution

For removing multiple layers of absolute value signs, we remove them layer by layer from outer layer to inner layer. From the given equation we have $2x + |x - 5| = 10$ or $2x + |x - 5| = -10$.

From the first equation $2x + |x - 5| = 10$ we have,

$$2x + |x - 5| = 10 \iff -2x + 10 = |x - 5|$$
$$\iff -2x + 10 = x - 5 \text{ or } -2x + 10 = -x + 5$$
$$\iff x = 5$$

Problem 18.4

If $|3k - 7| - c = 14$ is an equation in k, and it has three distinct solutions, find the value of the rational number c.

Solution

From the given equation we have

$|3k - 7| - c = 14$ or $|3k - 7| - c = -14|$

if $|3k - 7| - c = 14$ has exactly one solution, then c + 14 = 0, i.e. c = −14 which implies $|3k - 7| + 14 = -14$ should be $|3k - 7| = -28$, so no solutions. Thus c ≠ −14 and $|3k - 7| - c = 14$ has two solutions, but $|3k - 7| - c = -14$ has exactly one solution, so c − 14 = 0, i.e. c = 14. In fact, when c = 14 then $|3k - 7| - c = 14$ becomes $|3k - 7| = 28$.

If 3k − 7 = 28, then $k = \dfrac{35}{2}$. If 3k − 7 = −28, then k = −7.

Problem 18.5

Given that $|a - x| + |x - a| + |2a - 2x| = 8$, what is the sum of the values of x in terms of a?

A) $-2a$ B) 0   C) $a - 2$ D) $a + 2$ E) $2a$

Solution

From the given equation we have
$|a - x| + |a - x| + 2|a - x| = 8 \iff 4|a - x| = 8$
$\iff |a - x| = 2$. If $a - x = 2$, then $x = a - 2$, if
$a - x = -2$, then $x = a + 2$, so $a - 2 + a + 2 = 2a$.

Problem 18.6

Solve equation $|x + 1| + |x| - 2|x - 1| - |x - 2| = x$.

Solution

Letting each of $|x + 1|$, $|x|$, $|x - 1|$, $|x - 2|$ be 0 we get $x = -1, 0, 1, 2$, so we get five intervals as $x \le -1$, $-1 < x \le 0$, $0 < x \le 1$, $1 < x \le 2$ and $2 < x$.

1. When $x \le -1$, then
   $-x - 1 - x - 2(-x + 1) - (-x + 2) = x \iff 0 = 5$
   ∴ no solution.

2. When $-1 < x \le 0$, then
   $x + 1 - 2(-x + 1) - (-x + 2) = x \iff x = \frac{3}{2}$
   ∴ no solution.

3. When $0 < x \le 1$, then
   $x + 1 + x - 2(-x + 1) - (-x + 2) = x \iff x = \frac{3}{4}$.

4. When $1 < x \le 2$, then
   $x + 1 + x - 2(x - 1) - (-x + 2) = x \iff 0 = 1$
   ∴ no solution.

5. When $2 < x$, $x + 1 + x - 2(x - 1) - (x - 2) = x$
   $\iff x = \frac{5}{2}$.
   Thus there are two solutions, $x = \frac{3}{4}$ and $x = \frac{5}{2}$.

Problem 18.7

If $|x - 1| + |y - 2| + z^2 - 6z + 9 = 0$ and $\frac{ax - ay^2}{2z} = 3$, find the value of a.

Solution

$|x - 1| + |y - 2| + z^2 - 6z + 9 = 0 \iff$
$|x - 1| + |y - 2| + (z - 3)^2 = 0.$

Since $|x - 1| \ge 0, |y - 2| \ge 0$ and $(z - 3)^2 \ge 0$ for any real numbers x, y, z $x - 1 = 0$, $y - 2 = 0$ and $z - 3 = 0$, i.e. $x = 1$, $y = 2$ and $z = 3$.

By substituting them into $\frac{ax - ay^2}{2z} = 3$, it follows that $\frac{a - 4a}{6} = 3 \iff -3a = 18$, therefore $a = -6$.

Problem 18.8

Given that $-1 < x < 2$, $\sqrt{x^2 + 2x + 1} + \sqrt{x^2 - 4x + 4} = ?$

Solution

$\sqrt{x^2 + 2x + 1} + \sqrt{x^2 - 4x + 4} = \sqrt{(x + 1)^2} + \sqrt{(x - 1)^2}$
$= |x + 1| + |x - 2| = x + 1 - x + 2 = 3$

Problem 18.9

Find the product of all x−values that satisfy the equation $|4x + 9| = |2x + 13|$.

Solution

If $4x + 9 = 2x + 13$, then $x = 2$ and
if $4x + 9 = -2x - 13$,
then $x = -\frac{11}{3}$, so $2 \cdot -\frac{11}{3} = -\frac{22}{3}$.

RATIONAL EQUATIONS

A rational equation is an equation containing at least one fraction where numerator and denominator are polynomials, $\frac{P(x)}{Q(x)}$.

To solve a rational equation, we find all the values of the variable that make the equation true.

Strategy for Solving Rational Equations:

1. Determine which numbers cannot be solutions of the equation.

2. Multiply both sides of the equation by the LCD of all rational expressions in the equation. This clears the equation of fractions.

3. Solve the resulting equation.

4. Check all possible solutions in the original equation.

Example 18.2

To find all solutions of $\dfrac{1}{x} + \dfrac{2}{1-x} = \dfrac{11}{x}$

First we identify the LCM of the denominators

LCD $= x(1-x)$. $\dfrac{1\,(1-x)}{x\,(1-x)} + \dfrac{2\,(x)}{(1-x)\,(x)} = \dfrac{11\,(1-x)}{x\,(1-x)}$

$1 - x + 2x = 11 - 11x \Rightarrow 1 + x = 11 - 11x$

$\Rightarrow 12x = 10 \quad x = \dfrac{10}{12} = \dfrac{5}{6}$

Problem 18.10

Find the value of x for the given equation

$$\frac{3}{4-2x} - \frac{4}{8(1-x)} = \frac{3}{2-x} + \frac{5}{2-2x}$$

A) $\dfrac{2}{5}$ B) $\dfrac{5}{3}$ C) $-\dfrac{2}{3}$ D) $-\dfrac{5}{2}$ E) $-\dfrac{2}{5}$

Solution

$\dfrac{3}{2(2-x)} - \dfrac{3}{(2-x)} = \dfrac{5}{2(1-x)} + \dfrac{1}{2(1-x)}$

$\Rightarrow -\dfrac{3}{2(2-x)} = \dfrac{3}{(1-x)} \quad 4 - 2x = -1 + x \Rightarrow x = \dfrac{5}{3}$

RADICAL EQUATIONS

Solving an Equation Containing Radicals:

Step 1: Isolate a radical term on one side of the equation.

Step 2: Raise both sides of the equation to the power that is the same as the index of the radical.

MathTopia Press

Example 18.3

$\sqrt{2x-9} = x - 6$, we first square both sides of the equation. $2x - 9 = x^2 - 12x + 36$. We rewrite the quadratic in standard form. $x^2 - 14 + 45 = 0$ $(x-9)(x-5) = 0$. So, $x = 9$ or $x = 5$.

We need to check for extraneous solution. 5 is an extaneous solution, and 9 is the solution of the equation.

Problem 18.11

Solve $\sqrt{x^2 - 2} - \sqrt{x + 4} = 0$

Solution

Step 1: Isolate the radicals $\sqrt{x^2 - 2} - \sqrt{x + 4}$

Step 2: Square both sides $\left(\sqrt{x^2-2}\right)^2 - \left(\sqrt{x+4}\right)^2$

Step 3: Solve for x

$x^2 - 2 = x + 4$

$x^2 - 2 = x + 4$

$x^2 - x - 6 = 0$

$(x + 2)(x - 3) = 0$

$x = -2$ or $x = 3$

Step 4: Check answers

$x = -2 \quad \sqrt{4-2} - \sqrt{2} = 0$

$\sqrt{2} - \sqrt{2} = 0$

$0 = 0$

$x = 3 \quad \sqrt{9-2} - \sqrt{7} = 0$

$\sqrt{7} - \sqrt{7} = 0$

$0 = 0$

Problem 18.12

Solve $\sqrt{x+2} + \sqrt{x-1} = 3$

Solution

▶ isolate $\qquad \sqrt{x+2} = 3 - \sqrt{x-1}$

▶ take square $\quad x + 2 = 3^2 - 2 \cdot 3\sqrt{x-1} + \left(\sqrt{x-1}\right)^2$

$\qquad x + 2 = 9 - 6\sqrt{x-1} + x - 1$

$\qquad x + 2 = 8 + x - 6\sqrt{x-1}$

$\qquad\qquad 6 = -6\sqrt{x-1}$

$\qquad\qquad -1 = \sqrt{x-1}$

$\qquad\qquad 1 = x - 1$

$\qquad\qquad x = 2$

Check: $\sqrt{2+2} + \sqrt{2-1} = 3$

$\qquad\qquad \sqrt{4} + \sqrt{1} = 3$

$\qquad\qquad\qquad 3 = 3$

$x = 2$ is the solution to the equation.

Problem 18.13

How many pairs (x, y) of real numbers satisfy the following system of equations?

$x^2 + xy = 2y^2$ and $y^2 - xy = 1$

Solution

From the first equation,

$x^2 + xy - 2y^2 = (x - y)(x + 2y) = 1$

That is, either $x = y$ or $x = -2y$.

If $x = y$, the second equation is transformed into $0 = 1$, which is not possible.

If $x = -2y$, the second equation is transformed into $3y^2 = 1$, i.e. $y = \pm 1/\sqrt{3}$. Thus, the solutions are $(-2/\sqrt{3}, 1/\sqrt{3})$ and $(2/\sqrt{3}, -1/\sqrt{3})$.

Problem 18.14

How many real number solutions does the equation $5^x x^2 + 125 = 5^{x+2} + 5x^2$ have?

Solution

$5^x x^2 + 125 = 5^{x+2} + 5x^2$

$\Rightarrow 5^x(x^2 - 25) - 5(x^2 - 25) = 0$

$\Rightarrow (5^x - 5)(x^2 - 25) = 0$

Thus, either $5^x = 5$ or $x^2 - 25 = 0$.

In other words, x is either 1, 5 or −5.

There are three solutions.

Problem 18.15

x and y are two numbers such that $y < |x| < x$. What is the simplified version of $|x + y| - |x| + |y|$?

Solution

Since $y < |x| < x$, we have $y < 0 < x$ and so $-y = |y| < x$, i.e. $0 < x + y$. Thus,

$$|x + y| - |x| + |y| = (x + y) - (x) + (-y) = 0$$

Problem 18.16

Suppose x and y are real numbers that satisfy $2x^2 - 3y = -\dfrac{17}{2}$ and $y^2 - 4x = 7$.

What is the value of $x + y$?

Solution

As $4x^2 - 6y = -17$ and $y^2 - 4x = 7$, we have

$0 = (4x^2 - 6y) + (y^2 - 4x) + 10$

$= (4x^2 - 4x + 1) + (y^2 - 6y + 9)$

$= (2x - 1)^2 + (y - 3)^2.$

Then $2x - 1 = 0$ and $y - 3 = 0$.

In other word, $x = \dfrac{1}{2}$ and $y = 3$.

Thus $x + y = \dfrac{7}{2}$.

MathTopia Press

Problem 18.17

Given that

$$\frac{2^{2018} + 1}{2^{2019}} = x$$

and

$$x^2 - x = -\frac{1}{4} + c,$$

compute the value of c.

Solution

We can write

$$c = x^2 - x + \frac{1}{4} = (x - \frac{1}{2})^2,$$

and observe that

$$x - \frac{1}{2} = \frac{1}{2^{2019}}.$$

Thus $c = \dfrac{1}{2^{4038}}$.

Problem 18.19

Suppose x, y, and z are real numbers such that

xy + yz = 12

2x − 3y + 2z = 0

What is the value of y2?

Problem 18.20

The real number x satisfies the equation

$$x + \frac{1}{x} = \sqrt{3}.$$

What is the value of $x^9 - 3x^7 + x^5$?

Problem 18.18

$z^2 + y^2 = 36$

$z + y = 18$

Find $\dfrac{1}{\dfrac{1}{z} + \dfrac{1}{y}}$

Solution

We knot that

$z^2 + y^2 = (z + y)^2 - 2zy$

$36 = 18^2 - 2zy$

$\Rightarrow -2zy = 288$

$\Rightarrow zy = 144$

$$\frac{1}{\frac{1}{z} + \frac{1}{y}} = \frac{1}{\frac{z+y}{zy}} = \frac{zy}{z+y} = \frac{144}{18} = 8$$

Problem 18.21

If $\dfrac{a}{bc} = 4$, $\dfrac{b}{ac} = 8$, and $\dfrac{c}{ab} = 7$,

what is the value of $\dfrac{a^2 + b^2 + c^2}{abc}$?

1. If $y < |y| < x$, then $|x + y| - |x| + |y|$ is equivalent to which of the following expressions?

   A) 0   B) $2x + 2y$ C) $2x$ D) $2y$ E) $2x - 2y$

2. For how many values of x the equation $|x - 10| = |14 - x|$

   A) 0   B) 1   C) 2   D) 3   E) 4

3. What is the sum of all the values of x that satisfy $||x - 3| - 4| = 10$?

   A) –4   B) 0   C) 4   D) 6   E) 17

4. If $\sqrt{25 - \sqrt{n}} = 3$, then the value of n is

   A) 4   B) 9   C) 16   D) 64   E) 256

5. Find the sum of all positive values of a that make the fraction $\dfrac{5}{2 - \dfrac{1}{4 - a}}$ undefined.

   A) 4   B) $\dfrac{7}{2}$ C) 6   D) $\dfrac{15}{2}$ E) $\dfrac{17}{2}$

6. If $x(x(x + 1) + 3) + 5 = x^3 + x^2 + 2x + 1$ then $x^2 - 8$ is equal to

   A) –4   B) 0   C) 4   D) 8   E) 12

MathTopia Press

7. What is the value of x satisfying

$$\frac{2}{1300x - 2600} = \frac{1}{650} - \frac{1}{651} ?$$

    A) 1303   B) 1302   C) 653   D) 650   E) 651

8. What is the value of $\dfrac{x^4 + 9}{x^2}$ if $x^2 - 6x + 3 = 0$?

    A) 9   B) 12   C) 19   D) 24   E) 30

9. What is the sum of the solutions of the equation

$$\sqrt{3x + 3} + \sqrt{x + 2} = 5$$

    A) 2   B) 3   C) 4   D) 5   E) 6

10. If $|x + 2| + (y + 3)^2 = 0$ and $ax - 3ay = 8$, find the value of a

    A) –1   B) 0   C) 1   D) 2   E) 4

11. How many real numbers x are suh that $\sqrt{2 - x/2} = 2 + x$?

    A) 0   B) 1   C) 2   D) 3   E) 4

12. The first four terms in an arithmetic sequence are $x + y$, $x - y$, xy, and $\dfrac{x}{y}$, in that order.

    What is the fifty term?

    A) $-\dfrac{15}{8}$ B) $-\dfrac{6}{5}$ C) 0   D) $\dfrac{27}{20}$ E) $\dfrac{123}{40}$

MathTopia Press

1. Find the sum of the integer values of x that satisfy $|x - 19| + |x - 20| = 5$?

   A) 17   B) 19   C) 27   D) 39   E) 49

2. If $x^{\frac{1}{2}} + x^{-\frac{1}{2}} = 6$, what is the value of $x + x^{-1}$?

   A) 4   B) 24   C) 34   D) 36   E) 38

3. What is the possible value of xy from every (x, y) real number pairs that satisfy the two equations $x^2 + y^2 = 3$ and $(x + 1)(y + 1) = 1$

   A) –3   B) –1   C) 0   D) 1   E) 2

4. If x is a real number such that

   $\sqrt{x} + \sqrt{10} = \sqrt{x + 20}$, compute x.

   A) 1   B) $\frac{3}{2}$ C) 2   D) $\frac{5}{2}$ E) 9

5. For real numbers x, y, and z the expression $x^2 + y^2 + z^2 - 2x - 4y - 9z + 10$ has a minimum value m at x = n, y = k, and z = l. What is the value of m + n + k + l?

   A) –4   B) 1   C) 2   D) 3   E) 4

6. What is the sum of all possible solutions of the equation $\dfrac{x}{x + 1} - \dfrac{2}{x - 1} = \dfrac{-4}{x^2 - 1}$

   A) 2   B) 3   C) 4   D) 6   E) 8

MathTopia Press

7. How many real number solutions does the equation
$5^x x^2 + 125 = 5^{x+2} + 5x^2$ have?

    A) 0   B) 1   C) 2   D) 3   E) 5

8. If $\sqrt{x + 3 - 4\sqrt{x - 1}} + \sqrt{x + 8 - 6\sqrt{x - 1}} = 1$,
what is the sum of all integer values that x can take?

    A) 3   B) 8   C) 9   D) 10   E) 12

9. What is the sum of all the solutions of the equation
$(x - 5)(x - 7)(x + 6)(x + 4) = 504$

    A)   B)   C)   D)   E)

10. Given that a and b positive and c is negative real numbers and $a + b + c = 0$.

    Find the value of $x^{19} - 19x + 19$, where
    $$x = \frac{b + c}{|a|} + \frac{a + c}{|b|} + \frac{a + b}{|c|}.$$

    A) −39   B) −38   C) 0   D) 37   E) 38

11. What is the sum of all the solutions of the equation
$$x^2 + 4x + \frac{4}{x} + \frac{1}{x^2} + 6 = 0$$

    A) −1   B) 0   C) 2   D) 3   E) 5

12. What is the sum of all the solutions of the equation
$$\sqrt{2x^2 + 4x + 6} + \sqrt{3(x^2 + 2x + 1) + 9} = 4 - 2x - x^2 ?$$

    A) −1   B) 0   C) 2   D) 4   E) 6

MathTopia Press

Problem Set 1

1. Since $y < |y|$, y is negative. Also, $x > |y| \geq 0$, therefore, $y < 0 < x$. So,

   $y + |y| = 0 < x + y \Rightarrow |x + y| - |x| - |y|$
   $= x + y - x - y = 0$

   The answer is A

2. There are two possibilities,

   $x - 10 = 14 - x$ or $x - 10 = x - 14$.

   The second situation is impossible, hence,

   $x - 10 = 14 - x \Rightarrow 2x = 24 \Rightarrow x = 12$

   The answer is B

3. There are two main possibilities, $|x-3| - 4 = 10$ or $|x-3| - 4 = -10$.

   The second one is impossible, therefore,

   $|x - 3| = 14 \Rightarrow x - 3 = 14$ and $x - 3 = -14$

   So, $x = 17$ or $x = -11$. Their sum is 6.

   The answer is D

4. $25 - \sqrt{n} = 9$ implies $\sqrt{n} = 16$ and $n = 256$.

   The answer is E

5. If the given expression is undefined, then denominator of a fraction is 0. There are two possibilities, $4 - a = 0$ or $2 - \dfrac{1}{4 - a} = 0$.

   In the first case, $a = 4$. Second case,

   $2 = \dfrac{1}{4 - a} \Rightarrow 4 - a = \dfrac{1}{2} \Rightarrow a = 4 - \dfrac{1}{2} = \dfrac{7}{2}$

   Their sum is $\dfrac{15}{2}$.

   The answer is D

6. If we reorganize $x(x(x + 1) + 3) + 5$, we can find that it is $x^3 + x^2 + 3x + 5$.

   By the given equality,

   $x^3 + x^2 + 3x + 5 = x^3 + x^2 + 2x + 1 \Rightarrow x = -4$
   $\Rightarrow x^2 - 8 = 8$

   The answer is D

7. Because $\dfrac{1}{650} - \dfrac{1}{651} = \dfrac{1}{650 - 651}$,

   $\dfrac{2}{1300x - 2600} = \dfrac{1}{650 \cdot 651}$

   $\Rightarrow \dfrac{2}{2x - 4} = \dfrac{1}{x - 2} = \dfrac{1}{650} \Rightarrow x = 653$

   The answer is C

8. Because 0 is not a root of

   $x^2 - 6x + 3 = 0$, $x - 6\dfrac{3}{x} = 0$, and $x + \dfrac{3}{x} = 6$

   By that

   $36 = \left(x + \dfrac{3}{x}\right)^2 = x^2 + \dfrac{9}{x^2} + 6 \Rightarrow \dfrac{x^4 + 9}{x^2} = 30$

   The answer is E

9. Let's reorganize the equation,

   $\sqrt{3x + 3} = 5 - \sqrt{x + 2}$

   $\Rightarrow 3x + 3 = 25 + x + 2 - 10\sqrt{x + 2}$

   $\Rightarrow 12 - x = 5\sqrt{x + 2}$

   $\Rightarrow 25x + 50 = x^2 - 24x + 144$

   $\Rightarrow x^2 - 49x + 94 = (x - 2)(x - 47) = 0$

   However, for $x = 47$, the equation does not hold. So, $x = 2$.

   The answer is A

10. Since $|x + 2| \geq 0$ and $(y + 3)^2 \geq 0$ for all x, y numbers,

    $|x + 2| + (y + 3)^2 = 0 \Rightarrow x = -2$ and $y = -3$

    Hence,

    $ax - 3ay = -2a + 9a = 7a = 7 \Rightarrow a = 1$

    The answer is C

11. Let's take square of the both sides,

$2 - \dfrac{x}{2} = x^2 + 4x + 4 \Rightarrow 4 - x = 2x^2 + 8x + 8$

$\Rightarrow 3x^2 + 9x + 4 = 0$

By discriminant, the roots are $x_1 = \dfrac{-9 + \sqrt{33}}{x^2}$

and $x_2 = \dfrac{-9 - \sqrt{33}}{6}$.

However, $x^2 + 2 < 0$, therefore, it cannot be a solution. Only solution is x_1.

The answer is B

12. Assume that $x = yk$ for some k real number. Since first two terms are $x + y$ and $x - y$, third and fourth terms are $x - 3y$ and $x - 5y$ respectively.

$x - 3y = xy \Rightarrow yk - 3y = y^2k \Rightarrow k - 3 = yk$

$x - 5y = \dfrac{x}{y} \Rightarrow k - 5 = \dfrac{k}{y}$

By multiplying them, $(k - 3)(k - 5) = k^2$ and by that, $k^2 - 8k + 15 = k^2$ and $k = \dfrac{15}{8}$.

By putting this value to the equations, it can be found that $x = -\dfrac{9}{8}$ and $y = -\dfrac{3}{5}$.

The fifth term is $x - 7y = \dfrac{123}{40}$.

The answer is E

Problem Set 2

1. For $x - 20 = u$, the equation becomes

$|u| + |u + 1| = 5$.

If $u < -1$, then

$|u| + |u + 1| = -u - u - 1 = -2u - 1 = 5$

$\Rightarrow u = -3$

If $-1 \le u \le 0$, then

$|u| + |u + 1| = u - u - 1 \ne 5$

There is no solution.

If $u > 0$, then

$|u| + |u + 1| = 2u + 1 = 5 \Rightarrow u = 2$

So, x can be $u + 20 = 22$ or 17. Their sum is 39.

The answer is D

2. By taking square of the both sides,

$36 = \left(x^{\frac{1}{2}} + x^{-\frac{1}{2}}\right)^2 \Rightarrow x + x^{-1} + 2 = 36$

$\Rightarrow x + x^{-1} = 34$

The answer is C

3. By $(x + 1)(y + 1) = 1$, we can obtain that

$xy + x + y = 0$.

Hence,

$x^2 + y^2 + 2(xy + x + y) = (x + y)^2 + 2(x + y) = 3$

$\Rightarrow (x + y - 1)(x + y + 3) = 0$

If $x + y = 1$, then $xy = -1$.

$(x, y) = \left(\dfrac{1-\sqrt{5}}{2}, \dfrac{1+\sqrt{5}}{2}\right)$ satisfies these.

If $x + y = -3$, then $xy = 3$. However,

$(x - y)^2 = x^2 + y^2 - 2xy = -3 < 0$ is a contradiction. xy can be only -1.

The answer is B

4. Let's take square of the both sides,

$x + 10 + 2\sqrt{10x} = x + 20 \Rightarrow \sqrt{10x} = 5$

$\Rightarrow 10x = 25 \Rightarrow x = \dfrac{5}{2}$

The answer is D

5. Let's reorganize the expression,

$x^2 + y^2 + z^2 - 2x - 4y - 8x + 10$

$= (x^2 - 2x + 1) + (y^2 - 4y + 4) + (z^2 - 8z + 16) - 11$

$= (x - 1)^2 + (y - 2)^2 + (z - 4)^2 - 11 \ge -11$

Equality holds when $(x, y, z) = (1, 2, 4)$.

Hence, $m + n + k + l = 1 + 2 + 4 + (-11) = -4$.

The answer is A

MathTopia Press

6. Let's reorganize the equation,

$$\frac{x}{x+1} - \frac{2}{x-1} = \frac{x^2 - x - 2x - 2}{x^2 - 1} = \frac{-4}{x^2 - 1}$$

$$\Rightarrow x^2 - 3x + 2 = (x-2)(x-1) = 0$$

However, $x \neq 1$ becuase the numerator will be 0.

Only solution is $x = 2$. The answer is A

7. Let's reorganize the equation,

$$(5^x - 5)x^2 = 5^{x+2} - 125 = 25(5^x - 5)$$

$$\Rightarrow 5^x = 5 \text{ or } x^2 = 25$$

So, x can be $1, -5$ or 5.

The answer is D

8. Because for a, b > 0,

$$\sqrt{a + b - 2\sqrt{ab}} = |\sqrt{a} - \sqrt{b}|$$

We can find that

$$\sqrt{x + 3 - 2\sqrt{4(x-1)}} = |2 - \sqrt{x-1}|$$

$$\sqrt{x + 8 - 2\sqrt{9(x-1)}} = |2 - \sqrt{x-1}|$$

So, $|2 - \sqrt{x-1}| + |3 - \sqrt{x-1}| = 1$.

It is happened only when $2 \leq \sqrt{x-1} \leq 3$.

By that, $5 \leq x \leq 10$.

The sum of possible values is 45.

The answer is E

9. Let's group the factors,

$$((x-5)(x+4))((x-7)(x+6))$$

$$= (x^2 - x - 20)(x^2 - x - 42)$$

$$= (x^2 - x - 31)^2 - 11^2 = 504 \Rightarrow (x^2 - x - 31)^2$$

$$= 625$$

If $x^2 - x - 31 = 25$, then

$x^2 - x - 56 = (x+7)(x-8) = 0 \Rightarrow x = -7$ or

$x = 8$

If $x^2 - x - 31 = -25$, then

$x^2 - x - 6 = (x+2)(x-3) = 0 \Rightarrow x = -2$ or

$x = 3$

Solutions are $x = -7, -2, 3, 8$, and their sum is 2.

The answer is D

10. Let's calculate x,

$$x = \frac{b+c}{|a|} + \frac{a+c}{|b|} + \frac{a+b}{|c|} = \frac{-a}{a} + \frac{-b}{b} + \frac{-c}{c}$$

$$= -1 - 1 + 1 = -1$$

Hence,

$$x^{19} - 19x + 19 = (-1)^{19} - 19(-1) + 19 = 37$$

The answer is D

11. Let's group the terms,

$$\left(x^2 + \frac{1}{x^2} + 2\right) + 4\left(x + \frac{1}{x}\right) + 4 = 0$$

$$\Rightarrow \left(x + \frac{1}{x}\right)^2 + 4\left(x + \frac{1}{x}\right) + 4 = 0$$

$$\left(x + \frac{1}{x} + 2\right)^2 = 0 \Rightarrow x + \frac{1}{x} = \frac{x^2 + 1}{x} = -2$$

$$\Rightarrow x^2 + 2x + 1 = (x+1)^2 = 0$$

So, $x = -1$.

The answer is A

12. Let $x^2 + 2x + 3 = a$, then

$$\sqrt{2a} + \sqrt{3a + 3} = 7 - a$$

$\sqrt{2a} + \sqrt{3a + 3}$ is always increasing,

but $7 - a$ is decresing.

Hence, this equation can have at most 1 solution.

By checking some integer solutions, $a = 2$ can

be found as a solution.

Hence, it is the only solution.

$$x^2 + 2x + 3 = 2 \Rightarrow x^2 + 2x + 1 = (x+1)^2 = 0$$

So, $x = -1$.

The answer is A

MathTopia Press

MY NOTES

MathTopia Press

CHAPTER 19

GEOMETRY-ALGEBRA CONNECTIONS

Definition 19.1 — Distance Formula

In the figure, $\triangle ABC$ is a right triangle.

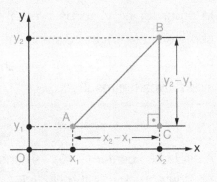

$AC = x_2 - x_1$

$BC = y_2 - y_1$

By the Pythagorean theorem,

$$AB^2 = AC^2 + BC^2$$

$$AB^2 = (x_2 - x_1)^2 + (y_2 - y_1)^2$$

and so $AB = \sqrt{(x_2 - x_1)^2 + (y_2 - y_1)^2}$ or

$$AB = \sqrt{(x_1 - x_2)^2 + (y_1 - y_2)^2}$$

Problem 19.1

A(a, 2), B(3, 4), and C(−2, 1) are given. If A is at the same distance from the points B and C, find a.

Solution

We are given AB = AC. By the distance formula between two points,

$$\sqrt{(3 - a)^2 + 2^2} = \sqrt{(a - 2)^2 + 1^2}$$

$$9 - 6a + a^2 + 4 = a^2 + 4a + 4 + 1$$

$$10a = 8$$

$$a = \frac{4}{5}.$$

Definition 19.2 — Mid-Point Formula

The point M halfway between points A and B is called the **midpoint** of line segment AB.

Consider the points A(3, 1) and B(5, 5). M is at (4, 3) on the line segment connecting A and B.

x-coordinate of A   x-coordinate of B

$$\frac{3 + 5}{2} = 4$$

x-coordinate of M

and

y-coordinate of A   y-coordinate of B

$$\frac{1 + 5}{2} = 3$$

y-coordinate of M

MathTopia Press

Problem 19.2

M is the midpoint of AB. If A is (−1, 4) and M is (2, 3), find the coordinates of B.

Solution

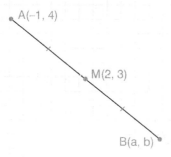

Let B have coordinates (a, b).

$$\therefore \quad \frac{a + (-1)}{2} = 2 \quad \text{and} \quad \frac{b + 4}{2} = 3$$

$$\therefore \quad a - 1 = 4 \quad \text{and} \quad b + 4 = 6$$

$$\therefore \quad a = 5 \quad \text{and} \quad b = 2$$

So, B is the point (5, 2).

Definition 19.3 — Completing The Square

The method of "completing the square" is important for changing a quadratic expression from standard form $ax^2 + bx + c$ to canonical form $a(x - k)^2 + d$

Example 19.1

The quadratic expression $x^2 - 18x + 112$ can be rewritten as $(x - a)^2 + b$.

What is the value of $a + b$?

First we take half of 18 which is 9. When we take square of 9 that goes as the last term.

So, we have $x^2 - 18x + 81 + 31 = (x - 9)^2 + 31$

Therefore, $a + b = 9 + 31 = 40$

Problem 19.3

If real numbers x and y satisfy the equation

$x^2 + y^2 - 2x - 14y + 50 = 0$,

what is the value of x + y?

Solution

We first organise the equation as

$$x^2 - 2x + \square + y^2 - 14y + \triangle = -50.$$

We need to replace 1 with $\square$ and 49 with $\triangle$. Once we add 50 on the left side then we need to add to the right side. We have $(x - 1)^2 + (y - 7)^2 = 0$

Therefore, x + y = 8

Definition 19.4 — Circle Equation

The equation of a circle centered at (a, b) with radius r is

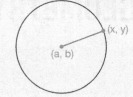

$(x - a)^2 + (y - b)^2 = r^2$.

By the distance formula, the distance between (x, y) and (a, b) is $\sqrt{(x - a)^2 + (y - b)^2}$

In order for (x, y) to be on the circle of radius r centered at (a, b), this distance must equal r, so we have $\sqrt{(x - a)^2 + (y - b)^2} = r$, and squaring both sides gives the result.

Example 19.2

A circle has center (−10, −4) and has radius 13. So, the equation of the circle is

$(x + 10)^2 + (y + 4)^2 = 13^2$

Problem 19.4

If (−2, −6) and (8, 8) are two endpoints of a diameter of a circle, what is the equation of the circle?

Solution

The mid-point (the center) is

$$\left(\frac{-2 + 8}{2}, \frac{-6 + 8}{2} \right) = (3, 1)$$

We also need to find the radius.

$r^2 = (8 - 3)^2 + (8 - 1)^2 = 25 + 49 = 74$

So, the equation of the circle is

$(x - 3)^2 + (y - 1)^2 = 74$.

MathTopia Press

Problem 19.5

Find q given that P(−2, 4) and Q(−1, q) are $\sqrt{10}$ units apart.

Solution

From P to Q, the x-step = $-1 - (-2) = 1$

and the y-step = $q - 4$

$$\therefore \quad \sqrt{1^2 + (q-4)^2} = \sqrt{10}$$

$$\therefore \quad 1 + (q-4)^2 = 10$$

$$\therefore \quad (q-4)^2 = 9$$

$$\therefore \quad q - 4 = \pm 3$$

$$\therefore \quad q = 4 \pm 3$$

$$\therefore \quad q = 1 \text{ or } 7$$

Problem 19.6

If the circle $x^2 + y^2 - 8x + 2y + 1 = 0$

has center (a, b) and radius r, what is the value of $a + b + r$?

Solution

If we organize the equation and complete the squares we get

$x^2 - 8x + 16 + y^2 + 2y + 1 = 16$

$(x - 4)^2 + (y + 1)^2 = 4^2$

So, $r = 4$, $(a, b) = (4, -1)$.

Therefore $a + b + r = 4 + 4 - 1 = 7$.

Pythagorean Theorem Applications

Remark 19.1

(Pythagoras' Theorem) For a right-angled triangle with two legs a, b and hypotenuse c, the sum of squares of legs is equal to the square of its hypotenuse, i.e. $a^2 + b^2 = c^2$.

(Inverse Theorem) If the lengths a, b, c of three sides of a triangle have the relation $a^2 + b^2 = c^2$, then the triangle must be a right-angled triangle with two legs a, b and hypotenuse c.

Problem 19.7

Given that the perimeter of a right angled triangle is $(2 + \sqrt{6})$ cm, the median on the hypotenuse is 1 cm, find the area of the triangle.

Solution

$a^2 + b^2 = 2^2 = 4$ and $a + b = \sqrt{6}$.

Therefore $6 = (a + b)^2 = a^2 + b^2 + 2ab$, so

$ab = \dfrac{6 - 4}{2} = 1$,

the area of ABC is $\dfrac{a \cdot b}{2} = \dfrac{1}{2}$.

Problem 19.8

Given that in a right triangle the length of a leg of the right angle is 11 and the lengths of the other two sides are both positive integers.

Find the perimeter of the triangle.

Solution

We have

$n^2 = m^2 + 11^2$,

$n^2 - m^2 = 11^2$,

$(n - m)(n + m) = 121 = 1 \cdot 121 = 11 \cdot 11$,

therefore the only pair works is n = 61 and m = 60.

Thus, the perimeter is $11 + 61 + 60 = 132$.

Problem 19.9

Two sides of an isosceles triangle △ABC have lengths 9 and 4. What is the area of △ABC?

Solution

The third side must be 9 (Why?).

$$h^2 = 9^2 - 2^2$$
$$h = \sqrt{77}$$

The are of the triangle is $\dfrac{4\sqrt{77}}{2} = 2 = \sqrt{77}$

MathTopia Press

Problem 19.10

A rectangle has area 120 cm² and perimeter 46 cm. Find the length of one of its diagonals.

Solution

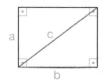

$$a \cdot b = 120$$
$$2a + 2b = 46 \Rightarrow a + b = 23$$

$$d = \sqrt{a^2 + b^2} = \sqrt{(a + b)^2 - 2ab} = \sqrt{23^2 - 2(120)}$$
$$d = \sqrt{529 - 240} = \sqrt{289}$$
$$d = 17$$

Trigonometry Basic

Definition 19.5

For an angle $0 < \alpha < 90°$, let $\triangle ABC$ be a right triangle with $\angle C = 90°$ such that $\angle BAC = \alpha$:

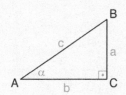

We define the sine, cosine, tangent, cosecant, secant, and cotangent functions as follows:

$$\sin \alpha = \frac{a}{c} \qquad \csc \alpha = \frac{1}{\sin \alpha} = \frac{c}{a}$$

$$\cos \alpha = \frac{b}{c} \qquad \sec \alpha = \frac{1}{\cos \alpha} = \frac{c}{b}$$

$$\tan \alpha = \frac{a}{b} \qquad \cot \alpha = \frac{1}{\tan \alpha} = \frac{b}{a}$$

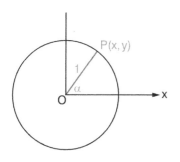

It is good to know sine, cosine, tangent of commonly used angles:

$$\sin 0° = 0 \qquad \sin 30° = \frac{1}{2} \qquad \sin 45° = \frac{\sqrt{2}}{2}$$

$$\sin 60° = \frac{\sqrt{3}}{2} \qquad \sin 90° = 1$$

$$\cos 0° = 1 \qquad \cos 30° = \frac{\sqrt{3}}{2} \qquad \cos 45° = \frac{\sqrt{2}}{2}$$

$$\cos 60° = \frac{1}{2} \qquad \cos 90° = 0$$

$$\tan 0° = 0 \qquad \tan 30° = \frac{\sqrt{3}}{3} \qquad \tan 45° = 1$$

$$\tan 60° = \sqrt{3} \qquad \tan 90° = \text{undefined}$$

The values of some other angles outside $[0°, 90°]$ (for example 120° or 150°) can be derived using the identities below:

Basic Identities

From the unit circle definition of cosine and sine, we can derive the following identities for any angle a (try to see them yourself):

- $\sin^2 \alpha + \cos^2 \alpha = 1$ (Pythagorean Identity)
- $\sin(90° - \alpha) = \cos \alpha$
- $\cos(-\alpha) = \cos \alpha$ and $\sin(-\alpha) = -\sin \alpha$
- $\sin(180° - \alpha) = \sin \alpha$ and $\cos(180 - \alpha) = -\cos \alpha$
- $\sin(\alpha + 360°) = \sin \alpha$ and $\cos(\alpha + 360°) = \cos \alpha$

Remark 19.2

Sum & Difference Identities

For any real x, y,

1. $\sin(x - y) = \sin x \cos y - \cos x \sin y$
2. $\cos(x - y) = \cos x \cos y + \sin x \sin y$
3. $\tan(x - y) = \dfrac{\tan x - \tan y}{1 + \tan x \tan y}$

Problem 19.11

Find $\sin 75°$.

Solution

We find that $\sin 75° = \sin(30 + 45)$
$$= \sin(30)\cos(45) + \sin(45)\cos(30) = \frac{\sqrt{6} + \sqrt{2}}{4}.$$

MathTopia Press

Example 19.3

Evaluate the ratio named by using the given ratio:

a) $\tan\theta$, if $\cot\theta = \dfrac{2}{3}$

If $\cot\theta = \dfrac{2}{3}$, then $\tan\theta = \dfrac{3}{2}$
(the reciprocal of $\cot\theta$).

b) $\sin\alpha$, if $\csc\alpha = 1.25$

If $\csc\alpha = 1.25$ or $\dfrac{5}{4}$, then $\sin\alpha = \dfrac{4}{5}$
(the reciprocal of $\csc\alpha$).

c) $\sec\beta$, if $\cos\beta = \dfrac{\sqrt{3}}{2}$

if $\cos\beta = \dfrac{\sqrt{3}}{2}$, then $\cos\beta = \dfrac{2}{\sqrt{3}}$ or $\dfrac{2\sqrt{3}}{3}$
(the reciprocal of $\csc\beta$).

d) $\csc\gamma$, if $\sin\gamma = 1$

if $\sin\gamma = 1$, then $\csc\gamma = 1$
(the reciprocal of $\sin\gamma$).

Problem 19.12

In right triangle ABC (not shown), $\sin\alpha = \dfrac{2}{3}$.
Find $\cos\alpha$.

Solution

$$\sin^2\alpha + \cos^2\alpha = 1$$
$$\left(\dfrac{2}{3}\right) + \cos^2\alpha = 1$$
$$\dfrac{4}{9} + \cos^2\alpha = 1$$
$$\cos^2\alpha = \dfrac{5}{9} \quad \cos\alpha = \dfrac{\sqrt{5}}{3}$$

Remark 19.3 — The Law of Cosines

In any $\triangle ABC$ with sides a, b, and c units in length, and opposite angles A, B, and C respectively:

$$a^2 = b^2 + c^2 - 2bc\cos A$$
$$\text{or } b^2 = a^2 + c^2 - 2ac\cos B$$
$$\text{or } c^2 = a^2 + b^2 - 2ab\cos C$$

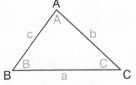

Problem 19.13

Find the length of $\overline{AB}$ in the triangle in Figure 11.43.

Solution

Referring to the 30° angle as γ, we use the following from the Law of Cosines:

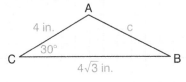

$$c^2 = a^2 + b^2 - 2ab\cos\gamma$$
$$c^2 = (4\sqrt{3})^2 - 4^2 - 2\cdot 4\sqrt{3}\cdot 4\cdot\cos 30°$$
$$c^2 = 48 + 16 - 2\cdot 4\sqrt{3}\cdot 4\cdot\dfrac{\sqrt{3}}{2}$$
$$c^2 = 48 + 16 - 48$$
$$c^2 = 16$$
$$c = 4$$

Therefore, AB = 4 in.

Problem 19.14

Find, to the nearest tenth, the diameter of the circle circumscribed about $\triangle ABC$.

Solution

According to the law of Cosines

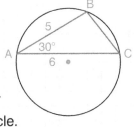

$$(BC)^2 = 5^2 + 6^2 - 2(5)(6)(\cos 30°)$$
$$= 25 + 36 - \dfrac{60\sqrt{3}}{2}$$
$$= 61 - 30\sqrt{3}$$
$$BC \approx 3.006$$

We now use the formula for the diameter of a circumcircle.

$$D = \dfrac{a}{\sin\angle A}$$
$$\approx \dfrac{3.006}{\sin 30°}$$
$$\approx \dfrac{3.006}{\dfrac{1}{2}} \approx 6.0$$

MathTopia Press

Problem 19.15

Let x be a real number such that $\sec x - \tan x = 2$.
Then evaluate $\sec x + \tan x$.

Solution

Use the identity $\tan^2 x + 1 = \sec^2 x$.

Rearranging terms gives $1 = \sec^2 x - \tan^2 x$,

and thus $1 = (\sec x - \tan x)(\sec x + \tan x)$,

which means $\sec x + \tan x = \dfrac{1}{2}$.

Problem 19.16

P(4, 8) is a point on a circle, centre O. The tangent at P intersects the axes at point A and B. What is the length of AB?

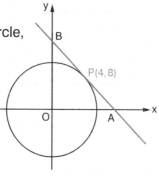

Problem 19.17

The line $y = 2x + p$ and the circle $x^2 + y^2 = 44$ intersect at points A and B. p is a positive integer. What is the solution of the equation $5x^2 + 4xp + p^2 - 44 = 0$?

Problem 19.18

What is the equation of the circle which passes through the two points (−3, 0) and (7, 4) and is centered at a point on the y-axis?

Problem 19.19

Triangle LMO has $L\hat{M}O = 120°$. LM = 3 cm, LO = 21 cm, and MO = x cm.

a) Using the cosine rule, show that $x^2 + 3x - 432 = 0$

b) Find the perimeter of triangle LMO.

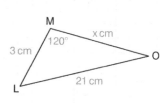

1. Point A lies at (2, 6) and point B lies at (–5, 10) in the standard (x, y) coordinate plane below.

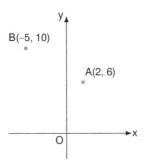

   What is the length, in coordinate units, of $\overline{AB}$?

   A) $\sqrt{40}$ B) $\sqrt{65}$ C) $\sqrt{125}$ D) 13   E) 17

2. Suppose (a, b, c) form a Pythagorean triple, with a < b < c.
   If c = 61 and c – b = 1, then the value of a is:

   A) 3.   B) 5.   C) 7.   D) 11.
   E) None of (A) or (B) or (C) or (D).

3. The sides of triangle ABC are a cm, b cm and c cm long. It is known that there exists natural numbers m and n such that the lengths of the three side lengths of triangle ABC are given by $a = m^2 + n^2$, $b = 2mn$, and $c = m^2 - n^2$, respectively. Which one of the following statements about triangle ABC must be true?

   A) ABC is **not** a right triangle.

   B) ABC is a right triangle, and angle A = 90°.

   C) ABC is a right triangle, and angle B = 90°.

   D) ABC is a right triangle, and angle C = 90°.

   E) None of (A), or (B) or (C) or (D).

4. Suppose you fold two rectangular sheets of card, each a inches by b inches (a < b), so that you make them into two cylinders, A and B say. For Cylinder A, the shorter edges (i.e., the a inch edges) of the rectangular card meet and the circumference of the base is b inches; and, for Cylinder B the longer edges (i.e., the b inch edges) meet, and the circumference of the base is a inches. If the cylinders are closed by adding circular tops and bottoms, what would the volume measure of Cylinder A divided by the volume measure of Cylinder B equal?

   A) $\dfrac{a}{b}$ B) $\dfrac{b}{A}$ C) $2\pi\dfrac{b}{a}$ D) $2\pi\dfrac{a}{b}$
   E) None of (A) or (B) or (C) or (D)

5. Suppose you had a rectangular piece of card, dimensions a inches by b inches (with a > b). Suppose, too, that you decided to cut squares, for which each side length was x inches, from each corner of the piece of card (with 0 < x < b/2), and to fold so that you got a box "without a lid." Then you added a flat lid to form a "closed box." A formula for the volume (in cubic inches) of the box would be V(x) equals

   A) x(a – x)(b – x).   B) x(a – 2x)(b – 2x).
   C) (ab – x)(2a – x)(2b – c).   D) $x^3 + ax^2 + bx$.
           E) None of (A) or (B) or (C) or (D).

6. In the figure,
   AB ⊥ BC,
   BA = 3x – 1,
   AC = 3x + 1, and
   BC = x√3.
   Find the value of x.

   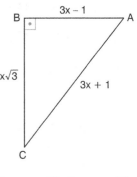

   A) 2   B) 4   C) 5   D) 6   E) 8

MathTopia Press

7. In the figure,

   $AD \perp BD$,

   $AB = 9$,

   $AC = 7$, and

   $BC = 5$.

   Find CD.

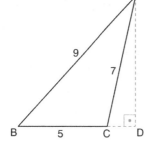

   A) $\dfrac{1}{2}$ B) $\dfrac{7}{10}$ C) $\dfrac{9}{10}$ D) $\dfrac{3}{2}$ E) $\dfrac{7}{2}$

8. What is the number of intersections between $y = 4$ and $x^2 + y^2 = 9$?

   A) 0   B) 1   C) 2   D) 3   E) 4

9. Find the equation of the circle with center $(-1, 7)$ and radius $\sqrt{2}$.

   A) $x^2 + 2x + y^2 - 14y + 48 = 0$

   B) $x^2 - 2x + y^2 - 14y + 48 = 0$

   C) $x^2 + 2x + y^2 + 14y + 48 = 0$

   D) $x^2 + 2x + 14y + 48 = 0$

   E) $x^2 + 14x + y^2 - 2y + 48 = 0$

10. If $\sin A = b$, what is the value of the product $\sin A \cdot \cos A \cdot \tan A$ in terms of b?

    A) 1   B) $\dfrac{1}{b}$ C) b D) b^2 E)

11.

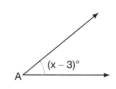 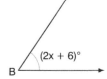

    If in the figure above $\dfrac{\sin A}{\cos B} = 1$, then $x =$

    A) 6   B) 26   C) 29   D) 59   E)

12. If $0 < x < \dfrac{\pi}{2}$ and $\dfrac{\cos x}{1 - \sin^2 x} = \dfrac{3}{2}$,

    what is the value of cos x?

    A) $\dfrac{1}{9}$ B) $\dfrac{1}{3}$ C) $\dfrac{4}{9}$ D) $\dfrac{2}{3}$ E)

MathTopia Press

1. Find the equation of the circle with center $(-3, 8)$ and radius $\sqrt{3}$.

   A) $x^2 - 6x - y^2 - 16y - 70 = 0$

   B) $x^2 - 16x + 70 + y^2 - 6y = 0$

   C) $x^2 - 6x - y^2 - 16y + 70 = 0$

   D) $x^2 + 16x + 70 + y^2 - 6y = 0$

   E) $x^2 + 6x + y^2 - 32y + 73 = 0$

4. (CEMC – Fermat-15 -16)

   In a diagram, the line segment with endpoints $(P(-4, 0)$ and $Q(16, 0)$ is the diameter of a semi-circle with $t > 0$, then t is

   A) 6   B) 10   C) 8   D) 9   E) 7

2. For real numbers x and y, the polynomial

   $$x^2 + 2y^2 + 2xy - 8x - 10y + 30$$

   has a minimum value m at $x = a$ and $y = b$.
   What is the value of abm?

   A)   B)   C)   D)   E)

5. (CEMC – Fermat-04 -20)

   In triangle ABC, if $AB = AC = x + 1$ and $BC = 2x - 2$, where $x > 1$, then the area of the triangle is always equal to

   A) $(x - 1)\sqrt{2x^2 + 2}$ B) $2(x - 1)$ C) $\frac{1}{2}(x + 1)^2$

   D) $(x + 1)(x - 1)$ E) $2(x - 1)\sqrt{x}$

3. $x^2 + y^2 - 8x + 2y + 1 = 0$

   has center (a, b) and radius r, what is the value of $a + b + r$?

   A)   B)   C)   D)   E)

6. What is the equation of the circle that passes through the origin, has its center on the line $x + y = 4$, and cuts the circle $x^2 + y^2 - 6x + 16y + 24 = 0$ orthogonally?

   A)   B)   C)   D)   E)

MathTopia Press

7. In △ABC we have AB = 1 and AC = 2. Side $\overline{BC}$ and the median from A to $\overline{BC}$ have the same length. What is BC?

A) $\dfrac{1+\sqrt{2}}{2}$ B) $\dfrac{1+\sqrt{3}}{2}$ C) $\sqrt{2}$ D) $\dfrac{3}{2}$ E) 3

10. OABC is a square inscribed in the semicircles as shown. If |AE| = 3 cm and |OA| = 6 cm, then what is the slope of the line going through the points D and B?

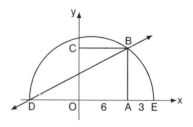

A) $\dfrac{2}{3}$ B) $\dfrac{1}{2}$ C) $\dfrac{3}{5}$ D) 1   E) $\dfrac{3}{2}$

8. What is the minimum value of $x^2 + y^2$ for all (x, y) satisfying $(x - 5)^2 + (y - 12)^2 = 196$?

MathTopia Press

11. ABCD is a square. FB = 2CF and ∠EAB = ∠FEA. Find tan∠DAE?

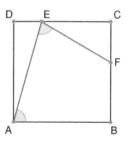

A) $\dfrac{2}{5}$ B) $\dfrac{3}{5}$ C) 1   D) 3   E) 5

9. We are given that sinx = 3 cosx. What is sinx cos x?

A) $\dfrac{1}{6}$ B) $\dfrac{1}{5}$ C) $\dfrac{2}{9}$ D) $\dfrac{1}{4}$ E) $\dfrac{3}{10}$

12. The figure is formed by connecting identical squares. What is the value of sin a?

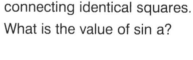

A) $\dfrac{\sqrt{3}}{2}$ B) $\dfrac{2}{\sqrt{3}}$ C) $\dfrac{\sqrt{13}}{2}$ D) $\dfrac{2}{\sqrt{13}}$

Problem Set 1

1. The length between A and B is
$$\sqrt{((-5) - 2)^2 + (10 - 6)^2} = \sqrt{65}$$
The answer is B

2. It is given that $a^2 + b^2 = c^2$ and $c = 61$ and $b = 60$,
$$a^2 + 60^2 = 61^2 \Rightarrow a^2 = 61^2 - 60^2$$
$$= (61 + 60)(61 - 60) = 121 \Rightarrow a = 11$$
The answer is D

3. Let's check if it satisfies Pythagoras' theorem,
$$b^2 + c^2 = (2mn)^2 + (m^2 - n^2)^2 = m^2 + n^2 + 2m^2n^2$$
$$= (m^2 + n^2)^2 = c^2$$
Therefore, it is a right triangle and $A = 90°$.
The answer is B

4. The volume of Cylinder A is $\pi \left(\dfrac{b}{2\pi}\right)^2 a$ and the volume of Cylinder
B is $\pi \left(\dfrac{a}{2\pi}\right)^2 b$. Therefore,
$$\frac{\text{The volume of Cylinder A}}{\text{The volume of Cylinder B}} = \frac{\pi \left(\dfrac{b}{2\pi}\right)^2 a}{\pi \left(\dfrac{a}{2\pi}\right)^2 a} = \frac{b}{a}$$
The answer is B

5. Dimension of the box will be $a - 2x$, $b - 2x$ and x. Therefore, the volume will be $x(a - 2x)(b - 2x)$.
The answer is B

6. By Pythagoras' theorem,
$$(x\sqrt{3})^2 + (3x - 1)^2 = (3x + 1)^2$$
$$\Rightarrow 3x^2 = (3x + 1)^2 - (3x - 1)^2 = 12x \Rightarrow x = 4$$
The answer is B

7. For $|CD| = a$ and $|AD| = b$,
By Pythagoras' Theorem,
$$a^2 + b^2 = 49 \text{ and } (a + 5)^2 + b^2 = 81$$
$$\Rightarrow (a + 5)^2 - a^2 = 10a + 25 = 9^2 - 7^2 = 32$$
$$\Rightarrow a = \frac{7}{10}$$
The answer is B

8. Since $x^2 + y^2 = 9$, $y^2 \leq 9$ and $y \leq 3$.
So, $y = 4$ does not intersect with $x^2 + y^2 = 9$.
The answer is A

9. The equation of the circle is
$$(x + 1)^2 + (y - 7)^2 = (\sqrt{2})^2$$
$$\Rightarrow x^2 + 2x + 1 + y^2 - 14y + 49 = 2$$
$$\Rightarrow x^2 + 2x + y^2 - 14y + 48 = 0$$
The answer is A

MathTopia Press

10. Because $\tan A = \dfrac{\sin A}{\cos A}$,

$\sin A \cdot \cos A \cdot \tan A = \sin A \cdot \sin A = b^2$

The answer is D

11. If $\sin A = \cos B$, then $A + B = 90°$.

$(x - 3)° + (2x + 6)° = 3x + 3 = 90° \Rightarrow x = 29°$

The answer is C

12. Because $1 - \sin^2 x = \cos^2 x$,

$\dfrac{\cos x}{1 - \sin^2 x} = \dfrac{\cos x}{\cos^2 x} = \dfrac{1}{\cos x} = \dfrac{3}{2} \Rightarrow \cos x = \dfrac{2}{3}$

The answer is D

Problem Set 2

1. The equation of the circle is

$(x + 3)^2 + (y - 8)^2 = (\sqrt{3})^2$

$\Rightarrow x^2 + 6x + 9 + y^2 - 16y + 64 = 3$

$\Rightarrow x^2 + 6x + y^2 - 16y + 73 = 0$

The answer is E

2. Let's reorganize the expression,

$x^2 + 2y^2 + 2xy - 8x - 10y + 30$

$= (x + y - 4)^2 + (y - 1)^2 + 13 \geq 13$

Equality holds when $(x, y) = (3, 1)$.

Hence, $abm = 3 \cdot 1 \cdot 13 = 39$.

The answer is C

3. By reorganizing the expression,

$x^2 + y^2 - 8x + 2y + 1$

$= (x - 4)^2 + (y + 1)^2 - 16 = 0$

Therefore, $(4, -1)$ is the center and radius is

$r = 4$. The sum $a + b + r = 7$.

The answer is E

4. The middle point of $[PQ]$ is $\left(\dfrac{16 + (-4)}{2}, 0\right) = (6, 0)$.

Let this point be M and origin be O. In OMR, by

Pythagoras' theorem, $|OR| = t = 8$.

The answer is C

5. The altitude is $\sqrt{(x + 1)^2 - (x - 1)^2} = 2\sqrt{x}$.

The area of ABC is $\dfrac{2(x - 1) \cdot 2\sqrt{x}}{2} = 2(x - 1)\sqrt{x}$.

The answer is E

6. The given circle's equation is

$x^2 + y^2 - 6x + 16y + 24$

$= (x - 3)^2 + (y + 8)^2 - 49 = 0$

Because the center is passing through $x + y = 4$,

the center is $(m, 4 - m)$ for some m. The equation

of this circle is

$(x - m)^2 + (y - 4 + m)^2 = r^2$

for radius r. Because the circle is passing through

origin, $m^2 + (m - 4)^2 = 2m^2 - 8m + 16 = r^2$.

Since $x^2 - 2mx + y^2 + 2(m - 4)y = 0$ cuts the

circle $x^2 + y^2 - 6x + 16y + 24 = 0$ orthogonally,

$2(-m)(-3) + 2(m - 4)8 = 0 + 24 \Rightarrow 22m = 88$

$\Rightarrow m = 4$

Therefore, the equation of the circle is

$x^2 + y^2 - 8x = 0$. So, $(x - 4)^2 + y^2 = 4^2$

The answer is D

MathTopia Press

7. Let the midpoint of [BC] be D.

For, $|BD| = |DC| = x$ and $|AD| = 2x$, by Steward's theorem,

$$\frac{|AB|^2|DC| + |AC|^2|BD|}{|BC|} - |BD||DC| = |AD|^2$$

$$\Rightarrow \frac{1^2x + 2^2x}{2x} - x^2 = 4x^2 \Rightarrow x = \frac{1}{\sqrt{2}}$$

$$\Rightarrow |BC| = 2x = \sqrt{2}$$

The answer is C

8. Let's change the variables as $x = 14\sin a + 5$ and $y = 14\cos a + 12$. By that,

$x^2 + y^2 = (14\sin a + 5)^2 + (14\cos a + 12)^2$

$= 14^2(\sin^2 a + \cos^2 a) + 28(5\sin a + 12\cos a)$

$+ 5^2 + 12^2$

$= 14^2 + 5^2 + 13^2 + 28(5\sin a + 12\cos a)$

$= 365 + 28(5\sin a + 12\cos a)$

Hence, we need to find the minimum value of $A = 5\sin a + 12\cos a$.

For $\cos b = \frac{5}{13}$ and $\sin b = \frac{12}{13}$,

$\frac{A}{13} = \frac{5}{13}\sin a + \frac{5}{13}\cos a = \sin a + b \geq -1$

Therefore, $A \geq -13$,

$x^2 + y^2 = 365 + 28A \geq 365 - 28 \cdot 13 = 1$

The answer is D

9. If $\sin x = 3\cos x$, then $\tan x = 3$. Hence,

$$\sin x = \pm \frac{3}{\sqrt{3^2 + 1^2}} = \pm \frac{3}{\sqrt{10}} \text{ and } \cos x = \pm \frac{1}{\sqrt{10}}$$

Therefore,

$$\sin x \cos x = \left(\pm \frac{3}{\sqrt{10}}\right)\left(\pm \frac{1}{\sqrt{10}}\right) = \frac{3}{10}$$

The answer is E

10. Because $|OE| = |OD| = 9$, $|AD| = 6 + 9 = 15$.

ABCD is a square, therefore, $|AB| = 6$.

Therefore, the slope of the line is $\frac{6}{15} = \frac{2}{5}$.

The answer is D

11. For $|FC| = x$, $|EC| = y$, and $|EF| = z$, if we extend EF and intersect AB at G.

Because $|FB| = 2x$, $|BG| = 2y$ and $|FG| = 2z$.

Also, it is given that $\widehat{EAB} = \widehat{FEA}$, therefore,

$|EG| = 3z = |AG| = 3x + 2y$.

If we say $y = 3k$, $z - x = 2k$.

By Pythagoras' theorem on ECF,

$x^2 + y^2 = z^2 \Rightarrow y^2 = 9k^2 = (z - x)(z + x)$

$= 2k(z + x) \Rightarrow z + x = \frac{9k}{2}$

Because we know both $z - x$ and $z + x$, we can find that $(x, y, z) = \left(\frac{5k}{4}, 3k, \frac{13k}{4}\right)$.

$$\tan(\widehat{DAE}) = \frac{|DE|}{|AD|} = \frac{3x - y}{3x} = \frac{\frac{15k}{4} - 3k}{\frac{15k}{4}} = \frac{1}{5}$$

The answer is A

12. a is an angle in the "$2 - 3 - \sqrt{13}$" right triangle. Hence, $\sin a = \frac{2}{\sqrt{13}}$.

The answer is D

MathTopia Press

MathTopia Press

CHAPTER 20

MODULAR ARITHMETIC ADVANCED

Definition 20.1

Euclidian Algorithm: the Euclidean algorithm, or Euclid's algorithm, is an efficient method for computing the greatest common divisor (gcd) of two numbers, the largest number that divides both of them without leaving a remainder.

Example 20.1

Find the gcd of 144 and 60.
$144 = 60 \cdot 2 + 24$, $60 = 24 \cdot 2 + 12$,
$24 = 12 \cdot 2 + 0 \Rightarrow \gcd(144,60) = 12$

Example 20.2

Find the gcd of 34 and 55.
$55 = 34 \cdot 1 + 21$, $34 = 21 \cdot 1 + 13$,
$21 = 13 \cdot 1 + 8$, $13 = 8 \cdot 1 + 5$, $8 = 5 \cdot 1 + 3$,
$5 = 3 \cdot 1 + 2$, $3 = 2 \cdot 1 + 1$, $2 = 2 \cdot 1 + 0$
$\Rightarrow \gcd(34,55) = 1$

Remark 20.1 — Bezout Theorem

$\gcd(a,b)$ can be represented by a linear combination of a and b with integral coefficients. In other words there are $x, y \in \mathbb{Z}$,
so that $\gcd(a,b) = ax + by$.

Remark 20.2

Two integers a and b are relatively prime if and only if there exist some $x, y \in \mathbb{Z}$ such that $ax + by = 1$

Example 20.3

Find a solution for the given equation,
$24a + 14b = \gcd(24,14)$ where $a, b \in \mathbb{Z}$.
$\gcd(24,14)$, $24 = 14 \cdot 1 + 10$, $14 = 10 \cdot 1 + 4$,
$10 = 4 \cdot 2 + 2$, $4 = 2 \cdot 2 + 0$,
So $\gcd(24,14) = 2$.
$2 = 10 - 2(14 - 1 \cdot 10) = 3 \cdot 10 - 2 \cdot 14$
$= 3(24 - 1 \cdot 14) - 2 \cdot 14 = 3 \cdot 24 - 5 \cdot 14$,
So $a = 3, b = -5$.

Remark 20.3

Important properties of gcd(A,B)

- If $\gcd(A,B) = \gcd(B,A) = d$, then $d|A$ and $d|B$
- $\gcd(A,B) = \gcd(-A,B) = \gcd(A,-B) = \gcd(-A,-B)$
- If $c|A$ and $c|B$, then $c|\gcd(A,B) = d$
- If $a|c, b|c$ and $\gcd(A,B) = 1$, then $a \cdot b|c$
- If B is 0, then $\gcd(A,0) = |A|$
- $\gcd(a,b) = \gcd(a,a+b) = \gcd(a,b-a)$

MathTopia Press

Example 20.4

Find a solution for gcd(−20,36) = 36a − 20b
gcd(−20,36) = gcd(20,36) = 4, So it is enough
to solve 36a + 20b = gcd(36,20) and change the
sign of b. If 36a + 20b = 4, then 9a + 5b = 1
and for a = −1 and b = 2 we get a solution for
36a − 20b = 4 as (−1,−2)

Example 20.5

Find the maximum value of gcd(4n + 5,n − 2) for
n ∈ ℤ.
gcd(4n + 5,n − 2) = gcd(4n + 5 − n + 2,n − 2)
= gcd(3n + 7,n − 2)
= gcd(3n + 7 − 3n + 6,n − 2)
= gcd(13,n − 2), since 13 is a prime number,
if n − 2 is not divisible by 13,
then gcd(4n + 5,n − 2) = 1
if not gcd(4n + 5,n − 2) = 13.

Remark 20.4 — Chineese Remainder Theorem

Let m and n be relatively prime positive integers.
For any integers a and b, the pair of congruences
x ≡ a (mod m) and x ≡ b (mod n) has a solution,
and this solution is uniquely determined modulo
mn.

The Chinese remainder theorem can be extended
from two congruences to any finite number of
congruences, but we have to be careful to make sure
that all of the moduli are pairwise relatively prime.

Remark 20.5

For ≥ 2, let m_1, m_2, ⋯, m_r be nonzero integers that
are pairwise relatively prime (that is
gcd(m_i, m_j) = 1 for i ≠ j). Then, for any integers
a_1, a_2, ⋯, ar, the system of congruences
x ≡ a_1 (mod m_1), x ≡ a_2 (mod m_2), ⋯, x ≡ a_r (mod
m_r), has a solution, and this solution is uniquely
determined (mod $m_1 m_2 \cdots m_r$).

MathTopia Press

Example 20.6

Find all solutions to x ≡ 1 (mod 3),
x ≡ 3 (mod 5), and x ≡ 4 (mod 7).
x ≡ 1 (mod 3) ⇒ x = 3k + 1 and x 3 (mod 5)
⇒ 3k + 1 ≡ 3 (mod 5) ⇒ 3k ≡ 2 (mod 5)
⇒ k ≡ 4 mod 5 ⇒ k = 4 + 5t.
If we substitute k = 4 + 5t into x = 3k + 1, then
x = 3(5t + 4) + 1 = 15t + 13.
x ≡ 4 (mod 7) ⇒ 15t + 13 ≡ 4 (mod 7)
⇒ t − 1 ≡ 4) t ≡ 5 (mod 7) ⇒ t = 7n + 5.
If we substitute t t = 7n + 5 into x = 15t + 13:
x = 15(7n + 5) + 13 = 105n + 88
⇒ x ≡ 88(mod 105)

Remark 20.6 — Wilson's Theorem

p is a prime Iff then (p − 1)! = −1 (mod p).

Example 20.7

What is the remainder when you divide 11 · 22!
by 23?
By Wilson's theorem, 22! ≡ −1 (mod 23),
So 11 · 22! ≡ 11 · (−1) ≡ 12 (mod 23).

Example 20.8

What is the remainder when you divide 20! by 23?
By wilson's theorem, 22! ≡ −1 (mod 23),
So 22 · 21 · 20! ≡ (−1) · (−2) · 20! ≡ 2 · 20! ≡ −1
(mod 23)
$20! \equiv \dfrac{-1}{2} \equiv \dfrac{-1 + 23}{2} \equiv 11$ (mod 23)

Problem 20.1

Let a be the integer such that

$$1+ \frac{1}{2} + \frac{1}{3} + \frac{1}{4} + \cdots + \frac{1}{22} + \frac{1}{23} = \frac{a}{23!}.$$

Compute the remainder when a is divided by 13. (ARML − 2002)

Solution

Multiplying both sides of the equation by 23!, we obtain

$$\frac{23!}{1} + \frac{23!}{2} + \frac{23!}{3} + \cdots + \frac{23!}{13} + \cdots + \frac{23!}{22} + \frac{23!}{23} = a.$$

Note that all the terms on the LHS except $\frac{23!}{13}$ are divisible by 13, so the answer is simply the modulo 13 of $\frac{23!}{13}$.

Note that $\frac{23!}{13} \equiv 12!10! \equiv \frac{1}{2} \equiv 7 \pmod{13}$, so $a \equiv 7 \pmod{13}$.

Remark 20.7 — Fermat's Theorem

Let a be a positive integer and p be a prime, then $a^p \equiv a \pmod p$, or If a is an integer, p is a prime number and a is not divisible by p, then $a^{p-1} \equiv 1 \pmod p$.

Example 20.9

Let's find each exponents in given (mod)

- $3^{31} \equiv \underset{3}{(3^7)^4} 3^3 \equiv 3^7 \equiv 3 \pmod 7$

- $2^{35} \equiv \underset{2}{(2^7)^5} \equiv 32 \equiv 4 \pmod 7$

Example 20.10

What is the remainder when you divide 2^{2010} by 23?

By Fermat's Theorem

$$2^{2010} = 2^{2002} \cdot 2^8 \equiv \underset{1}{(2^{22})^{91}} \cdot 2^8 \equiv 1 \cdot 256 \equiv 3 \pmod{23}$$

EULER'S THEOREM

Definition 20.2

Euler's Totient Function

The totient function Ø(n), also called Euler's totient function, is defined as the number of positive integers less than n that are relatively prime to n.

Properties of Totient Function:

Let p be a prime number and $n \in \mathbb{Z}^+$

- $\emptyset(p) = p - 1$

- $\emptyset(p^n) = p^n - p^{n-1}$

- If gcd(n,m) = 1, then $\emptyset(n \cdot m) = \emptyset(n) \cdot \emptyset(m)$

- If $n = p_1^{m_1} \cdot p_2^{m_2} \cdots p_s^{m_s}$, then

$$\emptyset(n) = \emptyset(p_1^{m_1}) \cdot \emptyset(p_2^{m_2}) \cdots \emptyset(p_s^{m_s})$$
$$= (p_1^{m_1} - p_1^{m_1-1}) \cdot (p_2^{m_2} - p_2^{m_2-1}) \cdots (p_s^{m_s} - p_s^{m_s-1})$$

Example 20.11

Let's find the totient value of the given numbers

- $\emptyset(7) = 7 - 1 = 6$

- $\emptyset(5^3) = 5^3 - 5^2 = 125 - 25 = 100$

- $\emptyset(150) = \emptyset(5^2 \cdot 2 \cdot 3) = \emptyset(5^2)\emptyset(2)\emptyset(3)$
  $= (5^2 - 5)(2 - 1)(3 - 1) = 20 \cdot 1 \cdot 2 = 40$

Remark 20.8

Euler's Theorem: Let Ø(n) be Euler's totient function, if a is an integer and m is a positive integer relatively prime to a, then $a^{\emptyset(m)} \equiv 1 \pmod m$.

Problem 20.2

What is the remainder when 8^{103} is divided by 13?

Solution

$$8^{103} \equiv \underset{1}{(8^{12})^8} \cdot 8^7 \equiv 8^7 \pmod{13},$$

$$\Rightarrow 8^7 \equiv \underset{-1}{(8^2)^3} \cdot 8 \equiv -8 \equiv 5 \pmod{13}.$$

MathTopia Press

Problem 20.3

Find the last two digits of 2002^{2001}

Solution

Let's find the x for $2002^{2001} \equiv 2^{2001} \equiv x \pmod{100}$.

It is very obvious that $2^{2001} \equiv 0 \pmod 4$,

since $\emptyset(25) = 20$ and $\gcd(2,25) = 1$

we get $2^{2001} \equiv (2^{\underset{1}{20}})^{50} \equiv 2 \equiv 2 \pmod{25}$,

So x can be one of the numbers $\{2, 27, 52, 77\}$,

52 satisfies the requirements for both (mod 4) and (mod 25).

Problem 20.4

What is the remainder when $2^{2^{17}} + 1$ is divided by 19?

Solution

From Euler we get $2^{18} \equiv 1 \pmod{19}$, now we need to find the value of 2^{17} in (mod 18).

$2^{17} \equiv 0 \pmod 2$ and $2^{17} \equiv (2^{\underset{1}{6}})^2 \cdot 2^5 \equiv 32 \equiv 5 \pmod 9$,

then we have possible solutions as $\{5, 14\}$, 14 is the only solution for both (mod 2) and (mod 9). Now we can write $2^{17} = 14 + 18k$ where $k \in \mathbb{Z}$.

$$\begin{aligned} 2^{2^{17}} + 1 \ &\equiv \ 2^{14+18k} + 1 \equiv (2^{18})^k \cdot 2^{14} + 1 \\ &= (2^{\underset{-3}{4}})^3 \cdot 2^2 + 1 \pmod{19} \\ &= (-27) \cdot 2^2 + 1 \equiv 6 + 1 \equiv 7 \pmod{19} \end{aligned}$$

DIOPHANTINE EQUATIONS

A Diophantine equation is a polynomial equation, usually in two or more unknowns, such that only the integer solutions are sought or studied (an integer solution is a solution such that all the unknowns take integer values). A linear Diophantine equation equates the sum of two or more monomials, each of degree 1 in one of the variables, to a constant.

LINEAR DIOPHANTINE EQUATIONS

The simplest linear Diophantine equation takes the form $ax+by = c$, where $a; b$ and c are given integers. This Diophantine equation has a solution (where x and y are integers) if and only if c is a multiple of the greatest common divisor of a and b. Moreover, if (x;y) is a solution, then the other solutions have the form $(x + kv, y - ku)$, where k is an arbitrary integer, and u and v are the quotients of a and b (respectively) by the greatest common divisor of a and b.

Problem 20.5

Find the solution to the linear equation $10x + 12y = 15$.

Solution

$10x + 12y = 15 \Rightarrow 10x \equiv 15 \equiv 3 \pmod{12}$, since $\gcd(10, 12) = 2$ and $2 \nmid 3$ there is no solution.

Problem 20.6

How many positive pairs of integers (x, y) satisfy the equation $2x + 3y = 1000$?

Solution

$2x + 3y = 1000 \Rightarrow y \equiv 0 \pmod 2$,

that is $y = 0 + 2k$ where $k \in \mathbb{Z}^+$.

So $y \in \{0, 2, 4, 6, \cdots 232\}$

which is $\dfrac{332 - 2}{2} + 1 = 166$.

Problem 20.7

How many positive pairs of integers (x, y) satisfy the equation $12x + 15y = 1203$?

Solution

$\gcd(12, 15) = 3 \Rightarrow 4x + 5y = 401$.

Since $y \equiv 1 \pmod 4$, $y = 4k + 1$ and $y < 80$

we get $y \in \{1, 5, 9, \cdots 77\}$, so there are

$\dfrac{77 - 1}{4} + 1 = 20$ solutions.

MathTopia Press

Problem 20.8

How many positive integers $x < 36$ satisfy the equation $15x + 36y = 3$?

Solution

$\gcd(15, 36) = 3 \Rightarrow 5x + 12y = 1$.
Since $5x \equiv 1 \pmod{12}$ we get $x \equiv 5 \pmod{12}$.
(we multiplied both sides by 5). $x \in \{5, 17, 29\}$

FACTORING METHOD

Factoring is a very powerful tool while solving Diophantine equations. Sometimes factoring can crack a Diophantine equation wide open. Instead of talking about how good and powerful it is, let's see a demonstration of how factoring can help solving certain Diophantine equations. We're going to start off with quadratic equations, which we already know how to factorize. This is a very powerful tool and can sometimes solve seemingly impossible problems.

Simon's favorite factoring trick (SFFT), also called completing the rectangle, is a simple but clever factorization of the expressions of the form $xy + xn + ym + mn$ where x and y are variables (usually integer variables), and m and n are integers.

Notice that this can be factorized as
$xy + xn + ym + mn = (x + m)(y + n)$

Problem 20.9

How many pairs of integers (x, y) satisfy the equation $x^2 = 210 + y^2$?

Solution

$x^2 = 210 + y^2 \Rightarrow (x - y)(x + y) = 210 = 2 \cdot 3 \cdot 5 \cdot 7$.
Since $x - y$ and $x + y$ are both even or odd there is no solution, because there is only one even number factor of 210.

MathTopia Press

Problem 20.10

Find the integer solutions of $x^4 = y^2 + 71$.

Solution

$x^4 = y^2 + 71 \Rightarrow x^4 - y^2 = 71 \Rightarrow (x^2 - y)(x^2 + y) = 71$, since 71 is a prime number we have $x^2 - y = 1$ and $x^2 + y = 71$. If we add those two equations $2x^2 = 72$ and $x = \mp 6$, $y = 35$.
And also for $x^2 - y = 71$ and $x^2 + y = 1$
we get $x = \mp 6$ and $y = -35$.
For the factors -1 and -71 there is no solution, so we have the solutions as $(-6, 35)$, $(-6, -35)$, $(6, 35)$, $(6, -35)$.

Problem 20.11

How many pairs of even integers (x, y) satisfy the equation $x^6 = y^2 + 60$.

Solution

$x^6 = y^2 + 60 \Rightarrow (x^3 - y)(x^3 + y) = 60$ and both of the factors $x^3 - y$ and $x^3 + y$ are even.
since $60 = 2^2 \cdot 3 \cdot 5$ we get the factors ∓ 10 and ∓ 6.

$\left. \begin{array}{l} x^3 - y = 10 \\ x^3 + y = 6 \end{array} \right\} \Rightarrow x = 2, y = -2,$

$\left. \begin{array}{l} x^3 - y = -10 \\ x^3 + y = -6 \end{array} \right\} \Rightarrow x = -2, y = 2,$

$\left. \begin{array}{l} x^3 - y = 6 \\ x^3 + y = 10 \end{array} \right\} \Rightarrow x = 2, y = 2,$

$\left. \begin{array}{l} x^3 - y = -6 \\ x^3 + y = -10 \end{array} \right\} \Rightarrow x = -2, y = -2,$

So there are four solutions.

Problem 20.12

How many pairs of positive integers (m, n) satisfy the equation $m = \dfrac{10n}{n-10}$?

Solution

$m = \dfrac{10n}{n-10} \Rightarrow mn - 10m - 10n = 0$

$\Rightarrow mn - 10m - 10n + 100 = 100$

$\Rightarrow m(n-10) - 10(n-10) = 100$

$\Rightarrow (m-10)(n-10) = 100 = 2^2 5^2$.

So the possible solutions are below;

$\left.\begin{array}{l} m-10=1 \\ n-10=100 \end{array}\right\}$, $\left.\begin{array}{l} m-10=2 \\ n-10=50 \end{array}\right\}$, $\left.\begin{array}{l} m-10=4 \\ n-10=25 \end{array}\right\}$

$\left.\begin{array}{l} m-10=5 \\ n-10=20 \end{array}\right\}$, $\left.\begin{array}{l} m-10=10 \\ n-10=10 \end{array}\right\}$

If we solve those equations we will get the solitions (11, 110), (12, 60), (14, 35), (15, 30), (20, 20) and because of the symetry we have (110, 11), (60, 12), (35, 14), and (30, 15) so is there are 9 solutions.

THE MODULAR ARITHMETIC METHOD

A useful technique for problems involving Diophantine equations is reducing (mod n) for some well-chosen modulus n. This is often a method for proving the nonexistence of solutions: if there are no solutions (mod n) for some n, then there are no solutions over the integers. Occasionally it is also useful to narrow down the possible solutions based on solutions (mod n), but finding a complete set of solutions, when the set is nonempty, will almost always require more advanced techniques.

Problem 20.13

How many pairs of integers (x, y) satisfy the equation $x^2 + 4x + 1 = 4y^2$?

Solution

Taking both sides modulo 4,

we get $x^2 + 1 \equiv 0 \pmod 4$,

Howewer $x^2 \equiv 0,1 \pmod 4$,

so $x^2 + 1 \equiv 1,2 \pmod 4$.

Therefore, since the left hand side is never divisible by 4, the equation has no solutions in positive integers.

Problem 20.14 (USAMO 1979)

Find all nonnegative solutions in integers to

$n_1^4 + n_2^4 + \cdots n_{14}^4 = 1599$

Solution

Let's solve in (mod 16), then $n_i^4 \equiv 0$ or 1, so the left side is in$\{0, 1, 2, \cdots 14\}$ in (mod 16), but the right side is 15 (mod 16). So there are no solutions.

Problem 20.15

How many pairs of integers (x;y) satisfy the equation $5x^2 + 4y^2 = 61$.

Solution

$5x^2 + 4y^2 = 61 \Rightarrow 4y^2 \equiv 1 \pmod 5$

$\Rightarrow y^2 \equiv 4 \pmod 5$, so $y \equiv 2 \pmod 5$ or $y \equiv 3 \pmod 5$.

Since $x^2 > 0$ and $y^2 > 0$ we get $y^2 \leq 15$ and $y = \mp 2$ or $y = \mp 3$

For $y = \mp 2$, $5x^2 = 45 \Rightarrow x = \mp 3$

For $y = \mp 3$, $x^2 = 5 \Rightarrow$ there is no solution.

MathTopia Press

Problem 20.16

Find all solutions in positive integers to
$3 \cdot 5^{2x+1} + 2^{3x+1} + 17y = 1870$.

Solution

Since $1870 = 17 \cdot 110$,

$$3 \cdot 5^{2x+1} + 2^{3x+1} \equiv 0 \pmod{17}$$
$$15 \cdot 5^{2x} + 2 \cdot 2^{3x} \equiv 0 \pmod{17}$$
$$15 \cdot 25^x + 2 \cdot 8^x \equiv 0 \pmod{17}$$
$$17 \cdot 8^x \equiv 0 \pmod{17}$$

That means it satisfies for all positive integers.

For $3 \cdot 5^{2x+1} + 2^{3x+1} \leq 1870$ we have two solutions as $(0,109)$ and $(1,87)$. So, only positive solution is $(1,87)$

Problem 20.17

Find all solutions in integers to
$(x + m)^3 + (x + 2m)^2 + (x + 3m)^2 + (x + 4m)^2 = 2009$

Solution

$(x + m)^3 + (x + 2m)^2 + (x + 3m)^2 + (x + 4m)^2$
$= 4x^2 + mx(2 + 4 + 6 + 8) + m^2(1 + 4 + 9 + 16)$
$= 4x^2 + 20mx + 30m^2 = 2009 \Rightarrow 2m^2 \equiv 1 \pmod 4$
and there is no solution.

Problem 20.18

How many pairs of integers (x, y) satisfy the equation
$6(x! + 2) = y^2 - 1$?

Solution

$6(x! + 2) = y^2 - 1 \Rightarrow 6x! + 13 = y^2$
For $x \geq 5$, we have $x! \equiv 0 \pmod 5$ that is
$y^2 \equiv 3 \pmod 5$, so there is no solution and $x \leq 4$.
If $x = 0$ or $x = 1$, then $y^2 = 19$, no solution.
If $x = 2$, then $y^2 = 25 \Rightarrow y = \pm 5$.
If $x = 3$, then $y^2 = 49 \Rightarrow y = \pm 7$.
If $x = 4$, then $y^2 = 157$, no solution.

Problem 20.19

How many ordered pairs of integers (x, y) satisfy the equation
$3x^2 + 6x + 5 = y^2$

Problem 20.20

Solve the equation
$x^2 = 2^y + 7$

MathTopia Press

KEN KEN.

KenKen was born in a Japanese classroom in 2004 and now boasts a proven track record of academic benefits–from increasing math skills and logical thinking to developing concentration, perseverance, and determination.

RULES FOR KENKEN

Fill the grid with digits so as not to repeat a digit in any row or column, and so the digits within each heavily outlined box or boxes (called a cage) will produce the target number shown in that cage by using the operation (addition, subtraction, multiplication, or division) shown by the symbol after the numeral.

For single box cages, simply enter the number that is shown in the corner. So, for example, the notation 6+ means that the numerals in the cage should add up to 6, and the notation 48× means that by multiplying the numbers in the cage you will get 48. A 4×4 grid will use the digits 1-4. A 5×5 grid will use 1-5. A 6×6 grid will use 1-6, and so on.

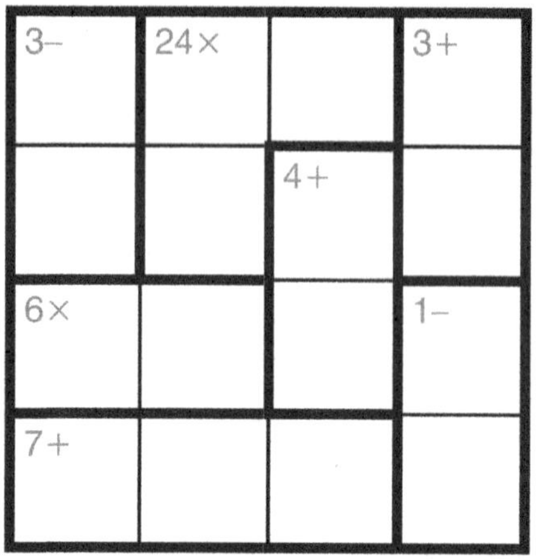

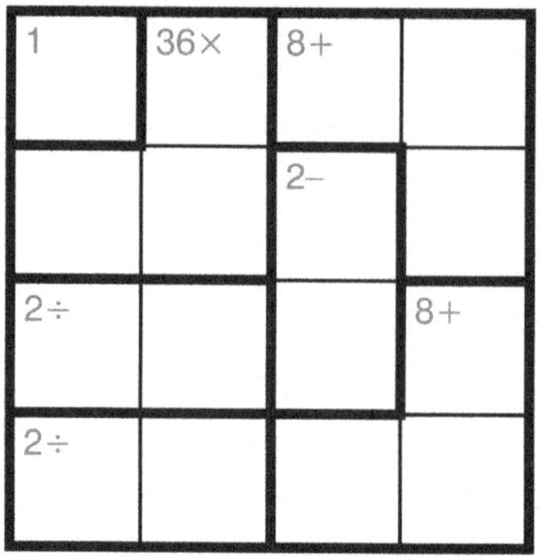

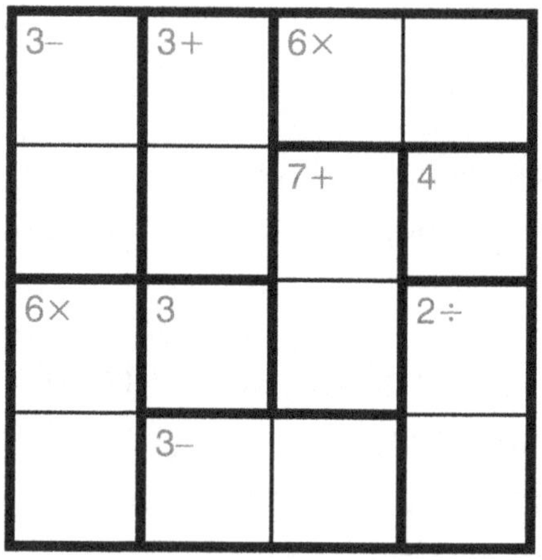

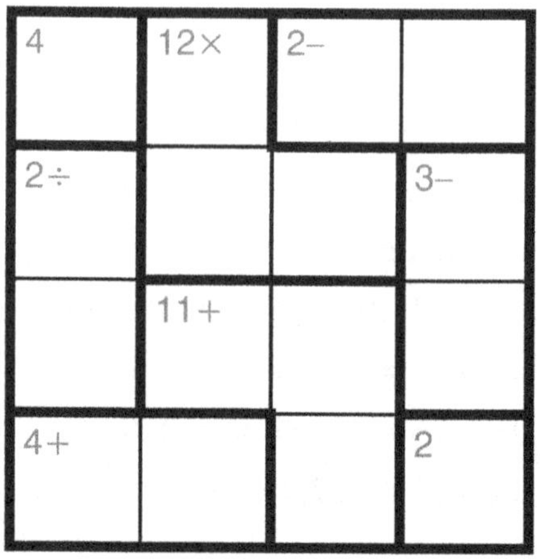

MathTopia Press

Puzzle 1 (top right):

1	36×	8+	
		2−	
2÷			8+
2÷			

Puzzle 2 (middle right):

3−	3+	6×	
		7+	4
6×	3		2÷
	3−		

Puzzle 3 (bottom left):

3−	24×		3+
		4+	
6×			1−
7+			

Puzzle 4 (bottom right):

4	12×	2−	
2÷			3−
	11+		
4+			2

1. What is the remainder when 2^{11215} is divided by 11?

   A) 10   B) 9   C) 8   D) 7   E) 5

2. What is the remainder when 143^{663} is divided by 14?

   A) 7   B) 9   C) 11   D) 12   E) 13

3. Find the last two digits of 3^{2002}.

   A) 09   B) 17   C) 19   D) 27   E) 89

4. What is the remainder when 2^{32003} is divided by 17?

   A) 7   B) 8   C) 11   D) 13   E) 14

5. For any integer n, what is the remainder when $n^{33} - n$ is divided by 15?

   A) 0   B) 1   C) 2   D) 11   E) 13

6. What is the remainder when $20^{15} - 1$ is divided by $11 \cdot 31 \cdot 61$?

   A) 11   B) 31   C) 61   D) 1   E) 0

MathTopia Press

7. What is the remainder when $43^{23} + 23^{43}$ is divided by 66?

    A) 33   B) 11   C) 6   D) 1   E) 0

8. What is the remainder when $2^{70} + 3^{70}$ is divided by 13?

    A) 0   B) 2   C) 3   D) 7   E) 11

9. What is the remainder when

    $(8^{80} + 1)(8^{40} + 1)(8^{20} + 1)(8^{10} + 1)(8^{10} - 1)$

    is divided by 13?

    A) 0   B) 2   C) 3   D) 9   E) 11

10. What is the remainder when

    $2 + (2 \cdot 4 \cdot 6 \ldots 196)(1 \cdot 3 \cdot 5 \ldots 195)$

    is divided by 197?

    A) 0   B) 1   C) 96   D) 196   E) none

11. Find the remainder when

    $3 + 3^2 + 3^{(2^2)} + 3^{(2^3)} + \ldots + 3^{(2^{2018})}$ is divided by 5?

    A) 0   B) 1   C) 2   D) 3   E) 4

12. Which of the following numbers can not divide $9^{18} - 1$?

    A) 20   B) 24   C) 16   D) 23   E) 27

1. What is the remainder when

   $1^1! + 2^2! + 3^3! + ... + 26^{26}!$ is divided by 7?

   A) 0   B) 1   C) 2   D) 3   E) 5

2. Among the numbers 1, 2, 3, ... 2020, how many are coprime to 2020?

   A) 101   B) 505   C) 800   D) 1010   E) 2000

3. Let m, n be positive integers, find the sum of the distinct remainders when $2012^n + m^2$ is divided by 11.

   A) 55   B) 46   C) 43   D) 39   E) 37

4. Find the last three digits of $49^{303} \cdot 3993^{202} \cdot 39^{606}$.

   A) 001   B) 081   C) 561   D) 721   E) 961

5. Which one of the followings can not be the positive integer n such that $1 + 3 + 3^2 + ... + 3^n$ is divisible by 100.

   A) 39   B) 69   C) 79   D) 119   E) 199

6. How many prime numbers p are there such that $29^p + 1$ is a multiple of p?

   A) 1   B) 2   C) 3   D) 4   E) 5

MathTopia Press

7. Calculuate the last three digits of
   $2005^{11} + 2005^{12} + ... + 2005^{2006}$

   A) 000   B) 100   C) 300   D) 500   E) 800

10. How many ordered pairs of positive integers
    (x, y) satisfy the equation $xy - 2x - 5y - 1 = 0$?

    A) 1   B) 2   C) 3   D) 4   E) 5

8. How many ordered pairs of integers (x, y) satisfy
   the equation $5x + 5y - xy = 0$?

   A) 2   B) 4   C) 6   D) 8   E) 10

11. How many ordered pairs of positive integers
    (x, y) satisfy the equation $xy - 4y^2 - 4x = 0$?

    A) 2   B) 3   C) 12   D) 13   E) 14

9. How many ordered pairs of positive integers
   (x, y) satisfy the equation
   $(x + y)^2 - 2xy = 124 + 2y^2$?

   A) 1   B) 2   C) 3   D) 4   E) 5

12. How many ordered pairs of positive integers
    (m, n) satisfy the equation
    $n(2n + 5m) = 4(3m^2 + 7)$?

    A) 0   B) 1   C) 2   D) 3   E) 4

MathTopia Press

1. How many integers n satisfy the equation $n^n = 2n^2 + 3n$?

   A) 0   B) 1   C) 2   D) 3   E) 4

4. How many ordered pairs of integers (x, y) satisfy the equation $(x + y)^2 - (x + y) - 3xy = 0$?

   A) 1   B) 2   C) 4   D) 6   E) 8

2. How many ordered pairs of positive integers (m, n) satisfy the equation $2n^2 - m^2 + mn = 36$?

   A) 0   B) 1   C) 2   D) 3   E) 4

5. How many ordered pairs of positive integers (x, y) satisfy the equation
   $x^2 - y^4 = (y + 1)^4 - (x + 1)^2$?

   A) 0   B) 1   C) 2   D) 3   E) 4

MathTopia Press

3. If x, y, x $\in \mathbb{Z}$ and $\left.\begin{array}{l} x - 3y = 1 - 2z \\ 2x + y = 7 + 5z \end{array}\right\}$, then find z.

   A) 3^{111} B) 2^{222} C) 5^{111} D) 6^{111} E) none

6. How many ordered pairs of positive integers (x, y) satisfy the equation $x^3 - y^3 = xy + 61$?

   A) 0   B) 1   C) 2   D) 3   E) 4

7. How many ordered pairs of integers (x, y) satisfy the equation $3x^2 + 6x + 5 = y^2$

A) 0   B) 1   C) 2   D) 3   E) 4

8. (21-2012-T04) (BmMT-2012-Team-4)

How many solutions (x, y) in the positive integers are there to $3x + 7y = 1337$?

A) 60   B) 63   C) 66   D) 72

E) None of the preceding

9. (CEMC-2016-Gauss8-24)

What is the tens digit of 3^{2016}?

A) 0   B) 2   C) 4   D) 6   E) 8

10. (21-2012-F31) (BmMT-2012-Ciphering-31)

What is the remainder when 19^{19} is divided by 17?

A) 3   B) 4   C) 5   D) 6   E) 7

11. For how many ordered pairs of positive integers (x, y) is $3x - 2y = 7$?

A) 0   B) 1   C) 2   D) 3   E) infinitely many

12. For how many ordered pairs of positive integers (x, n) is $x^2 + 615 = 2^n$?

A) 0   B) 1   C) 2   D) 3   E) infinitely many

MathTopia Press

Problem Set 1

1. 11 is a prime. By Fermat's theorem,

   $2^{10} \equiv 1 \ (mod\, 11)$

   $\Rightarrow 2^{11215} \equiv (2^{10})^{1121} \cdot 2^5 \cdot 32 \equiv 10 \ (mod\ 11)$

   The answer is A

2. $14 = 2 \cdot 7$ and $143^{663} \equiv 1 \ (mod\ 2)$.

   $143^{663} \equiv 3^{663} \equiv (3^6)^{110} \cdot 3^3 \equiv 27 \equiv 6 \ (mod\, 7)$

   by Fermat's theorem. So, $143^{663} \equiv 13 \ (mod\ 14)$.

   The answer is E

3. $100 = 2^2 \cdot 5^2$ and $3^{2002} \equiv (-1)^{2002} \equiv 1 \ (mod\ 4)$. Also,

   $\varnothing(25) = 5^2 - 5 = 20$, hence $3^{20} \equiv 1 \ (mod\, 25)$

   $3^{2002} \equiv (3^{20})^{100} \cdot 3^2 \equiv 9 \ (mod\, 25)$

   $\Rightarrow 3^{2002} \equiv 09 \ (mod\ 100)$

   The answer is A

4. $2^{16} \equiv 1 \ (mod\ 17)$ by Fermat's theorem,

   $3^{2003} \equiv (3^4)^{500} \cdot 3^3 \equiv 81^{500} \cdot 27 \equiv 27 \equiv 11 \ (mod\ 16)$

   $\Rightarrow 2^{3^{2003}} \equiv 2^{11} \equiv 2048 \equiv 8 \ (mod\, 17)$

   The answer is B

5. $15 = 3 \cdot 5$, hence,

   $n^{33} \equiv (n^3)11 \equiv n11 \equiv (n^3)^3 \cdot n^2 \equiv n^3 \cdot n^2 \equiv n \cdot n^2 \equiv n^3 \equiv n \ (mod\ 3)$

   $n^{33} \equiv (n^5)^6 \cdot n^3 \equiv n^6 \cdot n^3 \equiv n^5 \cdot n^4 \equiv n \cdot n^4 \equiv n^5 \equiv n$ (mod 5)

   Hence, $n^{33} - n$ is divisible by 15 for each n.

   The answer is A

6. Let's calculate for 11, 31, and 61,

   $20^{15} \equiv 9^{15} - 1 \equiv 3^{30} - 1 \equiv 27^{10} - 1 \equiv 1 - 1 \equiv 0$ $(mod\, 11)$

   $20^{15} - 1 \equiv (2^2 \cdot 5)^{15} - 1 \equiv 2^{30} \cdot 5^{15} - 1 \equiv 5^{15} - 1$
   $\equiv 125^5 - 1 \equiv 1 - 1 \equiv 0 \ (mod\, 31)$

   $20^{15} - 1 \equiv \left(\dfrac{60}{3}\right)^{15} - 1 \equiv -\dfrac{1}{3^{15}} - 1 \equiv -\dfrac{1}{243^3} - 1$

   $\equiv -\dfrac{1}{-1} - 1 \equiv 0$

   Therefore, $20^{15} - 1$ is divisible by $11 \cdot 31 \cdot 61$.

   The answer is E

7. $66 = 2 \cdot 3 \cdot 11$ and $43^{23} + 23^{43} \equiv 0 \ (mod\ 2)$.

   $43^{23} + 23^{43} \equiv 1^{23} + (-1)^{43} \equiv 0 \ (mod\, 3)$

   $43^{23} + 23^{43} \equiv (-1)^{23} + 1^{43} \equiv 0 \ (mod\, 11)$

   Hence, $43^{23} + 23^{43}$ is divisible by 66.

   The answer is E

8. Let's calculate

   $2^{70} \equiv (2^{12})^5 \cdot 2^{10} \equiv 2^{10} \equiv 1024 \equiv 10 \ (mod\ 13)$

   $3^{70} \equiv (3^{12})^5 \cdot 3^{10} \equiv 3^{10} \equiv (3^3)^3 \cdot 3 \equiv 3 \ (mod\, 13)$

   Hence their sum $2^{70} + 3^{70}$ is divisible by 13.

   The answer is A

9. By $a^2 - 1 = (a + 1)(a - 1)$,

   $(8^{80} + 1)(8^{40} + 1)(8^{20} + 1)(8^{10} + 1)(8^{10} - 1)$

   $= (8^{80} + 1)(8^{40} + 1)(8^{20} + 1)(8^{20} - 1)$

   $= (8^{80} + 1)(8^{40} + 1)(8^{40} - 1)$

   $= (8^{80} + 1)(8^{80} - 1) = 8^{160} - 1$

   Therefore,

   $8^{160} - 1 \equiv 2^{480} - 1 \equiv (2^{12})^{40} - 1 \equiv 1 - 1 \equiv 0 \ (mod\, 13)$

   The answer is A

MathTopia Press

10. The given number is equal to $196! + 2$.

Since 197 is a prime, by Wilson's theorem,

$196! \equiv -1 \pmod{197} \Rightarrow 196! + 2 \equiv 1 \pmod{197}$

The answer is B

11. $34 \equiv 1 \pmod 5$ by Fermat's theorem. Also,

$2^k \equiv 0 \pmod 4$ if $k \geq 2$. So,

$3 + 3^2 + 3^{2^2} + \cdots + 3^{2^{2018}}$

$\equiv 3 + 3^2 + \underbrace{1 + 1 + \cdots + 1}_{2017-\text{digits}} \equiv 3 + 9 + 2017 \equiv 4$

$\pmod 5$

The answer is E

12. We find

$\varnothing(20) = (2^2 - 1)(5 - 1) = 8$

$\varnothing(24) = (3^2 - 2^2)(3 - 1) = 8$

$\varnothing(16) = (2^4 - 2^3) = 8$

$\varnothing(23) = 23 - 1 = 22$

From Euler's Theorem,

$91^8 \equiv 11^8 \equiv 1 \pmod{20}$

$91^8 \equiv 19^8 \equiv 1 \pmod{24}$

$91^8 \equiv 11^8 \equiv 1 \pmod{16}$

$91^8 \equiv 22^8 \equiv (-1)^8 \equiv 1 \pmod{23}$

The answer is E

Problem Set 2

1. If $n \geq 7$, then $n! \geq 0 \pmod 7$.

Also, $n^n \geq 7$ if $n \geq 3$. So,

$(1^1)! + (2^2)! + (3^3)! + \cdots + (26^{26})! \equiv 1! + 4! \equiv$

$25 \equiv 4 \pmod 7$

The answer is E

2. The answer is $\varnothing(2020)$. Since $2020 = 2^2 \cdot 5 \cdot 101$,

$\varnothing(2020) = (2^2 - 2)(5 - 1)(101 - 1) = 800$

The answer is C

3. For each n,

$2012^n \equiv (-1)^n \equiv 1$ or $10 \pmod{11}$

Also,

$m^2 \equiv 0$ or 1 or 3 or 4 or 5 or $9 \pmod{11}$

Hence,

$2012^n + m^2 \equiv 0, 1, 2, 3, 4, 5, 6, 8, 10 \pmod{11}$

Sum of possible remainders is 39.

The answer is D

4. $1000 = 2^3 \cdot 5^3$ and

$49^{303} \cdot 3993^{202} \cdot 39^{606} \equiv 1 \cdot 1 \cdot (-1)^{606} \equiv 1 \pmod 8$

Also $\varnothing(125) = 5^3 - 5^2 = 100$, then

$49^{303} \cdot 3993^{202} \cdot 39^{606} \equiv 49^3 \cdot 3993^2 \cdot 39^6$

$\equiv 7^6 \cdot (-7)^2 \cdot 39^6$

$\equiv 7^8 \cdot 39^6 \equiv (7^4)^2 \cdot (39^2)^3 \equiv 2401^2 \cdot 1521^3$

$\equiv (-99)^2 \cdot 21^3$

$\equiv 9^2 \cdot 11^2 \cdot 3^3 \cdot 7^3 \equiv 3^7 \cdot 7^3 \cdot 11^2 \equiv 2187 \cdot 343 \cdot 121$

$\equiv 62 \cdot 93 \cdot (-4)$

$\equiv 5766 \cdot (-4) \equiv 16 \cdot (-4) \equiv -64 \equiv 61 \pmod{125}$

Since $61 + 2 \cdot 125 \equiv 561 \pmod 8$, the last three digits is 561.

The answer is C

5. Because $1 + 3 + 3^2 + \cdots + 3^n = \dfrac{3^{n+1} - 1}{2}$,

we should look for n such that $3^{n+1} - 1$ is divisible by $200 = 2^3 \cdot 5^2$. If $3^{n+1} - 1 \equiv 0 \pmod 8$, then $n + 1$ is even and n is odd because

$3^k \equiv 1 \pmod 8 \iff k \equiv 0 \pmod 2$ and $3^k \equiv 3 \pmod 8 \iff k \equiv 1 \pmod 2$

Since $\varnothing(25) = 20$, then $3^{20} - 1 \equiv 0 \pmod{25}$ and $n = 20k - 1$ satisfies. Since $20k - 1$ is odd, there is no problem. Only 69 is not in this form.

The answer is B

6. It is clear that p = 29 does not satisfy.

    By Fermat's theorem,

    $29^p + 1 \equiv 29 \cdot 29^{p-1} + 1 \equiv 29 + 1 \equiv 30 \pmod p$

    Hence, p can be 2, 3, 5.

    The answer is C

7. We know that $1000 = 2^3 \cdot 5^3$ and the sum is

    divisible by 125.

    For (mod 8), the sum is equivalent to

    $5^{11} + 5^{12} + \cdots + 5^{2006}$

    $\equiv 5 + 1 + 5 + 1 + \cdots + 5 + 1 \pmod 8$

    because $5^k \equiv 5 \pmod 8$ if k is odd and

    $5^k \equiv 1 \pmod 8$ if k is even.

    There are 998 many 5 and 1, therefore

    $\equiv (5 + 1) \cdot 998 \equiv (-2) \cdot (-2) \equiv 4 \pmod 8$ Hence,

    them is equivalent to $125 \cdot 4 \equiv 500 \pmod{1000}$.

    The answer is D

8. Let's reorganize the equation,

    $xy - 5x - 5y = 0 \Rightarrow (x - 5)(y - 5) = 25$

    x−5 is divisible by 25 and it has 6 many divisors
    and each divisor represent only one solution.

    There are 6 solutions.

    The answer is C

9. If we reorganize the equation,

    $(x + y)^2 - 2xy = x^2 + y^2 = 124 + 2y^2$

    $\Rightarrow x^2 - y^2 = (x - y)(x + y) = 124 = 31 \cdot 4$

    (x − y) and (x + y) have same parity, therefore
    they are both even. Hence,

    x − y = 2 and x + y = 62.

    By that, (x, y) = (32, 30).

    The answer is A

10. Let's reorganize the equation,

    $xy - 2x - 5y - 1 = 0 \Rightarrow xy - 2x - 5y + 10$

    $= (x - 5)(y - 2) = 11$

    Therefore, ((x − 5), (y − 2)) = (1, 11) or (11, 1).

    By that, (x, y) = (6, 13) or (16, 3).

    The answer is B

11. Since $x(y - 4) = 4y^2$,

    $x = \dfrac{4y^2}{y - 4} = 4y + 16 + \dfrac{64}{y - 4}$

    Because x is positive, y−4 is also positive.

    Therefore, y−4 can be 1, 2, 4, 8, 16, 32, 64.

    For each y value, there is exactly one x value.

    There are 7 solutions.

    The answer is B

12. Because $n(2n + 5m) = 4(3m^2 + 7)$,

    $2n^2 + 5mn = 12m^2 + 28 \Rightarrow 2n^2 + 5mn - 12m^2$

    $= (2n - 3m)(n + 4m) = 28$

    If 2n − 3m = a and n + 4m = b,

    $2n + 8m - 2n + 3m = 11m = 2b - a$

    $= \dfrac{56}{a} - a = \dfrac{56 - a^2}{y - 4}$

    Therefore, $56 - a^2$ is divisible by 11 and a is a
    factor of 28. Only a = 1 satisfies that.

    So, for a = 1, we obtain (m, n) = (5, 8) solution.

    The answer is B

Problem Set 3

1. n ≠ 0 because 0^0 is undefined. Also, n cannot be
    negative because n^n is not integer but $2n^2 + 3n$
    is. Since n^n is increasing extremely faster than
    $2n^2 + 3n$,

    $n^n > 2n^2 + 3n$ for n ≥ 4

    So, we need to check for n = 1, 2, 3.

    Only n = 3 satisfies.

    The answer is B

MathTopia Press

2. By factorizing the given expression

   $2n^2 + mn - m^2 = (2n - m)(n + m) = 36$

   For $2n - m = a$ and $n + m = b$, we can find that

   $n = \dfrac{a+b}{2}$ and $m = b - \dfrac{a+b}{2}$. Since $a + b$ and

   ab are divisible by 3, both a and b are divisible

   by 3. So, (a, b) can be $(3, 12)$, $(12, 3)$, $(6, 6)$.

   However, for $(a, b) = (12, 3)$, $m < 0$.

   So, there are two solutions.

   The answer is C

3. Let's solve for x and y,

   $7x = (x - 3y) + 3(2x + y) = (1 - 2z) + (21 + 15z)$

   $= 22 + 13z$

   $7y = (2x + y) - 2(x - 3y) = (7 + 5z) - (2 - 4z)$

   $= 9z + 5$

   Therefore, both $22 + 13z$ and $9z + 5$ are divisible

   by 7. It is satisfied when $z \equiv 1 \pmod 7$.

   Only 2^{222} satisfies that.

   $2^{222} \equiv (2^3)^{74} \equiv 1 \pmod 7$

   The answer is B

4. Let's reorganize the equation,

   $(x + y)^2 - (x + y) - 3xy$

   $= x^2 - x(y + 1) + (y^2 - y) = 0$

   Since it is a polynomial with second degree and

   x is an integer, discriminant must be perfect square.

   $\Delta = (y + 1)^2 - 4(y^2 - y) = -3y^2 + 6y + 1$

   However, if $y \geq 3$ or $y \leq -1$, discriminant will be

   negative. So, y can be 0, 1, 2.

   If $y = 0$, then $x^2 - x = 0$, so $x = 0$ or $x = 1$.

   If $y = 1$, then $x^2 - 2x = 0$, and $x = 0$ or $x = 2$.

   If $y = 2$, then $x^2 - 3x + 2 = (x - 1)(x - 2) = 0$,

   and $x = 1$ or $x = 3$.

   There are 6 solutions.

   The answer is D

5. The equation is $x^2 + (x + 1)^2 = y^4 + (y + 1)^4$,

   $2x^2 + 2x + 1 = 2y^4 + 4y^3 + 6y^2 + 4y + 1$

   $=) \; 4x^2 + 4x + 2 = 4y^4 + 8y^3 + 12y^2 + 8y + 2$

   $=) \; (2x + 1)^2 + 1 = (2y^2 + 2y + 2)^2 - 2$

   $=) \; (2y^2 + 2y + 2)^2 - (2x + 1)^2 = 3$

   Since x and y are positive integers,

   $2y^2 + 2y + 2 \$ 6$. However, 3 can be represented

   as only $(\pm 2)^2 - (\pm 1)^2$.

   Therefore, there is no solution.

   The answer is A

6. Because $x^3 - y^3 = xy + 61 > 0$, $x > y$.

   Let say $x - y = a > 0$ and $xy = b > 0$.

   $x^3 - y^3 = (x - y)((x - y)^2 + 3xy) = a(a^2 + 3b)$

   $= xy + 61 = b + 61 \Rightarrow a^3 + 3ab - b = 61$

   Since $3a > 1$, $61 = a^3 + 3ab - b > a^3$.

   Hence, a can be $a = 1, 2, 3$. By putting these

   values into equation, we can see that only $a = 1$

   and $b = 30$ satisfy. By that, $(x, y) = (6, 5)$ solution

   is found.

   The answer is B

7. We can see that $3x^2 + 6x + 5 = 3(x + 1)^2 + 2$.

   This expression cannot be a perfect square

   because none of the perfect squares are in form

   of $3k + 2$.

   The answer is A

8. In (mod 3),

    $3x + 7y \equiv y \equiv 1337 \equiv 2 \pmod 3$

    $\Rightarrow y = 3n + 2, n \geq 0$

    In (mod 7),

    $3x + 7y \equiv 3x \equiv 1337 \equiv 0 \pmod 7$

    $\Rightarrow x = 7m, m > 0$

    By putting these values into equation,

    $3(7m) + 7(3n + 2) = 21m + 21n + 14 = 1337$

    $\Rightarrow m + n = 63$

    All solutions are

    $(m, n) = (1, 62), (2, 61), \ldots, (63, 0)$.

    There are 63 many solutions.

    The answer is B

9. $100 = 4 \cdot 25$ and $\varnothing(25) = 5^2 - 5 = 20$,

    therefore $3^{20} \equiv 1 \pmod{25}$.

    $3^{2016} \equiv \dfrac{(3^{20})^{101}}{3^4} \equiv \dfrac{1}{81} \equiv \dfrac{1}{6} \equiv \dfrac{51}{6} \equiv \dfrac{17}{2} \equiv \dfrac{42}{2} \equiv 21$

    (mod 25)

    Also,

    $3^{2016} \equiv (-1)^{2016} \equiv 1 \pmod 4$

    Therefore, $3^{2016} \equiv 21 \pmod{100}$.

    The answer is B

10. By Fermat's theorem, $19^{16} \equiv 1 \pmod{17}$,

    $19^{19} \equiv 19^3 \equiv 2^3 \equiv 8 \pmod{17}$

    The answer is E

11. Since 2y is even and 7 is odd, x is also odd.

    For $x = 2m + 1$ $(m \geq 0)$,

    $3x - 2y = 3(2m + 1) - 2y \equiv y \equiv 1 \pmod 3$

    $\Rightarrow y = 3n + 1, n \geq 0$

    $\Rightarrow 7 = 3x - 2y = 3(2m + 1) - 2(3n + 1)$

    $= 6(m - n) + 1 \Rightarrow m - n = 1$

    Hence, there are infinitely many solutions.

    $(x, y) = (2n + 3, 3n + 1)$ is a solution for each $n \geq 0$.

    The answer is E

12. $x^2 \equiv 0, 1, 4 \pmod 5$ for all integers. $x^2 \not\equiv 0$ because $2^n \not\equiv 0$. Hence, $2n \equiv 1, 4 \pmod 5$.

    It is satisfied only when n is even. For $n = 2m$,

    $2^{2m} - x^2 = (2^m - x)(2^m + x) = 615 = 3 \cdot 5 \cdot 41$

    Since $2^m - x + 2^m + x = 2^{m+1}$ is a power of 2 and only $(2^m - x, 2^m + x) = (5, 123)$ satisfies that.

    By that $m = 6$, $n = 2m = 12$ and $x = 59$.

    The answer is B

MathTopia Press

MathTopia Press

CHAPTER 01

| Problem Set 1 | 1-D | 2-C | 3-B | 4-D | 5-E | 6-A | 7-E | 8-C | 9-E | 10-D | 11-D | 12-C |
| Problem Set 2 | 1-E | 2-C | 3-B | 4-B | 5-D | 6-B | 7-A | 8-B | 9-B | 10-D | 11-C | 12-D |

CHAPTER 02

| Problem Set 1 | 1-D | 2-D | 3-C | 4-A | 5-D | 6-C | 7-E | 8-C | 9-A | 10-C | 11-D | 12-B |
| Problem Set 2 | 1-D | 2-B | 3-B | 4-D | 5-E | 6-C | 7-A | 8-B | 9-B | 10-C | 11-A | 12-A |

CHAPTER 03

| Problem Set 1 | 1-C | 2-A | 3-C | 4-B | 5-D | 6-B | 7-C | 8-A | 9-D | 10-D | 11-A | 12-D |
| Problem Set 2 | 1-E | 2-A | 3-E | 4-B | 5-B | 6-C | 7-C | 8-C | 9-A | 10-B | 11-A | 12-B |

CHAPTER 04

| Problem Set 1 | 1-C | 2-A | 3-E | 4-D | 5-D | 6-B | 7-B | 8-E | 9-C | 10-C | 11-D | 12-C |
| Problem Set 2 | 1-E | 2-B | 3-E | 4-E | 5-E | 6-C | 7-E | 8-D | 9-C | 10-D | 11-B | 12-A |

CHAPTER 05

| Problem Set 1 | 1-B | 2-A | 3-E | 4-D | 5-C | 6-A | 7-C | 8-D | 9-A | 10-B | 11-A | 12-A |
| Problem Set 2 | 1-C | 2-C | 3-E | 4-C | 5-A | 6-A | 7-D | 8-D | 9-D | 10-C | 11-E | 12-B |

CHAPTER 06

| Problem Set 1 | 1-D | 2-D | 3-B | 4-A | 5-E | 6-D | 7-B | 8-A | 9-E | 10-E | 11-C | 12-D |
| Problem Set 2 | 1-E | 2-A | 3-E | 4-B | 5-C | 6-B | 7-B | 8-B | 9-E | 10-D | 11-B | 12-B |

CHAPTER 13

Problem Set 1	1-B	2-E	3-C	4-E	5-B	6-C	7-A	8-D	9-E	10-C	11-D	12-B
Problem Set 2	1-D	2-D	3-A	4-B	5-D	6-D	7-C	8-B	9-A	10-C	11-A	12-E

CHAPTER 14

Problem Set 1	1-D	2-B	3-B	4-D	5-D	6-E	7-C	8-E	9-C	10-E	11-B	12-A
Problem Set 2	1-B	2-D	3-B	4-D	5-B	6-B	7-A	8-C	9-B	10-B	11-B	12-D
Problem Set 3	1-A	2-E	3-D	4-E	5-C	6-A	7-D	8-A	9-D	10-C	11-D	12-A

CHAPTER 15

Problem Set 1	1-C	2-B	3-B	4-B	5-E	6-C	7-A	8-E	9-A	10-A	11-B	12-C
Problem Set 2	1-C	2-C	3-E	4-C	5-B	6-C	7-A	8-E	9-C	10-A	11-B	12-C
Problem Set 3	1-D	2-D	3-C	4-E	5-C	6-E	7-E	8-E	9-E	10-A	11-E	12-A

CHAPTER 16

Problem Set 1	1-E	2-B	3-D	4-E	5-A	6-D	7-A	8-C	9-B	10-A	11-A	12-B
Problem Set 2	1-B	2-A	3-D	4-A	5-C	6-B	7-D	8-C	9-C	10-A	11-C	12-D
Problem Set 3	1-B	2-A	3-C	4-A	5-A	6-E	7-A	8-B	9-C	10-B	11-D	12-C

CHAPTER 17

Problem Set 1	1-E	2-C	3-D	4-D	5-E	6-C	7-A	8-D	9-B	10-D	11-D	12-A
Problem Set 2	1-E	2-B	3-E	4-D	5-E	6-D	7-D	8-D	9-E	10-B	11-D	12-B

CHAPTER 18

Problem Set 1	1-A	2-B	3-D	4-E	5-D	6-D	7-C	8-E	9-A	10-C	11-B	12-E
Problem Set 2	1-D	2-C	3-B	4-D	5-A	6-A	7-D	8-E	9-D	10-D	11-A	12-A

CHAPTER 19

Problem Set 1	1-B	2-D	3-B	4-B	5-B	6-B	7-B	8-A	9-A	10-D	11-C	12-D
Problem Set 2	1-E	2-C	3-E	4-C	5-E	6-D	7-C	8-D	9-E	10-D	11-A	12-D

CHAPTER 20

Problem Set 1	1-A	2-E	3-A	4-B	5-A	6-E	7-E	8-A	9-A	10-B	11-E	12-E
Problem Set 2	1-E	2-C	3-D	4-C	5-B	6-C	7-D	8-C	9-A	10-B	11-B	12-B
Problem Set 3	1-B	2-C	3-B	4-D	5-A	6-B	7-A	8-B	9-B	10-E	11-E	12-B

Made in the USA
Las Vegas, NV
21 September 2023